ON THE **GUARD**

THE YMCA LIFEGUARD MANUAL

YMCA OF THE USA

Library of Congress Cataloging-in-Publication Data is available.

On the Guard: The YMCA Lifeguard Manual. YMCA of the USA. Fifth edition.

ISBN 978-1-935727-02-6

Published by YMCA of the USA.

Printed in United States of America.

10 9 8 7 6 5 4 3 2 1

Cover feature photo courtesy of Brian Mueller. Copies of this book may be purchased from the Program Store at www.ymcaprogramstore.com or 800-747-0089.

Note

Thank you for choosing the YMCA's Lifeguard Training Program, the next generation of YMCA aquatic excellence.

This text represents best practices for lifeguarding and reflects the high standard that YMCA of the USA encourages all YMCAs and other aquatic facilities to uphold. It is designed to be used with YMCA of the USA's Lifeguard courses. However, this manual is not intended as a set of standards; rather, it presents recommendations that each aquatic facility and lifeguard can apply given the conditions, policies, and practices of its local community and management.

Each aquatic facility must comply with its local and state bathing codes, state and federal legislations, and its own policies. This text is not intended as a replacement for those regulations.

This text does not and cannot stand alone as a lifesaving policy manual. It has been written expressly to be used in conjunction with a facility's specific policies and procedures pertaining to the information provided in this text. The material contained in this text constitutes the considered and expert opinion of the authors. The authors make no express or implied warranty or guarantee as to the material, opinions, or methods contained in this text.

The procedures, techniques, and equipment used in lifeguarding and the science of lifesaving are constantly changing. For the latest information in the field of aquatics and the Y's priority on aquatic safety, visit www.ymcaexchange.org.

Because of the extensive development and testing time required to include the highest quality aquatic knowledge and practices in our most-used piece of curriculum, not all components of YMCA Lifeguard, including the *On the Guard* manual and the YMCA Lifeguard Program DVD, are aligned with the Y's new brand, launched in July 2010. We regret this in large part because our brand promise of strengthening community is represented on a grand and practical scale with the program.

Kids, parents, individuals, and families make use of YMCA pools, waterparks, waterfronts, and programs every day in large numbers. Keeping them safe requires well-trained, confident, and responsible lifeguards. YMCA Lifeguard gives you the tools to ensure your lifeguarding is the best in the business, and that means a safer community.

The look and feel of YMCA Lifeguard will be fully aligned with the new brand in its next published iteration. Until then, know that the content and outcomes of this program are hallmarks of our brand.

TABLE OF CONTENTS

RECOGNIZE (section two)

CHAPTER 4 Scanning and Recognizing Potential Victims page 66

CHAPTER 5 Drowning Victims page 78

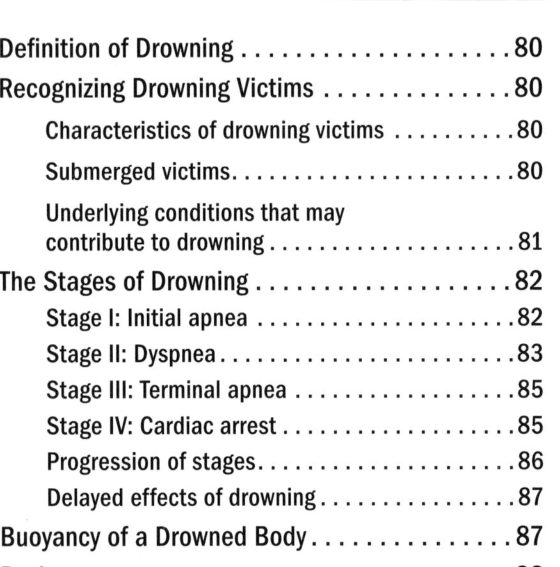

ACTIVATE EAP (section three)

CHAPTER 6 Emergency Action Plans page 90

RESCUE (section four)

CHAPTER 7 Rescue Strokes, Equipment, and Assists page 106

CHAPTER 8 Rescue Procedures page 124

PREFACE

About This Manual

On the Guard is designed to help the student of the YMCA Lifeguard course become a YMCA-certified lifeguard. It focuses on accident prevention strategies, victim recognition and scanning techniques, emergency action plans, problem-solving skills, rescue skills, emergency care, and incident reporting. *On the Guard* also serves as a resource for continued learning and a reference for lifeguards and aquatic professionals who are already certified.

Every lifeguard should be skilled in prevention, victim recognition, rescues, and emergency care, and the YMCA Lifeguard course teaches each of these skill sets and more. However, wherever possible, the YMCA Lifeguard course and *On the Guard* emphasize prevention: it is far better to prevent an incident before it happens than wait to see a person in distress and then execute a rescue.

The core of *On the Guard* is six sections that emphasize the key stages of lifeguarding:

- ***Prevent*** addresses lifeguard procedures such as decision making, supervision systems, lifeguard locations, and guard communications; rules and regulations designed to prevent accidents and injuries; and methods such as swim tests to help prevent accidents.
- ***Recognize*** discusses scanning techniques and victim recognition. A chapter on drowning victims emphasizes that prevention is key because time is short once an incident progresses to a drowning.
- ***Activate EAP*** (emergency action plan) focuses on being prepared to respond. This section addresses developing and carrying out emergency plans and reviews many types of medical and nonmedical emergencies.
- ***Rescue*** reviews rescue skills and equipment, from nonswimming assists to water entries, rescue towing, and water exits. In addition, this section provides information about managing rescues of victims with spinal injuries.
- ***Emergency care*** outlines what equipment should be in the first-aid station and how to safely respond to medical emergencies such as heart attacks, bleeding, dental injuries, hyperthermia and hypothermia, and emergencies that arise from asthma, allergies, diabetes, and epilepsy.
- ***Report*** discusses the legal responsibilities of lifeguards and the importance of completing reports and other paperwork.

In addition, this manual provides information about lifeguarding at different locations, including swimming pools, waterfronts, waterparks, and water attractions. You will also learn about pool maintenance and basic pool chemistry. Finally, you will receive helpful information about getting and keeping a lifeguarding job and opportunities for your professional development and growth. A few detailed appendixes complement the information in the manual, including key information about preventing child abuse. A helpful glossary rounds out the book.

The YMCA Lifeguard course aims to develop lifeguards who not only know a lot about preventing and responding to accidents on and around water but also care deeply about lifeguarding and those they are trained to serve. As you train to become a lifeguard, you learn more than just skills—you also grow in your ability and desire to help others. In this sense, lifeguarding is not just a job but a value as well. Becoming a YMCA-certified lifeguard presents a perfect opportunity to develop leadership and service skills while making a significant contribution to your community.

Acknowledgments

This manual represents the contributions of many people and would not have been possible without the support of a number of individuals, YMCAs, and other organizations. We would like to express our heartfelt appreciation to everyone who participated in the development of *On the Guard* and the *YMCA Lifeguard Training Video*. (Titles and organizations were current at the time of involvement in the project and may have changed since.)

Kay Smiley coordinated staff leadership for this project.

Technical advisors

Kevin S. Bottomley	YMCA of Greensboro, NC
Cory Brazeal	YMCA of Arlington, TX
Gerald DeMers, PhD	California Polytechnic State University, San Luis Obispo, CA
Mike Espino	YMCA of the USA, Chicago, IL
Monica J. Isgren	YMCA of Greater Houston, TX
Ralph L. Johnson, PhD	North Greenville University, Tigerville, SC
Rosemary McGreer-Lengefeld	YMCA of Greater Houston, TX
Kristine Meyerson, MA	YMCA of Greater Houston, TX
Kay Smiley	YMCA of the USA, Chicago, IL

Reviewers and contributors

Kevin S. Bottomley	YMCA of Greensboro, NC
Cory Brazeal	YMCA of Arlington, TX
B. Chris Brewster	International Life Saving Federation, San Diego, CA
Alexandra Cramer	YMCA of Florida's First Coast, Jacksonville, FL
Holly Colón	Ralph J. Stolle Countryside YMCA, Lebanon, OH
Gerald DeMers, PhD	California Polytechnic State University, San Luis Obispo, CA
Mike Espino	YMCA of the USA, Chicago, IL
Beth M. Ferguson	YMCA of Greater Louisville, KY
Carole L. Forbes	Heart of the Valley YMCA, Huntsville, AL
Gareth Hedges	The Redwoods Group Inc., Morrisville, NC
Christine Hughes	YMCA of Youngstown, OH
Monica J. Isgren	YMCA of Greater Houston, TX
Terri Johnson	YMCA of Greater Oklahoma City, OK
Ralph L. Johnson, PhD	North Greenville University, Tigerville, SC
Tomas A. Leclerc, MS	City of Albuquerque, NM
Jonathan B. Lee	YMCA of Metropolitan Atlanta, GA
Terri Lees	North Kansas City Community Center, North Kansas City, MO
Rosemary McGreer-Lengefeld	YMCA of Greater Houston, TX
Kristine Meyerson, MA	YMCA of Greater Houston, TX
Jason T. Pirnie	YMCA of Greater Springfield, MA
Linda Pourchot	YMCA of Greater St. Louis, MO
Laura J. Slane	YMCA of Greater St. Louis, MO
Kay Smiley	YMCA of the USA, Chicago, IL

Perry Smith	Lifesaving Society, Toronto, ON, Canada
Joy Thomen	Greater Wichita YMCA, Wichita, KS
Zack Tolbert	University of Alabama, Tuscaloosa, AL
Teresa L. Trammel	The Redwoods Group Inc., Morrisville, NC
Mary Zoller	YMCA of the USA, Chicago, IL

Field testers

Thanks to the staff of the following YMCAs who participated in field testing of the improvements made to the YMCA Lifeguard program.

Family YMCA of Southeast Mississippi, Hattiesburg, MS

Ralph J. Stolle Countryside YMCA, Lebanon, OH

Tampa Metropolitan Area YMCA, Tampa, FL

Volusia Flagler Family YMCA, DeLand, FL

YMCA of Central Florida, Orlando, FL

YMCA of Florida's First Coast, Jacksonville, FL

YMCA of Greater Houston, TX

YMCA of Greater Oklahoma City, OK

YMCA of Greater St. Louis, MO

Special thanks

Special thanks to Laura J. Slane, who provided research, support, coaching, and mentorship, and answered countless questions throughout this project.

Thanks also to Dr. Gerald DeMers and Dr. Ralph L. Johnson for their outstanding assistance on this project through answering numerous questions and sharing their expertise.

Thank you to B. Chris Brewster, who was extremely valuable in reviewing and editing *On the Guard.*

We also would like to thank the following for their support:

YMCA of Florida's First Coast for repeatedly providing staff and volunteers to assist in field testing, brainstorming sessions, and numerous photo shoots.

Kristine Meyerson and the rest of the staff of the YMCA of Greater Houston for their outstanding hospitality and professionalism during the multiple video and photo shoots throughout this project.

YMCA of Central Florida for hosting and participating in the Orlando video shoot.

Camp Tecumseh YMCA for its contributions to the video and photo shoots.

YMCA of Greater St. Louis for hosting the photo shoot for the cover.

Adolph Kiefer and Associates and Adolph Kiefer for his dedication to water safety and for the contribution of equipment for the photo and video shoots.

American Safety and Health Institute for its support and for providing equipment for the photo and video shoots.

Affinity Teamwear for its support of the YMCA Lifeguard program and for providing the swimsuits, shirts, and visors for the photo and video shoots.

List of Abbreviations

ADA	Americans with Disabilities Act
AED	automated external defibrillator
AGE	arterial gas embolism
AIDS	acquired immunodeficiency syndrome
ASHI	American Safety and Health Institute
BC	buoyancy compensator
BVM	bag-valve mask
CARE	cognizance, assessment, rescue, and evacuation (scuba and skin diving rescue procedures)
CDC	Centers for Disease Control and Prevention
CPR	cardiopulmonary resuscitation
CPR Pro	CPR for the professional rescuer
DAN	Divers Alert Network
DCS	decompression sickness
EAP	emergency action plan
EMP	electromagnetic pulse
EMS	emergency medical services
HBV	hepatitis B virus
HCV	hepatitis C virus
HELP	heat escape lessening position
HIPAA	Health Insurance Portability and Accountability Act
HIV	human immunodeficiency virus
IRB	inflatable rescue boat
LSI	Langelier Saturation Index
MSDS	material safety data sheet
NOAA	National Oceanic and Atmospheric Administration
NWS	National Weather Service
O2	The chemical symbol for oxygen, this is sometimes used to represent the oxygen administration training and emergency oxygen delivery
OSHA	Occupational Safety and Health Administration
PACA	problem, alternatives, consequences, and action (decision-making model)
PFD	personal flotation device
pH	measure of acidity and alkalinity of a substance (from the German for power + hydrogen)
POOL	Pool Operator on Location (YMCA training and certification)
PPE	personal protective equipment
ppm	parts per million
PWC	personal watercraft
Q-1-2	question, warning, take a break/ask to leave (accident prevention system)
RFD	rescue flotation device
RWI	recreational water illness
SCA	sudden cardiac arrest
SPF	sun protection factor
TDS	total dissolved solids
TTY	text telephone
USCG	United States Coast Guard
USLA	United States Lifesaving Association
UVA	ultraviolet A
UVB	ultraviolet B
V-fib	ventricular fibrillation
VGB	Virginia Graeme Baker Act
Y-USA	YMCA of the USA

INTRODUCTION
TO YMCA LIFEGUARD

YMCA staff and volunteers have led the way in swimming and water safety for more than 125 years, and they continue to improve the quality of millions of lives through YMCA programs. *On the Guard* explains the technical skills and knowledge necessary for YMCA-certified lifeguard candidates seeking swimming pool, waterpark, and waterfront positions.

In this section, we introduce the following:

- The importance of aquatic safety
- The Y's role in swimming and water safety
- What drives the Y's swimming and water safety programs
- YMCA Lifeguard and other water safety programs

The Importance of Aquatic Safety

In the past 30 years, interest in aquatic activities has exploded. With greater access to swimming facilities and waterparks, people can easily include aquatic activities in their recreational and physical activity routines. Aquatic enthusiasts are found in the water, in recreational and competitive swimming, synchronized swimming, waterpark activities, and water polo; on the water, in activities such as rafting, kayaking, canoeing, sailing, and boating; under the water, in skin diving and scuba diving; and even above the water, in parasailing. The popularity of aquatic activities has generated a new awareness of the need for aquatic education and safety for all age groups.

For participants without awareness and proper training, the aquatic environment can be as dangerous as it is fun for those who know how to swim. Even those who do not participate in water sports need water safety knowledge. Drowning claims almost 3,600 lives each year in the United States. More than one in four fatal drowning victims are children ages 14 and younger (CDC 2010a). Many drowning victims are nonswimmers who never intended to go into the water. These drowning scenarios include accidents in a bathtub and home spas, wading too far into the surf, and falling off a fishing pier or into a backyard swimming pool. In addition, over 700 people die each year in boating-related incidents, either from drowning or other causes.

Carelessness, rough play, and unsafe headfirst entries into shallow water can lead to serious injuries, including spinal injuries. According to the CDC (2010a), "For every child who dies from drowning, another four received emergency department care for nonfatal submersion injuries. Nonfatal drownings can cause brain damage that may result in long-term disabilities including memory problems, learning disabilities, and permanent loss of basic functioning (i.e., permanent vegetative state)." The Y's swimming and aquatic programs strive to make a difference in helping everyone be safe in and around water.

The Y's Role in Swimming and Water Safety

YMCAs and other community agencies have taken on the responsibility of providing swimming instruction and aquatic safety training for people of all ages. Even though water recreation activities are increasingly popular, many people in the U.S. do not know how to swim, and thousands drown annually. Offering education in water skills and aquatic safety is even more important now that public schools have cut back on physical education and aquatic course offerings. Through programs like swim lessons and the Splash water safety program, YMCA of the USA has developed swimming instruction methods to address the needs of all participants, from beginners to advanced swimmers, from preschoolers to older adults.

What drives the Y's swimming and water safety programs

Millions of people learn to swim at the Y every year, and each one gains more than just swimming skills. This is because the Y is committed to strengthening community, and programs such as swimming and aquatic safety support individuals and communities in becoming more connected, confident, and secure. In addition, each YMCA program is designed to meet certain program goals and to help people learn, grow, and thrive. Through YMCA Lifeguard, you have the opportunity not only to benefit as a participant in this YMCA program but also to help others reach their full potential through swimming and water safety programs at the Y.

The goals of developing character and building assets are central to the YMCA philosophy and make YMCA programs different from those offered by any other organization. By taking the YMCA Lifeguard course, you will develop specific skills while growing in spirit, mind, and body. You will have the opportunity to:

- Develop self-esteem and self-reliance
- Strengthen positive values in yourself and others
- Improve your personal and family relationships by learning to care, communicate, and cooperate with others
- Appreciate people of different ages, abilities, races, religions, cultures, incomes, and beliefs
- Become a better leader and supporter by learning to work toward a common goal
- Have fun

These objectives, which are central to the Y's purpose, make our programs different from those offered by any other organization. Ys use programs as a vehicle to deliver their unique mission.

Character development

Character development is an essential element of every YMCA program. Values are the cornerstones that make our society safe and workable. They are the principles of thought and conduct that help us distinguish right from wrong and provide a foundation for decision making. Values, which are sometimes referred to as character, are the basis of who we are, how we live, and how we treat others.

These are the Y's core values:

- **Caring**. Put others before yourself, love others, be sensitive to the well-being of others, and help others. Related values include compassion, forgiveness, generosity, and kindness.
- **Honesty**. Tell the truth, act in such a way that you are worthy of trust, have integrity, and make sure your actions match your values. Related values include integrity, fairness, and trustworthiness.
- **Respect**. Treat others as you would have them treat you and value the worth of every person (including yourself). Related values include acceptance, empathy, and self-respect.
- **Responsibility**. Do what you should do and be accountable for your behavior and obligations. Related values include commitment, courage, health, and service (citizenship).

Consider what it means to be a lifeguard: people trust you to keep them safe. These core values are a vital reason they can and do trust you to do your job effectively.

Your decision to train to become a lifeguard demonstrates that you have goals and are willing to do the work needed to achieve them, that you want to learn something new, that you want to challenge yourself, that you believe in your ability to successfully complete the training and become a vigilant lifeguard, that you make constructive use of your time, and that you have a strong sense of your own worth and abilities. That is fantastic! Throughout your life, you have been influenced, sometimes without even knowing it, by parents, family members, neighbors, teachers, religious community members, and others in your community. These people have helped you develop this confidence in yourself and your abilities.

When you become a lifeguard, you assume a leadership role that allows you to continue this chain of positive development in others. Through the way you conduct yourself as you work and interact with others, especially with children and youth, you will have the opportunity to help shape others as they grow and develop.

Supporting healthy living, youth development, and social responsibility

It is no secret that the United States is facing a health crisis of epidemic rates of obesity and diabetes, and related diseases such as heart disease. What you may not know is that you can help combat this health crisis through your work as a lifeguard. Swimming is a lifelong sport. That is, it is a healthful activity that people of all ages and abilities can take part in throughout their lives. As a lifeguard, you can create a safe, supportive environment for all people—children, youth, teens, adults, and families—who want to improve their health and well-being in spirit, mind, and body.

Swimming is a popular family activity and an important skill for young people to learn. In your experience as a professional lifeguard, you will have the opportunity to be part of the Y's commitment to youth development. The Y's swimming and

water safety programs also give you an opportunity to support people in getting involved in their community. When you make the pool or waterfront a welcoming and safe place to be, you encourage people to keep coming, and you help the Y achieve its goal of helping to give everyone the opportunity to learn, grow, and thrive.

YMCA Lifeguard Program

You are probably reading this book in preparation for becoming a YMCA-certified lifeguard. The YMCA Lifeguard course and certification is the first level of the YMCA Lifeguard program. This section outlines the course contents, prerequisites, and certification requirements for YMCA Lifeguard. There are two additional levels of certification in YMCA Lifeguard: YMCA Lifeguard instructor and YMCA Lifeguard trainer. See chapter 15, Pursuing Your Job and Your Future, to learn more about the course contents, prerequisites, and certification requirements for these two levels.

YMCA Lifeguard

YMCA Lifeguard is a unique program that prepares lifeguards with skills for this demanding and important responsibility. By definition, a lifeguard has a legal duty to use reasonable care to protect the safety of people in an assigned area. Lifeguards have a moral and professional obligation to prevent potential situations by enforcing the rules and regulations of their aquatic setting and to respond to any emergencies that occur. Lifeguards have a legal duty to respond only if they are on duty at their facility.

The YMCA Lifeguard course provides a comprehensive education centered on preventing accidents in aquatic environments and using rescue skills when needed. The program focuses on the practical knowledge that lifeguards need, including accident prevention, patron safety, victim recognition, rescue skills, and problem solving as well as how to give emergency care and document an incident. The YMCA Lifeguard course enables you to learn and apply safety principles vital to your own well-being, develop leadership skills, learn how to maintain a healthy lifestyle, and improve your decision-making skills.

To become a YMCA-certified lifeguard, you need more than advanced-level swimming ability. You also need to be caring, strong, quick to respond, confident, fit, and intelligent, and you need good interpersonal skills. As a professional lifeguard, you must be mentally, physically, and emotionally prepared to perform your job at all times. YMCA of the USA strives to include all people in its programs; however, the demands of lifeguarding may disqualify some individuals with certain physical, mental, or emotional conditions from becoming certified.

Minimum entrance requirements

To successfully complete the YMCA Lifeguard course and receive certification, you must be able to meet the minimum entrance requirements, complete the coursework as described, and fulfill all other certification requirements.

To become a YMCA-certified lifeguard, you must be able to accomplish the following:

- Sit for extended periods of time in an elevated chair. A candidate must remain alert and focused on the entire zone of responsibility for extended periods of time, even under conditions of high heat and humidity, with no lapses in consciousness. Move safely to various locations, including entering and exiting an elevated chair, while scanning the zone of responsibility.

- Communicate with others immediately when responding to an incident or an emergency. Candidates must be able to communicate verbally, including projecting their voice across distances; communicate swiftly and clearly with emergency personnel over the telephone and in person; and effectively give and receive directions.
- Hear noises and distress signals in the aquatic environment, including in the water and anywhere around the zone of responsibility. Candidates must understand that significant background noise exists in all indoor and outdoor aquatic environments. In addition, lifeguard candidates should have a minimum hearing threshold of no more than an average of a 25-decibel loss in both ears over a range of frequencies (500Hz, 1000Hz, 2000Hz, 788 and 3000Hz). Candidates who use hearing aids or other corrective devices for hearing should be able to perform all rescue skills and emergency procedures without interruptions to adjust, retrieve, or install or attach a hearing aid or corrective device.
- Observe all sections of an assigned zone or area of responsibility. Candidates who use corrective eyewear should be able to perform all rescue skills and emergency procedures without interruptions to adjust, clear, or retrieve corrective eyewear.
- Perform all rescue, resuscitation, and survival skills. Candidates must be able to perform basic first aid such as manual suction, use a bag-valve mask resuscitator, administer oxygen (O2), use an AED (automated external defibrillator), and perform professional rescuer CPR.
- Think in the abstract, solve problems, make quick decisions, instruct, evaluate, supervise, and recognize the potential for danger or injury.
- Have adequate memory skills and be able to retain and apply the knowledge learned in lifeguard training.
- Act swiftly in an emergency and take action even when unsure whether a person is really in danger.

To participate in the YMCA Lifeguard course, you must meet the following prerequisites:

- Be at least 16 years old by the last day of the scheduled course. Note that parental consent is required for those younger than 18 years old prior to the start of the first class.
- Pass the following minimum physical-screening requirements:
    - Phase 1
        - Tread water for two minutes
        - Swim 100 yards of front crawl
    - Phase 2
        - Swim 50 yards each of
            1. Front crawl with the head up
            2. Sidestroke
            3. Breaststroke
            4. Breaststroke with the head up
            5. Elementary backstroke kick with hands on the stomach
        - Perform a feetfirst surface dive in 8 to 10 feet of water (or maximum depth of training facility). Then swim underwater for 15 feet.

- Phase 3
    - Listen to directions from the instructor.
    - Start in the water at the shallow end of the pool.
    - Sprint for a distance of 60 feet and then perform an arm-over-arm surface dive in 8 to 10 feet of water (or maximum depth of training facility pool).
    - Pick up an object (dive ring) from the bottom of the swim area, tread water for at least 1 minute using the legs only, and then place the object back on the pool bottom.
    - Swim the remaining length of the pool and hoist yourself out of the water without using a ladder or other assistance.
    - Immediately begin compressions on an adult manikin for 1 minute or 100 compressions, and then stand and listen to directions from the instructor.

Course content

The YMCA Lifeguard course includes classroom and pool sessions plus practical experience. The course covers the following topics:

- Importance of aquatic safety
- Swimming strokes
- Aquatic environments and aquatic science
- Prevention of aquatic incidents
- Aquatic rescues, including situation assessment, scanning and victim recognition, use of a rescue tube or buoy (required for rescue) and other rescue equipment, nonswimming assists, and swimming rescues
- Special situations, such as spinal injuries, rescue breathing, scuba rescue, waterfront guarding and rescue, search and recovery operations, waterpark rescue, and first aid and procedures specific to the aquatic environment
- Lifeguard responsibilities and administration, including duties, rules, legal responsibilities, emergency procedures, reports, and pool maintenance
- Lifeguarding techniques
- Personal health and safety of lifeguards
- Job searches and additional training opportunities
- CPR for the Professional Rescuer (CPR Pro)/AED, first aid, and oxygen administration certifications

Certification requirements

A currently certified YMCA Lifeguard instructor must conduct the course. The candidate must meet the minimum entrance requirements and certification requirements listed, complete all required coursework, and fulfill other certification requirements. A medical clearance may also be required before participating in a YMCA Lifeguard course. To be certified you must:

- Successfully complete the entire YMCA Lifeguard course and the CPR Pro/AED, first aid, and oxygen administration courses.

- Score at least 80 percent on each section of the tests, written or oral knowledge.
- Successfully perform all skills in a practical skills test.

Note that certification may also include your instructor's subjective judgment regarding your maturity, attitude, and overall participation.

Your certification is reported to YMCA of the USA Program Certifications, 101 North Wacker Drive, Chicago, Illinois 60606. Certifications become effective once entered into the YMCA of the USA system. YMCA Lifeguard certifications are renewable every two years.

The YMCA Lifeguard course also provides you with certifications in CPR Pro/AED, first aid, and oxygen administration; however, some of these certifications expire after one year. You must maintain current certification in CPR Pro/AED, first aid, and oxygen administration for your YMCA Lifeguard certification to be valid. See Maintaining your CPR Pro/AED, first aid, and oxygen administration certifications in chapter 15 for additional information.

Lifeguard Employment

The YMCA Lifeguard course provides the basic skills and knowledge needed for an entry-level lifeguard position. Successful entry and completion of the YMCA Lifeguard course does not guarantee employment as a lifeguard. YMCA Lifeguard certification acknowledges that the participant has completed the required educational and testing requirements to complete this course of study. It does not imply a participant's readiness or suitability for employment; employment decisions are left to the individual employer.

Lifeguard employment requirements and criteria are set by a hiring agency based on minimum standards established by federal, state, and local laws and regulations. In addition to lifeguard certification, an employer may have additional employment requirements that may include the following:

- Minimum age requirement
- Minimum education requirement
- Additional certification requirements
- Pre-employment testing of lifeguard knowledge and skills; including decision-making skills
- Medical examination
- Minimum vision requirements
- Minimum hearing requirements
- Drug testing

Before applying for a lifeguard position, make sure you meet the minimum requirements of your potential employer.

Review

Review Questions

1. How long has the Y been involved in swimming and aquatic safety?
2. What makes YMCA Lifeguard programs different from those of other organizations?
3. List five of the minimum entrance requirements for this lifeguard course.
4. What are the certification requirements for the YMCA Lifeguard course?
5. What other certifications must you maintain to keep your YMCA Lifeguard certification valid?

Prevent

SECTION one

CHAPTER 1

Lifeguarding Procedures and Prevention

Being a lifeguard is a rewarding and challenging experience. People of all ages love to swim. As a lifeguard, your job is to help everyone be safe while they are having fun in and around the water. While on duty, you have to be vigilant and prepared to make split-second decisions. With consistent practice, you will learn to recognize and respond to minor incidents to keep them from escalating into serious emergencies.

In this chapter, you will learn the following:

- Decision-making skills
- Lifeguard supervision systems
- Lifeguard communication systems
- Safety systems
- Handling special guarding assignments
- Being inclusive and communicating with all patrons

1
CHAPTER

The Successful Lifeguard

The best lifeguards are successful because of particular personal characteristics. They are people-oriented professionals who share their aquatic skills, enabling others to safely enjoy water activities. A successful professional lifeguard candidate possesses these basic skills and personal characteristics:

- Cares about others
- Is strong and fit
- Is a good swimmer
- Is responsible and dedicated—a role model
- Wants to help others
- Can stay cool under pressure

Do these characteristics describe you? If so, you are on your way to becoming a professional lifeguard. If not, think carefully about whether you really want to pursue the job of a professional lifeguard.

Once you have learned lifeguarding skills, your attitude and professionalism will largely determine your success as a lifeguard.

Attitude

Lifeguards need to have the right attitude to be successful. Do you genuinely care about people? Are you ready to take responsibility for the safety of others?

You give managers and patrons clues to your attitude and work ethic by the example you set at work and in social situations. The image you present greatly influences how much respect observers will have for you. Whatever your intentions are, patrons of your facility develop an impression of you based on your personal interactions with other patrons, peers, and staff. As a lifeguard, leadership will be expected of you. Make it a point to lead others at your facility by your example:

- Try to prevent accidents before they occur.
- Be familiar with your area and its potential hazards.
- Cooperate with fellow lifeguards—you are an important part of a team.
- Look professional.
- Be punctual.
- Follow the rules. (You cannot expect others to follow them if you do not.)
- Be alert at all times.
- Stay focused while scanning.
- Do not have personal conversations, joke around, read, text, or use personal electronic devices while on duty.
- Be courteous; avoid shouting or arguing.
- Direct questions for which you do not know the answer to a supervisor.
- Never report for your shift under the influence of alcohol or drugs.
- Do not abuse your authority.
- Maintain control of your assigned area.

Using common sense and common courtesy will go a long way toward demonstrating that you want to serve patrons and that you are worthy of their respect and trust. It will make your lifeguarding service pleasant, satisfying, and rewarding.

Physical conditioning and wellness

By doing a good job, you will help prevent accidents that could require your rescue skills. But when called upon to use these skills, you need the strength and endurance to carry out a rescue. Regular exercise

Lifestyle Assessment

Here are some questions to help you assess your lifestyle:

1. Are you kind and caring toward others?
2. Do you balance your needs with the needs of others?
3. Do you have a purpose to your life—a goal?
4. Are you in good physical condition?
5. Do you regularly spend time doing some kind of physical fitness activity?
6. Do you eat healthy foods?
7. Do you get 7 to 8 hours of sleep every night?
8. Do you drink enough water each day to stay hydrated?
9. Do you control your emotions effectively?
10. Are you overweight?
11. Are you underweight?
12. Do you smoke? Drink alcohol? Take drugs?

If you answered no to some of questions 1 through 9 or yes to some of questions 10 through 12, you may want to consider changes in your lifestyle. The changes you make are important to your personal development and the patrons of your facility.

What changes would you like to make in your lifestyle?

is vital to maintaining your physical conditioning (**figure 1.1**). The best exercise for a lifeguard is swimming. Try lap swimming, stroke drills, sprints, and water games to help you build and maintain your strength, endurance, speed, breath control, agility, and skill at the levels essential for effective lifeguarding.

Your attentiveness, vigilance, and fitness are crucial to the safety of those who use your facility. Your lifestyle will influence these areas of your preparation. Take some time to evaluate your lifestyle—your personal way of life. The lifestyle you choose affects your social, spiritual, intellectual, physical, and emotional wellness. Becoming a lifeguard will support your health and well-being as you develop both physical skills and mental and emotional maturity and decision-making abilities. However, you are likely to be most successful if you begin from a strong foundation of health in your spirit, mind, and body.

Figure 1.1 Regular exercise, such as weight lifting, will help you stay in good physical condition.

Decision Making

There is a consequence for every decision you make. For instance, imagine you are driving and notice your gas gauge is near empty. You can decide either to fill up at the nearest gas station or to try to make it to your destination with the gas you have. If you fill up the tank, it will cost you some money, but you will not have to worry about running out of gas on a deserted road. If you do not fill up, you could end up on foot!

As a YMCA lifeguard, you will be responsible for making decisions quickly based on the information you have at the time. The YMCA decision-making model, PACA, can help you make these important decisions.

Decision-Making Exercise

Try this exercise to sharpen your decision-making skills. On a piece of paper, describe a situation about which you need to make an important decision. Using that situation as an example, complete these steps:

- Describe the **problem** or situation.
- Consider ways to resolve the problem or situation. Try to list at least three **alternatives.**
- List the **consequences** of each alternative.
- Make your decision and write a brief justification of the **action** you will take.

The PACA decision-making model

PACA is an acronym representing the four steps in the YMCA decision-making process. As you make decisions, systematically follow the PACA model to ensure you have considered the possible consequences. Memorizing the acronym will help you remember the steps:

P: What is the *problem* or situation?

A: What are the *alternatives*?

C: What are the *consequences* of the alternatives: are they positive or negative?

A: What is the *action* or decision?

Preparation

Because we are responsible for our own decisions, we need to think through possible consequences that might result from them. This is especially true as you take on the role of a lifeguard. Choosing to intervene—and the actions you take in an intervention—may mean the difference between safety and serious injury or death.

As a lifeguard, you may have little time to make critical decisions. You will often have only seconds to respond. Therefore, it is important to think through what to do in certain situations before you need to take action. The emergency drills and in-service training at your facility will help you prepare, but it is also important that you personally consider what to do in given situations. For example, how would you react if someone

- broke a minor safety rule, such as sitting on a ladder or running on deck;
- looked frightened, unsure, or tired while swimming or diving;
- was reported missing; or
- broke a major safety rule, by pushing or dunking another swimmer?

When you consider what to do, it is not enough to tell yourself, "I'd just talk to him" or "I'd use my whistle and ask her to get out of the pool." In a real-life situation, you might find you have forgotten to prepare for crucial actions. Instead, you need to know ahead of time each step you would take and what you would say. Use the following accident prevention system to plan what you would do if you encountered these situations.

Q-1-2 accident prevention system

An effective lifeguard is always watching for potential problems and acting on them before they become emergencies. But constant intervention becomes annoying to both you and your patrons. How can you enforce the rules without blowing your whistle constantly?

One solution is to learn the Q-1-2 system, which works with children and adults alike. There are three advantages to this system:

- It helps you be consistent and fair.
- It reduces the stress and emotion of enforcing rules.
- It allows you to remain focused on your assigned area.

Next we look at each step of this three-part system.

Q: Question

The Q-1-2 process begins before someone actually violates a rule or does something potentially dangerous. You will frequently notice people preparing to do something that might put them or someone else in danger. Consider these examples:

- A person walks very tentatively to the edge of a slide, diving board, or deep end.
- A swimmer starts across the pool but returns, struggling and gasping for air.
- Someone floats a kickboard a few feet from the deck and appears to be preparing to jump onto or over it.

Q-1-2 Key Points: Question

- Watch for situations in which it appears a patron is about to do something unsafe or against pool rules.
- Ask the person to come to where you are.
- Ask a question to determine whether the person was preparing to do something unsafe or against the rules and whether the person is aware of the danger.
- Give corrective information or instruction and provide the reason.
- Watch your area of responsibility at all times.

- A patron on the deck says to another, "Race you to the deep end."
- Someone is sneaking up behind another person.
- A person is walking faster than normal.

Although no one in these situations has violated a rule or done anything dangerous, the potential is clear. The first step, Q, is to ask the person a question (**figure 1.2**). Ask him or her to stand beside you so you can ask your question without looking away from your assigned area or shouting.

Do not use questions to accuse. Rather, ask questions to help people understand for themselves the danger

Figure 1.2 Q-1-2: First, ask the person a question.

Q-1-2 Key Points: Warning

- State the warning using "I saw...," "That is...," and "Please..." statements.
- Do not argue with the patron.
- Watch your area of responsibility at all times.
- Make it clear that repeating the undesirable behavior is unacceptable and doing so may require the patron to take a break or leave.

they may be risking. The following questions might be useful in the scenarios just described:

- Have you ever gone down the slide before? Can you swim across the pool? Can you show me?
- Have you ever had swimming lessons? Can you stand up in that depth? Did you take a safety swim test yet?
- Were you going to jump on the kickboard? Do you know what could happen if you landed on it?
- How are you going to race? In the water? On the deck? Underwater?
- What were you planning to do to the person you were approaching from the back?
- Do you know we have a rule against running on the deck? Do you know why?

Sometimes the question itself gets the point across. However, be sure to listen to the answer. If it indicates that the person is not aware of the potential problem, give more information or instructions:

- For your safety, you need to be able to swim across the swimming pool before going down the slide. Wait until my break and I'll give you a safety swim test. If you pass and it is okay with your parents, you can go down the slide.
- Stay in the shallow end until you've taken and passed the safety swim test.
- Do not jump on or over the kickboard; it could fly up and hit someone.
- There are too many people in the pool for you to race now; you could bump into people as you race.
- You cannot push (dunk, splash) another person, even if it is your friend and you are playing a game. Splashing will bother other people in the pool, and dunking is not a safe game to play.
- The deck is wet. Please walk a little slower so you don't injure yourself or someone else.

1: Warning

Use the next step of the Q-1-2 system—warning—when a patron does something unsafe or against pool rules. First, call the person to your side so you do not have to shout or look away from the water (**figure 1.3**). Next, tell the person what you saw. This may sound silly—it might have been obvious. But people sometimes do not realize what they have just done. Also, you want to be certain the person knows why you are issuing the warning.

Because this will be the offender's only warning, make simple, direct statements using this format:

- I saw...
- That is...
- Please...

Here are some specific examples:

- *I saw* you jump off the side of the diving board. *That is* dangerous because it is too near the deck. *Please* jump off the end of the board.
- *I saw* you running. *That is* unsafe because the deck is wet. *Please* walk.
- *I saw* you dive into shallow water. *That is* very dangerous because you could hit your head and injure your neck. *Please* dive only in the deep end.
- *I saw* you enter the pool without taking a shower. *That is* against our pool rules because it makes the water dirty. *Please* shower before entering the pool.

Be sure to make simple, direct statements without emotion. Use statements of fact that do not require discussion. People will often argue in their defense, but you should try to avoid long discussions. You can listen, but maintain your focus on the water. Make it clear to the patrons that if they repeat the undesirable behavior, you will ask them to leave or take a break from swimming (discussed in the next step).

2: Take a break (child or teen)

Use the final Q-1-2 step—take a break—if a child or teen repeats the unacceptable behavior after being warned. If the person is a child, direct the child to take a break from the pool. Giving break time means removing the child from the water and from the company of others. If the person is a teen, use your facility's guidelines and your own judgment to decide whether to ask the person to leave the pool (see the next section) or take a break.

Again call the person to your side. Then, without emotion, say, "I saw you run (push, jump off the side of the board) again. Please take a break in the assigned area for 5 minutes. Then come back and see me."

The purpose of a break is not public humiliation but to have the child think about proper behavior. The break area should be away from the edge of the pool and out of the sun but within sight of a lifeguard or other staff member. Post the pool rules in the break area so people can think about what they should be doing rather than what they did wrong.

Keeping track of the time should be the responsibility of the child, not the lifeguard. An easy way to assist in timekeeping is to give a youngster an inexpensive plastic stopwatch or kitchen timer. Set the watch or timer to the designated time and hand it to the child with instructions to bring it back when the time is up. Break times should be age appropriate. A good rule of thumb is one minute for each year of age, not to exceed six minutes. Allow shorter breaks for minor infractions.

Figure 1.3 Call the person to you.

Q-1-2 Key Points: **Take a Break/Ask to Leave**

- Send a child to the break area with a timer for a specified period.
- After the break, ask the child to tell you what he or she should do in the same situation in the future.
- Ask an adult to leave the pool area.

When a child returns to you from the break area, ask for a description of what to do in the future in the same situation. (Basically, you are asking the person to repeat the warning you gave.) If the person cannot answer appropriately, explain the warning and ask the person to repeat it to you.

2: Asking a patron to leave

If an adult repeats undesirable behavior after a warning, or a child does so after one or more breaks, inform management (for example, head lifeguard, manager) to request that the patron leave the premises voluntarily (**figure 1.4**). If a minor is involved, management should contact the parent or guardian. File an incident report soon after. To help lifeguards act consistently and fairly, effective managers discuss the issue of dismissing patrons from the facility at staff meetings and clarify procedures and chain of command.

Figure 1.4 If the problem persists, ask management to talk to the person.

What if a child repeats the same behavior after taking a break from the pool? What behaviors require immediate removal of a patron (for example, intentionally wearing the wrong safety band)? Every facility has different rules, so be sure you know the steps for your facility and enforce them consistently. However, every repeated behavior need not be treated the same way: Not showering before swimming may earn a break away from the pool; dangerous behavior may merit removal from the area.

Q-1-2 exceptions

The Q-1-2 system is designed to be fair and consistent, but exceptions will certainly arise. Keep in mind that the system is merely a tool. Your judgment may override the system when needed.

For example, a young swimmer may do several different things that merit warnings but never repeat the same behavior, thus avoiding a break. Explain to the child that you have seen several offenses and want the child to take a break from the pool. After the child returns from break time, ask him or her to list all of the actions for which he or she received warnings.

A regular young patron who receives a warning one day and repeats the behavior the following day should go to the break area without a new warning. You may reasonably hold higher expectations for those who use the facility regularly.

Remember, maintain a professional attitude regardless of what occurs. Treat patrons courteously, without displaying anger or harsh emotions, and focus on the behavior to be corrected, not the individual. Never shout, use abusive language, or use physical actions.

Supervision Systems and Lifeguard Locations

Your role as a professional lifeguard is to ensure safe practices, prevent accidents, and enforce the facility's policies. The role of management is to create policies and procedures to support and guide the lifeguard and to protect patrons. This section addresses factors that management considers when establishing staffing levels, supervision systems, and lifeguard locations. For more information, see *YMCA Aquatic Management*, available from the YMCA Program Store.

Staffing levels

The quality of any facility is due in large part to the commitment management makes to its patrons and staff. All facility managers should be committed to providing a safe and fun environment for patrons by ensuring that there are sufficient lifeguards on duty and that lifeguards

- are trained and certified;
- are actively scanning their zone;
- are focused on watching the patrons in their zone;
- are positioned at waterside to assist swimmers;
- have no responsibilities other than patron safety while on duty; and
- receive adequate rotations and breaks.

An important element in determining the necessary number of lifeguards on duty is the capacity of the pool or pool area. Management should ensure that each pool has a minimum of one certified lifeguard on duty whenever the pool is open. Facilities may set their own stricter standards and are required to follow state and local ordinances that prescribe additional requirements. Facilities may also determine the number of lifeguards on duty based on the following conditions:

- Size and shape of the pool
- Equipment in the pool areas
- Bather load
- Skill level of swimmers
- Activity or activities in the pool area
- Sun glare that makes viewing areas of the water difficult
- Number of high-use or high-risk areas or activities
- Ability to handle emergencies properly and effectively
- Meeting or exceeding compliance with applicable state and local codes

As a starting point (and a rule of thumb), facility management could use a ratio of one lifeguard per 25 patrons and then evaluate the size and shape of the pool, the equipment in the pool, the number of swimmers in the pool and their skill levels, and environmental issues. Management could then change the lifeguard-to-patron ratio (for example, to one lifeguard per 18 patrons), depending on the factors in the list above. Management is also likely to divide the facility into zones for particular activities, such as slides or diving, wading, or lap swimming. These zones help both lifeguards and patrons identify appropriate behavior in each area, while minimizing conflicts.

Your facility management should also ensure that there are sufficient lifeguards to respond to an emergency. It may take three or four people—either lifeguards or staff members trained in aquatic emergencies—to effectively manage a serious emergency procedure. Facility management also should ensure that any staff who has a role to play in the emergency action plan (EAP) be included in and practice the in-service training, in addition to lifeguards and other aquatic staff.

To assist in lifeguard supervision and to help lifeguards stay vigilant, facility management may appoint a head lifeguard as part of the chain of command. The head lifeguard is responsible for ensuring the safe conduct of classes and any swim testing and that aquatic safety emergency procedures are being followed. It is a common practice to have in the vicinity a supervisor who is at least 21 years old and in the pool area at least one aquatic staff member who is at least 18 years old.

Supervision systems

Supervision systems define the positions, zones, and rotations for lifeguards so that the entire aquatic area is supervised at all times. If even one lifeguard neglects his or her area or duties, a serious accident may result. A number of factors influence what is considered a proper supervision system:

- Size and shape of the facility
- Typical swimming skill levels of those using the facility
- Number of people in the water
- Number of lifeguards available
- Aquatic experience of swimmers and lifeguards
- Environmental conditions
- Lighting conditions or glare
- Types of activities
- Positioning of lifeguards
- Placement of lifeguard chairs or towers
- Ability of each lifeguard to reach all points in an assigned zone within 10 seconds

Two common supervision systems are entire-area coverage and zone coverage. When formulating these areas, management should make sure that any assigned area allows the lifeguard to reach a distressed swimmer in 10 seconds or less. The zones may have to change due to bather load or programming. Management should also formulate and communicate an emergency coverage plan (discussed later in this chapter).

Entire-area coverage

In entire-area coverage, a single lifeguard supervises the entire swimming area (**figure 1.5**) and depends on backup personnel to maintain vigilance and respond to an emergency. The entire-area coverage system can work when the swimming area is small, there are few swimmers, and other certified lifeguards are available to give breaks to the lifeguard on duty. In addition, more lifeguards or staff members trained to assist a lifeguard in an emergency should be available near the lifeguard on duty. Entire-area coverage has advantages and disadvantages:

Advantages

- Fewer on-duty lifeguards are required.
- The lifeguard can easily understand the coverage area.

Disadvantages

- The lifeguard may be responsible for too large an area.
- The lifeguard tends to concentrate on boundaries rather than the entire swimming area.

- A lifeguard who gets little change of pace when scanning often becomes fixated and fatigued.
- It may be challenging to keep second and third trained responders near the pool for fast response.
- It may be more difficult for the lifeguard to take the necessary breaks and rotations to maintain vigilance. It is necessary to rotate lifeguards every 20 to 30 minutes. Each hour, the lifeguard should get a break from guarding. As the temperature and humidity rise, for both indoor and outdoor pools, lifeguard rotation and breaks should occur more often.

Although entire-area coverage may be suitable for some small-pool settings with no obstructions, it is difficult to use in a large, complex facility. When a single lifeguard is on duty, it is critical that additional trained staff be available to assist in emergency situations during all hours of operation.

Zone coverage

The zone coverage system allows the greatest flexibility for handling the changing needs of a dynamic aquatic environment. In zone coverage, the swimming area is broken into smaller units, or zones, with one lifeguard responsible for each zone.

Figure 1.5 Entire-area coverage: One lifeguard supervises the whole swimming area.

When designating zones, management considers several factors:

- Zones are not wider than 180 degrees. Placing lifeguard chairs at corners of rectangular pools so that lifeguards scan no more than 90 degrees may help improve scanning efficiency.
- Zones do not include blind spots.
- Zones of responsibility for multiple lifeguards overlap to ensure complete pool coverage (**figure 1.6**). This is especially critical in high-risk areas.
- Zones are designed so it is possible for lifeguards to reach any location in their zone within 10 seconds.

Zone coverage is usually accompanied by a rotation system, which is discussed later in this chapter. Zone coverage has its own advantages and disadvantages:

Advantages

- Lifeguards concentrate on limited areas.
- There is double coverage in overlap areas.
- Rotation keeps lifeguards refreshed.
- Lifeguards can interact with patrons more easily.
- Additional lifeguards are available to assist with the EAP.

Figure 1.6 Example of zone coverage. *Photo courtesy of Water Design, Inc.*

Disadvantages

- More on-duty lifeguards are required.
- If zones of responsibility are not clearly identified to all lifeguards, gaps in surveillance coverage may occur.

Rotation systems

When two or more lifeguards are on duty, regular rotation is necessary every 20 to 30 minutes. Rotation relieves the tedium of watching the same area for an entire shift, distributes the most and least interesting areas among all lifeguards, and keeps lifeguards alert. Rotation also allows management to shift zone responsibilities when necessary. Each on-duty lifeguard is responsible for carrying a rescue tube or buoy at all times, along with a whistle and rescue pack.

Most rotation systems are set on a time schedule. A lifeguard returning from break usually initiates the rotation, temporarily putting one extra lifeguard on duty until the rotation is complete. Between rotation cycles, the lifeguard who rotates off duty gets a short break from scanning. In some facilities, a "duty break" may be used. In a duty break, the lifeguard is rotated not to a break but to another task, such as routine maintenance or covering the first aid station.

A secondary way to rotate lifeguards is to use a prearranged signal. This type of rotation is usually set in motion by a change in the number of swimmers in an area, a buzzer or bell, or a change in the music. The signal should be initiated only by the head lifeguard or another lifeguard assigned to that duty by the management. Individual lifeguards should not make such a rotation decision.

Rotation systems can be designed in different ways. **Figure 1.7** illustrates a generic approach to rotation triggered by a lifeguard returning from break.

When using elevated lifeguard stands, the replacement lifeguard should scan as the seated lifeguard climbs down. Once on the ground, that lifeguard should scan the assigned area until the replacement lifeguard is in position on the elevated stand. At this time, the lifeguard being replaced shares any special issues or concerns about patrons with the incoming lifeguard. The incoming lifeguard checks the bottom, middle, and surface of the pool in the specified zone, determines that it is clear, and verbally states "clear." The outgoing lifeguard then reconfirms that the bottom, middle, and surface of the zone are clear and verbally states "clear." When both lifeguards are certain the bottom, middle, and surface are clear, the lifeguards can then complete the rotation. This procedure of

Figure 1.7 Example of a rotation system. *Photo courtesy of Water Design, Inc.*

visual and verbal confirmation supports continuity of coverage and patron safety during rotation (**figure 1.8**).

If there are not enough lifeguards on duty to provide an extra lifeguard for rotation, lifeguards should exchange positions in a prearranged order, watching their zones as they switch. As one lifeguard moves to replace another, the lifeguards exchange any necessary information about potential hazards or weak swimmers. The relieved lifeguard then moves to the next assigned position, and so on. An alternative is to close one zone (for example, the slide or the splash pool), perform the rotation, and then reopen the zone.

Regardless of the type of rotation system in operation at a facility, these important guidelines help management establish safe practices:

- Rotate lifeguards regularly, every 20 to 30 minutes.
- Rotate lifeguards systematically.
- Design rotations to move lifeguards from the most demanding position to a break period or a less demanding spot.
- As lifeguards rotate, they should remain alert to potential problems and patron needs.
- Make sure each zone is always under visual surveillance.

Sight lines

Your ability to clearly see your entire zone is critical for effective guarding. This may require you to move within your station. Human vision is most sharply focused when the observed object is directly in front of the eyes. Patrons or objects observed with your peripheral vision cannot be seen clearly or in detail. This is why it is important for you to move your head and eyes as you scan. Lifeguard positions on pool corners offer good sight lines because the field of vision encompassing the pool is V-shaped, or 90 degrees. Where possible, it is best to have V-shaped zones that create the desired sight lines.

Figure 1.8 Lifeguard rotation: The replacement lifeguard scans the water as the outgoing lifeguard climbs down from the lifeguard stand. Once on the ground, the outgoing lifeguard scans the water while the replacement lifeguard climbs onto the stand. The outgoing lifeguard shares any concerns. To complete the rotation, both lifeguards indicate "clear."

Emergency coverage

Each facility requires an emergency coverage plan. When there are two or more lifeguards on duty and one must enter the water, this plan guides the remaining lifeguards to expand their zones of responsibility so that the entire area remains covered. Lifeguards remaining out of the water will probably have to move to new positions to cover the pool or waterfront effectively and to perform emergency procedures. If your facility uses entire-area coverage, there should be a trained responder(s) nearby to assist in calling for help and retrieving resuscitation equipment. If coverage of all swimmers is not feasible during an emergency (due to the number of lifeguards needed to address the emergency and the number left to guard), a plan should be in place to clear the pool of swimmers.

All lifeguards should know the emergency coverage procedures. Management is responsible for informing staff of their responsibilities. An emergency coverage diagram should be posted, and emergency coverage procedures should be regularly practiced during in-service training. If you or other lifeguards are unsure of your responsibilities, ask. Your preparation could prevent an injury or accident.

Lifeguard locations

Where you are located affects your ability to scan your zone and react quickly to an emergency. Understanding the advantages and disadvantages of different locations will help you manage your responsibilities more effectively. For example, if the sun streams through the windows of an indoor pool at a certain time of day, the resulting glare affects where lifeguards and lifeguard stands should be located.

Lifeguards can stand, sit, or rove. Lifeguards may be stationed on the ground, either as stationary or roving lifeguards, or in elevated chairs (or towers) that are at least 5 to 6 feet high. Each position has different advantages as described in the following sections. Often a good solution is the combination of elevated and roving lifeguards.

Towers and elevated chairs

Elevated lifeguard chairs are very effective for supervising swimming areas. Towers and elevated lifeguard chairs provide a better viewing point and reduce distractions more effectively than do stations on the ground (**figure 1.9**). At ground level, waves or other swimmers may obscure some patrons from view. Lower chairs may reduce your scanning efficiency because, in a more accessible position, you

Figure 1.9 Elevated chairs are effective for supervising swimming areas.

Tip

If you find that an elevated lifeguard chair is not placed properly, do not use it. Instead, guard in a roving position, maintaining coverage at all times, until the elevated lifeguard chair can be moved safely to a proper location.

may be more likely to turn to face patrons who speak to you and get distracted by passing foot traffic.

While elevated lifeguard chairs higher than 5 feet are more effective than lower chairs and provide for command and control of the lifeguarding zone, their use necessitates certain precautions. When you are using an elevated chair, be aware of and scan any blind spots next to and beneath the chair. Also, before you initiate a rescue by diving or jumping into the water from an elevated chair, check that the water beneath the chair is deep enough and clear enough to do so.

One of the best types of elevated chairs for lifeguards, regardless of water depth, has steps on one or both sides. This type of stand allows the lifeguard to keep a victim in view while descending to make a rescue, and it allows the lifeguard the ability to observe the zone while ascending the chair during a rotation.

Because the placement of elevated stands affects your ability to scan effectively, be aware if your stand is placed appropriately. Elevated lifeguard chairs should be located near the pool edge and should face all entrances to the pool facility. They should be placed according to the zone coverage used. Often the best location for these stands is at the corner of the pool, because this gives you a good field of vision and reduces your zone to less than 180 degrees (it is preferable to limit scanning areas to between 45 to 90 degrees).

Tips for Safely Using an Elevated Tower or Chair

Keep your rescue tube across your lap. Protect the extra line from the rescue tube so it does not get tangled on either you or the chair. Gather it in your hand.

Regardless of how you descend from the chair, always grasp tightly any equipment you are taking with you, being careful of lines that can get caught. Maintain control of your rescue equipment at all times.

Either in your rescue tube or in your rescue pack, have a resuscitation mask with the dome pushed out and the valve in place so that you always have the mask with you and ready to use.

Practice getting up and down from the station.

To prevent injury, do not allow patrons or staff to congregate below or around elevated towers or chairs.

When jumping or climbing down from any height, look before you leap! Check the area beneath you to avoid landing on a swimmer or injuring yourself. Bend your knees and flex your feet when you land; landing with locked knees can be very painful and can cause serious injury to your knees and back. Practice getting down from the tower or chair until you can do it fluidly. Every second counts in an emergency.

If you intend to perform a compact jump directly into the water from the stand, be sure that the water is clear and at least 5 feet deep. In a wave pool, you need to time your jump so you hit the water at the peak of the swell. In a river, the depth and speed of the water change with rainfall or drought. Know the conditions in your area before you jump from a tower or an elevated chair into the water.

Roving lifeguards

When you are positioned on the ground, you are closer to patrons, which makes it easier to give advice, warnings, and directives (**figure 1.10**). Roving lifeguards, when combined with elevated lifeguards, provide an additional layer of safety. Many times, roving lifeguards are assigned to shallow-water areas so they can carefully supervise the water and surrounding deck, beach, or play structures. Roving lifeguards may also serve as a communication link between lifeguard towers, particularly at beaches. At all times, roving lifeguards should carry rescue tubes or buoys that are ready for use along with a whistle and rescue pack.

Additional lifeguards are often needed in high-risk areas and when a facility is crowded. These additional roving lifeguards can also provide educational tips to patrons because they are more accessible.

Lifeguard Communication Systems

Your success as a lifeguard requires effective communication skills. You will need to communicate not only with patrons of diverse ages, communication skills and styles, and backgrounds but also with other members of the lifeguard team. Several communication systems exist for lifeguards, and your management will select one or more of these systems. Every lifeguard should be well trained in how to use the facility's communication systems:

- **Whistle signals**. Patterns of whistle blows are used to signal particular situations. One common whistle signal system is as follows:
    - One short blast: used to get swimmers' attention
    - Two short blasts: used to get other lifeguards' attention

Figure 1.10 Roving lifeguards are closer to patrons, making communication easier.

- One long blast: used to initiate emergency procedures (necessary to overcome crowd noise or poor acoustics in indoor pools)

- **Hand signals.** Lifeguards frequently use hand signals to communicate with patrons and other lifeguards. Some examples are illustrated in **figure 1.11**. Be sure to hold your signal a few seconds to ensure it has been recognized. These signals are frequently accompanied by whistle signals.
- **Rescue equipment signals.** Some signals can be made using a rescue tube or buoy (**figure 1.12**, next page). Rescue equipment held vertically and moved from side to side means assistance is needed. Rescue equipment held horizontally over the head means the situation is under control.
- **Flags.** Flags are not used in most swimming pools but can be used at waterfront areas, water slides, and waterparks. Waving a red flag means danger or stop sending patrons down a slide. Waving a green flag indicates that all is well. To signal at waterslides, some waterparks use paddles that are red on one side and green on the other side.
- **Radios.** Two-way radios are most frequently used in large waterfront areas where visual contact is difficult. These radios are for lifeguarding business only, not socializing. Radios are particularly valuable because they can be taken to the scene of an emergency and provide an open line of communication that allows all lifeguards with radios to hear and understand what is taking place.

Figure 1.11 Common hand signals: (**A**) Giving direction; (**B**) Need help; (**C**) Stop sending people down the slide; (**D**) Activity can resume; (**E**) Need another lifeguard to cover zone temporarily.

- **Telephones.** Phones are important for use in emergencies. Emergency numbers should be listed on or near telephones. If mobile or cordless phones are used, management should make a standard phone available in case the mobile or cordless phones do not work. Restrict phones to business and emergency use only. While on duty, do not use mobile phones for social purposes, such as calls or texting.
- **Megaphones.** A megaphone is a cone-shaped device used to intensify and direct the voice. Using a megaphone can be helpful when a facility is crowded (**figure 1.13**, next page).
- **Air horns.** Air horns may be used in large natatoriums or outside pools where noise levels could hamper communication in an emergency. They are useful for getting the attention of a large group to clear the pool and to signal there has been an emergency.

E

- **Safety technology.** Alarm and monitoring systems can help save lives. A system that works with your EAP is best.
    - Wireless alarms and water-activated alarm systems: These are aquatic emergency summoning devices; see the box on this page.
    - Surveillance systems: Underwater and surface video-monitoring systems can help analyze activity in the pool and assist lifeguards in monitoring swimmers. Some can alert the lifeguard when a swimmer is in trouble.

About Alarm Systems

A water-activated alarm is a portable, aquatic-emergency summoning device that may be employed instead of a hard-wired emergency button or a telephone in the pool area. This alarm allows the lifeguard to respond almost immediately to an aquatic emergency, rather than first having to travel to the emergency call button before responding to the distressed swimmer.

Other alarm systems are wireless and can be activated from anywhere on the pool deck. With a wireless system, a lifeguard has a wristband or a device similar to those used with car alarms and door locks. Pressing the button signals the service desk or front desk staff members to begin their part of the EAP.

Appropriate protocols, combined with a wireless or water-activated alarm, can save time during an emergency.

Figure 1.12 Rescue equipment signals: (A) Urgent, additional help needed; (B) Additional help needed, but less urgent; (C) Situation under control, no additional help needed.

Special Guarding Situations

You will undoubtedly experience many different situations while lifeguarding, and special events often carry the greatest risk. Some situations are more common than others. Spend time considering how you should react to each of the following situations. If you are likely to encounter one of these special situations at your facility, consider additional specialized training.

Instructional programming

When you are assigned to lifeguard during classes, your role is solely to provide lifeguarding services. Watch every swimmer in any class situation, just as you would watch every swimmer during a recreational swim period. Assess the comfort and skill level of each swimmer, and use that information to guide your attention. Be sure to keep all class members grouped together (the instructor should help). Be sure to continuously scan your entire area. You may find the swim class interesting and possibly distracting; however, the entire zone is your responsibility.

Competitive events

At a competitive event, a lifeguard commonly becomes involved in assisting distressed swimmers or divers, controlling crowds, maintaining safety, and responding to potential spinal injuries. It is important to establish

communication with the meet director so that any incident can be handled effectively.

Even at swim meets, be prepared to assist or rescue a swimmer. Wear your lifeguard uniform and have your rescue tube and rescue pack with you while guarding. Have rescue equipment available in the usual locations. If an incident does occur, react efficiently and effectively. Stay alert and be ready to respond. Do not assume that because the participants are competitive swimmers they will never need your assistance. Medical problems, for example, can arise instantaneously, even in seemingly fit individuals.

Working with groups of children

In group situations such as day camp, child care, rental groups, and special events, give a safety swim test to all children and to any adult who gives concern (see chapter 3). Then divide swimmers into groups by skill level and use a wristband or neckband to identify each child and adult for swim ability. Depending on water depth, facility management may require nonswimmers to wear Coast Guard–approved PFDs (personal flotation devices), commonly known as life jackets. Your job will be easier when you know every swimmer's individual swim ability. Swim tests should be administered by

Figure 1.13 A megaphone can be useful at a crowded facility.

a separate lifeguard or supervisor—not the lifeguard responsible for the zone.

Review rules frequently with children (**figure 1.14**). Repetition helps them learn and understand the rules. Train the camp or child-care staff to watch their groups, assist in teaching the rules, give restroom breaks, and know the facility's emergency system; however, make it clear to staff that you, as the lifeguard, are in charge of all swimming activities and the safety of all patrons.

Figure 1.14 Review rules and safety positions.

Clear the water periodically. In a waterfront situation, check attendance carefully. These out-of-water safety checks are good teaching opportunities and give swimmers a chance to rest and use the restroom.

When working with a group of young children, it is useful to station one lifeguard on the deck near the group. This places a certified lifeguard nearby in case a child becomes frightened or needs help in the water. In addition, this lifeguard will be close by to begin teaching the rules to these young swimmers. Be sure, however, to check with your supervisor before independently changing guard positions based on the group using your area.

YMCA staff can find guidelines for aquatics in day camps and child care at www.ymcaexchange.org.

Rental groups and special events

Groups that rent a facility for a party or event need additional preparation before the event. Some patrons may need to be reminded that the rules are not relaxed because they are the only ones at the facility. All groups should be given a safety swim test and marked for swimming ability, and nonswimmers may be placed in Coast Guard–approved PFDs, depending on the facility and water depth. Swim tests should be administered by an off-duty lifeguard or a supervisor—not the lifeguards on duty.

Your facility's management should have a signed agreement with any rental group that clearly states the rules, number of adults to accompany the children in the water, and enforcement procedures. Enforce these rules as you would in any other guarding situation. Your supervisor should review with you any special agreements a rental group may have made with management.

Your supervisor or management will need to determine which individual patron is in charge when the group arrives at your facility. That person will be the contact should any incident occur. Next, review the rules with the group and conduct safety swim test procedures (see chapter 3). Remind group members that the rules are necessary to ensure their safety. If group members do not follow the rules, they will be asked to leave and risk not being able to use the facility in the future.

Some groups may bring their own lifeguards to your facility. The visiting group's lifeguards will need to meet with on-duty lifeguards before the swim session begins. Management should make clear to the visiting lifeguards that they will be considered water watchers, or extra eyes on deck. Visiting lifeguards will need to learn the facility's rules and hazards specific to the facility. They will need to clearly understand their responsibility during the swim session. Visiting group lifeguards are not counted in lifeguard-to-swimmer ratios—they are considered extra eyes only. Visiting lifeguards are not to participate in a rescue, resuscitation, first aid, or any part of an EAP unless instructed by facility staff.

Practicing Inclusion

Language differences

You may face a situation in which a swimmer does not speak your language. There may be another lifeguard or patron on hand who can translate. Get to know those around you who can help. If there is no one to translate, use common hand signals to communicate. You also can teach yourself key phrases in languages present in your community. See **table 1.1** later in this chapter for sample phrases.

People with disabilities

Under the Americans with Disabilities Act (ADA), people with disabilities must have access to all facilities and must receive equal opportunity to use the facilities. Furthermore, patrons with disabilities must be treated by the same standards you treat all patrons. Those with disabilities are people first. Aquatic facilities must determine how to work with each patron with disabilities. Find out if your facility has an ADA policy and if there is a person assigned to address ADA issues. If so, consult that person for additional guidance.

Disabilities can be categorized into three categories: sensory, physical, and developmental and cognitive disabilities:

Sensory disabilities: People who cannot see or hear rely on their other senses to receive communication. Practice giving instructions using only your hands and no words. Then use your voice and no hand signals. If patrons who are deaf frequent your facility, take the opportunity to learn American Sign Language and have a board to write on available.

Physical disabilities: People with physical disabilities may not have sufficient buoyancy, strength, flexibility, or agility to navigate certain areas of your facility safely. Be prepared to give them attention while respecting their independence.

Developmental and cognitive disabilities: People with these disabilities may have excellent physical skills or strength but may need assistance understanding and following the rules and communicating with others.

To help all patrons safely participate in aquatic activities, know how to handle emergencies involving people with disabilities. Be alert to patrons at your facility who have a disability and work with them and their companions to ensure you and your fellow staff can help them stay safe and enjoy their time around the water.

Tips for Working With Individuals Who Have Disabilities

Aquatic activities can be made very accessible for people of all abilities. While improvements have been made in expanding access to full participation in U.S. society for individuals with disabilities, progress is still needed in the way many people communicate about and interact with people with disabilities. Often people are concerned that they will say the "wrong" thing, so they say nothing at all–thus isolating people with disabilities. Here are some suggestions on how to relate to and communicate with people with disabilities so you can help create a welcoming, fun, and safe aquatic environment for all.

Words

Positive language empowers. When speaking about people with disabilities, put the person first. Group designations such as "the blind" or "the disabled" are inappropriate because they do not reflect the individuality, equality, or dignity of people with disabilities. Further, terms such as "normal person" imply that the person with a disability is not normal, whereas "person without a disability" is descriptive but not negative. Use positive language when talking to people who have disabilities or when describing their abilities or conditions. Remember the Y's core values of caring, honesty, respect, and responsibility.

Actions

Appropriate ways to interact with people who have disabilities are based on respect and courtesy. Outlined below are tips to help you in communicating with persons with disabilities.

General tips for communicating with people with disabilities

- When introduced to a person with a disability, it is appropriate to offer to shake hands. People with limited hand use or who wear an artificial limb can usually shake hands. (Shaking hands with the left hand is an acceptable greeting.)
- If you offer assistance, wait until the offer is accepted. Then listen to or ask for instructions.
- Treat adults as adults. Address people who have disabilities by their first names only when extending the same familiarity to all others.
- Relax. Do not be embarrassed if you happen to use common expressions such as "See you later," or "Did you hear about that?" that seem to relate to a person's disability.
- Do not be afraid to ask questions when you are unsure of what to do.

Individuals who are blind or visually impaired

- Speak to the individual when you approach him or her.
- State clearly who you are; speak in a normal tone of voice.
- When conversing in a group, remember to identify yourself and the person to whom you are speaking.
- Never touch or distract a service dog without first asking the owner.
- Tell the individual when you are leaving.
- Always ask first if you wish to lead the individual somewhere; allow the person to hold your arm and to control her or his own movements.
- Be descriptive when giving directions; verbally give the person information that is visually obvious to individuals who can see. For example, if you are approaching steps, mention how many steps.
- If you are offering a seat, gently place the individual's hand on the back or arm of the chair so that the person can locate the seat.

Individuals who are deaf or hard of hearing

- Gain the person's attention before starting a conversation (e.g., tap the person gently on the shoulder or arm).
- Look directly at the individual, face the light, speak clearly in a normal tone of voice, and keep your hands away from your face. Use short, simple sentences. Avoid smoking or chewing gum.
- If the individual uses a sign-language interpreter, speak directly to the person, not the interpreter.
- If you telephone an individual who is hard of hearing, let the phone ring longer than usual. Speak clearly and be prepared to repeat the reason for the call and who you are.
- If you do not have a text telephone (TTY), dial 711 to reach the national telecommunications relay service, which facilitates the call between you and an individual who uses a TTY.

Individuals with mobility impairments

- If possible, put yourself at the wheelchair user's eye level.
- Do not lean on a wheelchair or any other assistive device.
- Never patronize people who use wheelchairs by patting them on the head or shoulder.
- If you think it would be helpful to push the person's wheelchair, always ask first.
- Offer assistance if the individual appears to be having difficulty opening a door.
- If you telephone the individual, allow the phone to ring longer than usual to allow extra time for the person to reach the telephone.

Individuals with speech impairments

- If you do not understand something the individual says, do not pretend that you do. Ask the individual to repeat what he or she said and then repeat it back.
- Be patient. Take as much time as necessary.
- Try to ask questions that require only short answers or a nod of the head.
- Concentrate on what the individual is saying.
- Allow the person to speak for herself or himself; avoid speaking for the person or attempting to finish her or his sentences.
- If you are having difficulty understanding the individual, consider writing as an alternative means of communicating, but first ask the individual if that is OK.

Individuals with cognitive disabilities

- If you are in a public area with many distractions, consider moving to a quiet location.
- Be prepared to repeat what you say, orally or in writing.
- Offer assistance completing forms or understanding written instructions and provide extra time for decision making. Wait for the individual to accept the offer of assistance; take care not to "over assist" or be patronizing.
- Be patient, flexible, and supportive. Take time to understand the individual and to make sure the individual understands you.

Remember

- Relax.
- Treat the individual with dignity, respect, and courtesy.
- Listen to the individual.
- Offer assistance but do not insist or be offended if your offer is not accepted.

U.S. Department of Labor 1995/2002.

Remember always that people with disabilities are people first. Most individuals are open to discussing their disabilities if you approach them in a supportive, professional manner that respects their privacy. Be sure that all patrons understand the rules and policies of the facility and follow requirements for safety swim testing and color banding (see chapter 3).

While you can use the same rescue techniques you will learn in chapter 8 to assist people with disabilities, you may need to be flexible. If a person does not have both arms, for example, you may need to adjust your rescue technique. If a swimmer cannot see the equipment you are extending, you need to figure out how to help the person grab it. As you encounter specific disabilities among patrons in your facility, think through how you would assist that person should the need arise. Be sensitive and try to help without calling unnecessary attention to the person or the situation. Plan ahead, be respectful, and use what works. If you have specific questions about an individual's needs, ask your manager and work out a plan. Be sure to include the patron (and/or caregiver) in the discussion.

Table 1.1 Key Phrases in Spanish and French

English	Spanish	French
Stop	Pare [PAH-ray]	Arrêtez [ah-reh-TAY]
Please walk	Camine, por favor [kah-MEE-nay por fah-VOR]	Ne pas courir, s'il vous plaît [ne pah cur-REER see voo play]
Clear the pool	Sálganse de la piscina [SAL-gun-say day lah pee-SEE-nah]	Sortez de la piscine [sor-TAY duh lah pis-SEEN]
Danger	Cuidado [kwee-DAH-doh]	Attention / Danger [AH-tan-see-YAWN] / [dan-ZHAY]
Thank you	Gracias [grah-SEE-as]	Merci [mer-SEE]
Yes	Sí [SEE]	Oui [WEE]
No	No [NO]	Non [NOH]
No diving	*Text on sign:* Se prohibe tirarse de cabeza [say pro-EE-bay tee-RAR-se day kah-BAY-sah] *Verbal warning:* No se tire de cabeza [no say TEE-ray day kah-BAY-sah]	*Text on sign:* Interdiction de plonger [ENH-ter-dik-see-AWN duh PLAWN-zhay] *Verbal warning:* Ne plongez pas [neh PLAWN-zhay pah]

Review

Review Topics

Lifeguards help people stay safe and have fun in the water. In this chapter, you learned about being aware of your surroundings and making sound decisions. Here are some of the key points to know in this chapter:

1) Importance of emotional and physical fitness for a lifeguard
2) Decision-making tools
3) Different coverage systems
4) Different lifeguard stations and their requirements
5) Kinds of communication systems for lifeguards
6) How to work with special events and gatherings
7) Steps and procedures for working with groups
8) How to include and protect people who do not speak English and who have disabilities

Review Questions

1. List some basic characteristics required to be a successful lifeguard.
2. How are attitude and physical fitness important to being a lifeguard?
3. List and explain the four steps of PACA.
4. Explain what Q-1-2 represents and how you would use it.
5. What are zone coverage and entire-area coverage? When is each one used?
6. Describe the different lifeguard stations and the advantages and disadvantages of each one.
7. Name four of the methods lifeguards use to communicate. Describe when or how each is used.
8. Choose a special guarding situation (class, competition, day camp, child care, rental group, other special event) and tell what steps to take to ensure patrons' safety before they enter the pool.
9. Asking people who have disabilities how they would like you to work with them is a first step in welcoming and including people of differing abilities. List some other communication practices you can use when a patron has a disability.

CHAPTER 2

Rules and Regulations

Knowing your swimming facility and its potential hazards is critical to your ability to prevent accidents. Facility management establishes rules to help minimize potential dangers, and your consistent enforcement of these rules is key to aquatic safety.

In this chapter, you will learn the following:

- Communicating rules in your facility
- Rules and precautions for high-risk locations
- Enforcing the rules
- Handling special situations as problems arise

CHAPTER 2

Communicating Facility Rules

In most facilities, management tries to keep the number of rules for patrons to a minimum to keep the atmosphere as enjoyable as possible. When additional rules are needed, management has to consider both the safety and the enjoyment of patrons. Effective rules are realistic, specific, and understandable.

Once management establishes the rules, lifeguards are responsible for consistently enforcing them. Inconsistent enforcement can make people feel singled out and may create the impression that the rules can be broken in some cases. The first step to enforcing the rules is communicating them. One way to inform a facility's patrons of the rules is to post them: walls, fences, lifeguard stands, near diving boards, and even the backside of dressing room doors are all appropriate spots to mount signs. Copies of the rules can be handed out with pool passes or perhaps listed in a facility newsletter. All programs should include a rule review with each session, especially those with nonmember participation.

COMMON RULES

- Walk, do not run.

Rules and Precautions for High-Risk Locations

In any aquatic environment, certain areas can be more dangerous than others. Effective lifeguards closely supervise the areas where accidents occur most frequently (**figure 2.1**). The following section describes each area's potential dangers along with some suggested safety rules. (For more on safety and water play elements, see chapter 11.)

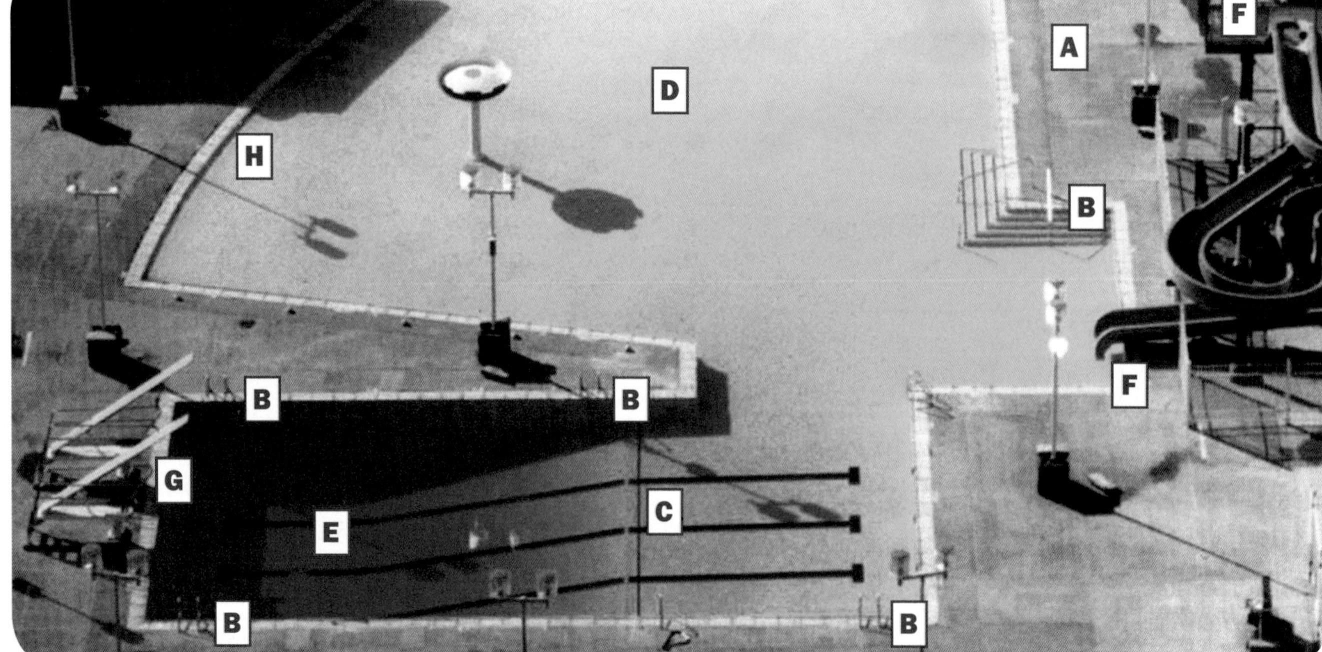

Figure 2.1 Some high-risk areas: (A) Pool deck; (B) Ladders; (C) Lifeline; (D) Shallow water; (E) Deep water; (F) Slides; (G) Springboard diving area; (H) Zero-depth entry. *Photo courtesy of Water Design, Inc.*

Entrance

Trying to get into the water as quickly as possible often leads swimmers to run to the pool from dressing rooms or entrances (**figure 2.2**). A wet and slippery deck poses a high risk, and one swimmer can easily collide with another or with the deck itself.

Pool deck

Running and rough play are the primary concerns on the pool deck. Many falls are the result of runners skidding or bumping into other patrons. Nonswimmers can be knocked into the water by people running on the deck. Good-natured rough play can escalate, causing participants or bystanders to be pushed or knocked to the ground or into the water. This behavior detracts from the enjoyment of others at your facility.

Obstructions on the deck

Sunbathers lying too close to the pool's edge can cause swimmers walking around the pool to stumble or trip. Generally, sunbathers should stay at least 6 feet from the edge to allow adequate room for swimmers to enter and exit the water (**figure 2.3**); however, know any requirements imposed by your own state or local health codes. A 2- to 4-inch-wide safety stripe placed at least 6 feet from the pool's perimeter can help remind patrons to observe this rule.

Do not permit breakable items in the deck area.

COMMON RULES

- Be considerate and play safely. No pushing or rough play.

COMMON RULES

- Sunbathe at least 6 feet from the edge of the pool.
- Only plastic containers and toys are allowed at the pool, observation deck, and locker/shower areas.

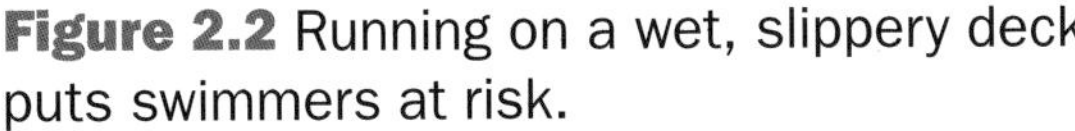

Figure 2.2 Running on a wet, slippery deck puts swimmers at risk.

Figure 2.3 Keep sunbathers away from the edge of the pool.

COMMON RULES

- Use ladders only for getting into or out of the water.
- Only one swimmer on the ladder at a time.

Ladders

Ladders (**figure 2.4**) are to be used only for getting into and out of the pool; other uses can pose hazards. People who sit on the ladders to talk can block access for tired swimmers. Other dangers include swimmers who use ladders to pull themselves underwater and back to the surface; they risk getting caught in a rung, shoved off the ladder, or stepped on. Slippery ladders are dangerous when swimmers swing on them or dive from them. Swimmers who swim between the ladder and the wall risk being caught, either on the surface or underwater. Inspect ladders daily and report any dangerous conditions, such as loose ladders and damaged rungs.

Figure 2.4 Allow ladders to be used only for entering and exiting the pool.

Pool gutters

Pool overflow gutters or troughs pose several potential dangers. Nonswimmers may use the gutters to travel from shallow to deep water, "wall walking" along the side of the pool hand over hand. Danger can arise if the nonswimmer is pushed away from the wall or attempts to climb out of the water and traps a knee or elbow in the gutter. If you spot a nonswimmer moving along the gutter, have the person exit the pool on the nearest ladder and return to shallow water.

Gutters are often slippery. Prohibit patrons from standing on the gutters or climbing into them. An arm, hand, leg, or foot can get wedged into the gutter and cause an injury, particularly if the person loses balance.

Children may want to turn and grab the gutter for support while jumping into the water. Trying to turn around while in the air may result in injury, so stop this activity immediately. Remind children to jump first, and then turn and swim to the side.

COMMON RULES

- Nonswimmers are allowed in shallow water only (water lower than the person's armpits).
- Exit the pool using the ladders.
- Jump clear of the gutter when entering the pool.

Lifelines

Lifelines mark the breakpoint between shallow and deep water (**figure 2.5**) and help define zones for both patrons and lifeguards. The chief danger with lifelines is small children or nonswimmers who move into deep water by pulling themselves along the lifelines. A nonswimmer who is pushed or otherwise loses hold of the line while in deep water will be in danger. People should not sit, hang, or play on lifelines: a lifeline submerged by a chatting swimmer is much more difficult for a distressed swimmer to find.

The lifelines should be strong and strung tightly enough to be visible and support panicky swimmers: the lifeline should not submerge more than a foot when supporting an adult whose head is above water. Lifelines should be in place at all times, except during end-to-end activities such as lap swim. If only a few lanes are set up for lap swimming, a lifeline should be strung across the lanes not used for end-to-end activities. A zero-depth pool should have a lifeline marking the 2.5- to 3-foot depth. (A facility will need lifelines of different lengths to fit various swim area configurations.)

COMMON RULES

- All youth (and any adult swimmer who gives concern) must take a safety swim test and wear a safety band at the pool or swim area.
- Use lifelines only for temporary support.

The water

Any water area is potentially hazardous if swimmers are not careful. One general concern is the use of flotation devices such as inner tubes and plastic toys. These can be dangerous if a nonswimming user floats into deep water or the device deflates and traps the person in it. These swimming aids are even more dangerous on crowded days when swimmers may accidentally bump into them, causing the user to fall away from the flotation device. They also

Figure 2.5 Lifelines separate shallow water areas from deep water areas.

COMMON RULES

- Only Coast Guard–approved PFDs are permitted.
- Adults must actively supervise children at all times.
- Breath-holding and prolonged underwater swimming are prohibited.

obstruct the lifeguard's view of the bottom of the pool. When someone is using a flotation device, it may be impossible for lifeguards to judge their swimming skills—until the person becomes separated from the device.

Many parents buy swimming aids for their children and perhaps gain a false sense of security from them. Parents are responsible for supervising their children at all times, whether or not the children are using swimming aids. Nonswimmers require a parent or adult guardian within arm's reach at all times. But keep in mind that parental presence does not mean that you do not have to keep watch on those children as well.

A second general concern in any aquatic facility is patrons entering the water at an unsafe depth. Consider a nonswimmer unknowingly entering deep water or a swimmer diving into the shallow end of the pool.

Depth markers are necessary on every side of the pool, on the vertical wall (if possible) and on the deck or coping. Note depths in the American system (feet and inches) and the metric system (meters and centimeters) so everyone will understand the depth. At some pools, a contour depth line, usually marked on a wall or fence beside the pool, provides a profile of the pool's depth. Patrons can easily stand next to the contour line to see exactly how deep the water is in relation to their height.

A third general concern is underwater swimming and breath-holding activities. Underwater swimmers can be jumped on, possibly suffering injuries. Underwater swimmers also can black out from breath-holding activities and hyperventilation because they take a series of deep breaths before swimming across the pool underwater. This decreases the amount of carbon dioxide in the blood, and because carbon dioxide tells the brain when to breathe, that reduction interferes with the breathing process. In effect, a swimmer can black out—and possibly drown—because of failure to breathe when necessary. For lifeguards, it can be hard to observe people swimming underwater, making the practice even more dangerous. (For additional information on hyperventilation, see chapter 3.)

Do not allow swimmers to do prolonged underwater swims or breath-holding activities. If you see someone performing these activities, intervene, using the Q-1-2 system. Be alert for high-risk activities such as the following:

- Hyperventilating
- Swimming multiple lengths or widths underwater
- Performing multiple sprints without taking breaths between strokes
- Breath-holding games or contests

Shallow water

Shallow water is a relationship of water depth to swimmer height. For small children, the shallow end of your pool may still be deep. Shallow water is considered water that is lower than the individual swimmer's armpits.

The primary dangers in shallow water are diving and dunking. Even an experienced diver may hit the bottom, causing injuries to the fingers, hands, head, neck, or back. Depths should be marked at regular intervals and at 1-foot changes in water depth and contour to alert divers to the conditions. Standing front dives require that the water be at least 9 feet deep. (See the appendix for YMCA guidelines on diving and water depth.)

Dunking is also a common activity for playful children and adults. The unsuspecting swimmer may ingest water and become scared or be injured by hitting the side or bottom of the pool. Rules should prohibit dunking and rough play.

COMMON RULES

- Diving is allowed only in marked areas.
- Play safely. No dunking.

Danger!

Shallow Water, No Diving

To promote the safety of swimmers, any facility with water shallower than 9 feet deep requires posted warning signs indicating that diving in shallow water is not allowed. These signs are posted on the deck near the edge of the pool and on walls adjacent to shallow water. They should be visible to anyone entering the pool and approaching shallow water.

Signs can be posted in a variety of ways:

- Lettering painted on the deck
- Tiled lettering embedded in the deck
- The universal "No diving" symbol tiled into or painted on the deck
- Plastic signs mounted on walls, fences, or stands

Because most spinal cord injuries occur the first time someone is at a facility, it is crucial to warn patrons of hazards. Multiple signs placed in strategic locations can help prevent injuries.

COMMON RULES

- Deep diving entries are prohibited.
- Diving from the deck is allowed only where the water is more than 9 feet deep.

Deep water

Those who are most in danger in deep water (**figure 2.6**) are nonswimmers and underwater swimmers. The nonswimmers can be spotted moving to the deep water along the gutter, on the deck, or from the diving board. Before entering the water, they may look apprehensive and usually have their arms folded or wrapped around themselves. Prevent nonswimmers from getting into the deep water. As noted previously, lifelines should be in place between the deep and shallow water, except where end-to-end activities such as lap swimming are taking place.

All children (and any adult patron with questionable swimming abilities) should take a safety swim test and wear a swim test band showing they passed before being allowed to swim in the deep water (for more on safety swim testing, see the sidebar on this page and also chapter 3).

Figure 2.6 Deep water can be extremely dangerous to nonswimmers or underwater swimmers.

Safety Swim Test

It is best to give a swim test to all youth and have them wear color-coded bands, for example:

- Give green bands to those who pass the deep-water test.
- Give yellow bands to those who pass the shallow-water test but not the deep-water test. Yellow-band swimmers may not enter water that is more than armpit deep.
- Give red bands to nonswimmers—those who do not pass or will not take the shallow-water test. Nonswimmers may not use the deep end of the pool at any time, and they require active adult supervision at all times. For children, this means the adult is within arm's reach. Depending on depth of shallow water, PFDs may be required.
- Swim tests may be given to adults who give concern.

For details about giving safety swim tests, see chapter 3.

Masks, fins, and snorkels may lure poor swimmers into deep water by providing a false sense of security. Keep a close watch on anyone using such equipment (if your facility allows its use). Goggles, while safe in water up to 5 feet deep, should not be worn at greater depths. The pressure on the eyes may cause discomfort or injury.

Allow diving from the deck only where the water is more than 9 feet deep.

Starting blocks

Starting blocks and platforms (**figure 2.7**) pose a significant hazard, especially to the inexperienced swimmer. No one should be allowed to dive from a starting block or platform except during a supervised competitive swim program or under proper supervision during instruction. Your management should check local and state bathing codes for guidelines on placement of the blocks and the water depth required. They should also check their insurance carrier's regulations. YMCA of the USA recommends that starting blocks be placed in

COMMON RULES

- Starting blocks are for competitive swimming program use only.
- Only dive in water at least 9 feet deep.

Figure 2.7 Starting blocks and platforms should be capped off except when used for a competitive event or supervised program.

the deep end (with a water depth of at least 5 feet) and that dives should be taught in water at least 9 feet deep. YMCA of the USA also recommends that coaches prohibit swimmers from performing "pike," "scoop," and "shoot" starts from the starting blocks, even if the water depth is 5 feet or deeper.

If the starting blocks or platforms cannot be removed during recreational swims, YMCA of the USA recommends that they be capped and that warning signs be posted to stop patrons from using them. (Also see the appendix about risk management involving starting blocks.)

Slides

Slides, which vary in height, shape, and location, can provide safe fun as long as proper precautions are taken.

The speed of a swimmer entering the water from a slide depends on the height, friction, and design of the slide and the alignment of the swimmer. For example, a swimmer who enters 3-foot-deep water at a near vertical angle from a slide that is 6 to 12 feet high achieves the same velocity as someone diving from a 1-meter diving board, which can cause spinal injury if the swimmer's head hits the bottom of the pool or another swimmer.

COMMON RULES

- Swimming is prohibited in the slide area.
- Move away from the bottom of the slide immediately.
- Use only the ladder to get onto the slide.
- One person on the slide at a time.
- Go down the slide feetfirst in a sitting position. Headfirst sliding is prohibited.
- Cross your legs when sliding.

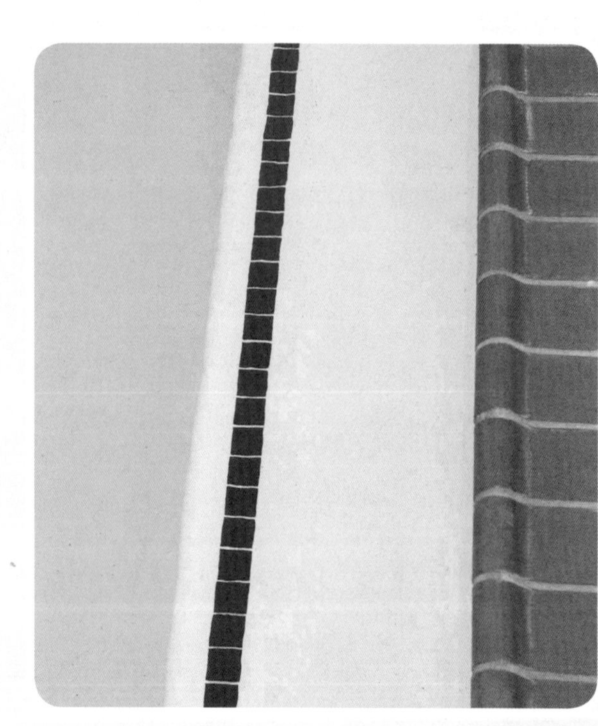

Underwater Safety Ledges

Some older swimming pools have underwater ledges, sometimes called *safety ledges,* constructed so that swimmers can stand up in deep water at the side of the pool. These ledges present a hazard related to head and spinal injuries. If it is difficult to see the ledge, a swimmer can dive or jump into deep water and hit it unexpectedly. To reduce or eliminate this possibility, black stripes can be painted on the top side of the ledge with a black line on the border so swimmers can identify the location and width of the ledge.

Pools with slides require at least one lifeguard whose main responsibility is to control the slide area. Have swimmers enter the water feetfirst in a sitting position to avoid head injuries. Have them cross their legs while sliding to prevent groin and internal injuries. Watch carefully that each slider returns to the surface and clears the area before the next person begins; lifeguards then signal when it is safe for the next person to start sliding.

Insist that the area at the bottom of the slide be kept open to avoid injuries to swimmers. The plunge area of the slide should be separated from the rest of the pool by a floating lifeline. Also be aware that outdoor slides can get hot enough to cause burns, particularly on hot days. Outdoor slides should have a water spray to prevent burns. See chapter 11 for more on slides and aquatic attractions.

Recreational springboard diving areas

Diving off a 1-meter board (**figure 2.8**) may be done either in a separate well or in an area of the pool that is at least 11 feet, 6 inches deep and measures at least 16 feet, 6 inches from the tip of the diving

Figure 2.8 A 1-meter board.

COMMON RULES

- Use the ladder to get on the diving board.
- Keep the area under the board clear of swimmers at all times.
- Only one diver is allowed on the board at a time.
- Sitting on the guardrails is prohibited.
- Wait for the previous diver to swim clear before diving.
- Only one bounce is allowed.
- Dive off the front of the board only.
- Hands must enter the water first in headfirst dives.
- Swim to the ladder immediately after diving.
- Swim in designated areas only.
- Only front dives are allowed.
- Use 3-meter boards and towers for competitive events only.

Risks Associated With Small-Facility Pool Designs and Diving Boards

As a lifeguard, you may find yourself guarding small-facility pools—such as therapy pools and those found in private day-care facilities, hotels, and apartment complexes—that present risks involving diving and diving boards. It is important that you understand these risks and the guidelines for depth marking so you can assure a safe work environment.

Most spinal cord injuries in small-facility pools result from diving into shallow water. Facility management should clearly mark depths on the deck near the edge of the pool, on the side of the pool coping, and on each side of the breakpoint that distinguishes shallow water from deep water. Where the water is shallow, signs that read "Danger! Shallow Water—No Diving" are necessary on the deck, on fences or walls enclosing the pool, and on a stand at the entrance to the pool area.

Hazards associated with diving into deep water, especially in small-facility pools, often relate to the configuration of the bottom and sides of the pool and the placement of the diving board. Two specific pool designs present an increased risk for spinal injuries associated with diving from a diving board: hopper-bottom and spoon-shaped pools.

Hopper-bottom pools

The hopper-bottom pool slopes on all four sides from the deepest point of the pool up to the breakpoint (**figure 2.9**). There is generally a very limited landing area for diving in the deepest part of the pool; in fact, diving into a hopper-bottom pool is like diving into a funnel. The sides of the pool all angle toward the deepest point, which may be only 2 feet by 2 feet. The depth markers on the deck and sides of the pool indicate the depth at the deepest point but do not give any indication of the side depths. The diver may think the depth is safe but find it shallower than expected because of the sloping sides. As a result, anyone who dives in the deep water area could strike the bottom or the upslope of the pool.

Spoon-shaped pools

Another design that creates potential hazards is the spoon-shaped pool (**figure 2.10**). The bottom contour of this pool gives a false sense of depth and bottom surface area throughout the deep section of the pool. If a diving board is present, the distance from the end of the board to the upslope of the pool bottom is greatly reduced in spoon-shaped pools, as it is in hopper-bottom pools. Striking the slope can cause serious neck and back injuries. The bottom also slopes up under the diving board and along the side.

Management should carefully assess the depth of a small-facility pool to assure minimum standards are met before diving is permitted. Research has shown that it is dangerous to dive from the deck into water less than 9 feet deep. If the pool is no deeper than 9 feet, do not allow diving from the deck. Further, it is best to remove the diving board from any pool that is less than 11 feet 6 inches deep and measures less than 16 feet 6 inches from the tip of the diving board to the start of the upslope.

If management decides not to remove the diving board from a small-facility pool, only feetfirst entries should be allowed off the diving board. Do not let people run on the diving board or attempt to travel for long distances through the air. In addition, caution people from aiming toward the side if there is the slightest chance that they will

- strike the upslope of the pool that rises from the deepest section to the shallow section;
- strike a floating line marking the boundary of the diving area; or
- strike a swimmer inside the diving area.

Key factors in preventing diving injuries are correct diving instruction, active supervision of swimmers, and participant awareness of the hazards of diving in shallow water. To minimize the risk of injury, conduct diving instruction from the deck in no less than 9 feet of water. Catastrophic injuries can be avoided by prohibiting diving in facilities that do not meet standards. All swimming pools with diving equipment should display diving rules and regulations near the boards and towers such as those listed in this chapter. It is your responsibility as a lifeguard to strictly enforce these rules.

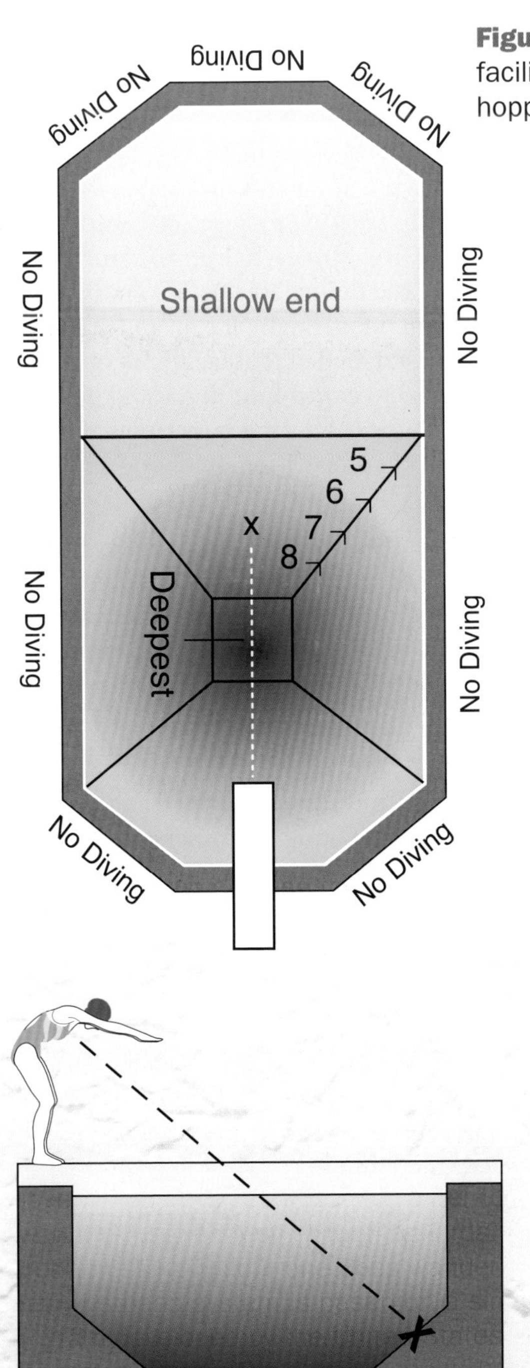

Figure 2.9 Typical small-facility or residential hopper-bottom pool.

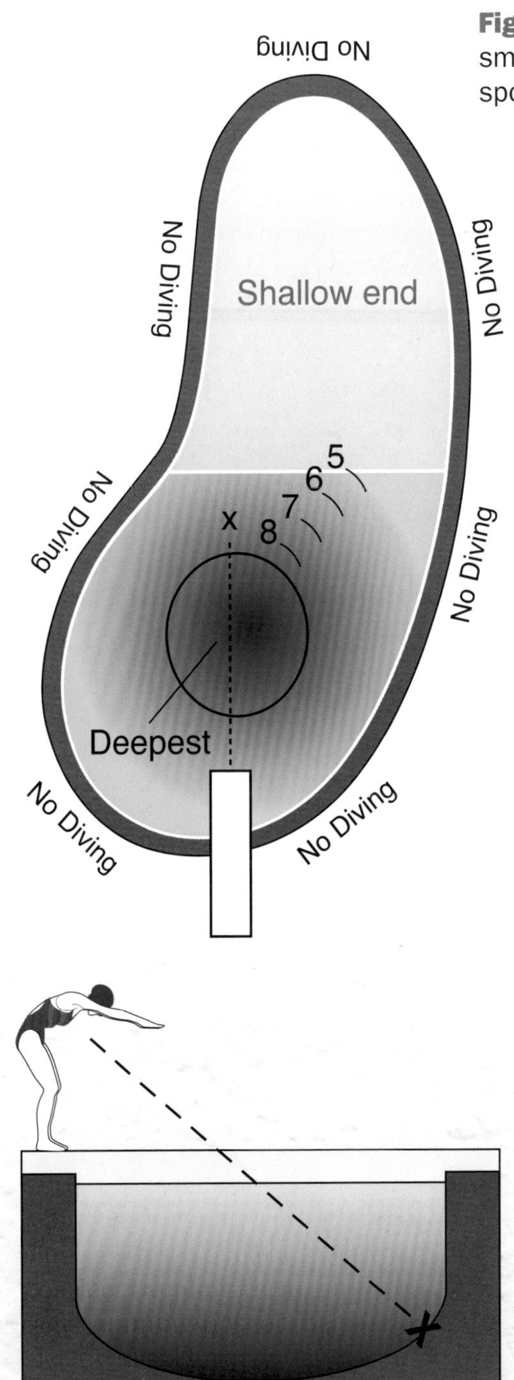

Figure 2.10 Typical small-facility or residential spoon-shaped pool.

board to the start of the upslope (the angled section of the pool bottom that transitions between the deep and shallow ends). In either case, give these diving areas special attention and enforce the rules consistently. Many accidents associated with diving can be prevented by vigilant and alert lifeguards. Some of the many causes of diving accidents include the condition and arrangement of the equipment and diving areas, visibility into the water, numerous weather factors, and the depth and distance to the upslope of the pool bottom.

Check the diving boards regularly throughout the day. Set the fulcrum as far forward as possible, and chain or lock it in position to keep the board stiff for recreational use. Require each diver to return to the surface and exit the diving area before another diver approaches. Watch for rough play on and around the boards. It is recommended that facility management assign a lifeguard to control the entry and plunge area of the springboard during busy times. See the appendix for more information on diving and risk management.

Do not allow recreational use of a 3-meter board or tower if this equipment is available in your facility. Such equipment is for competition diving only and should be used only by participants in a supervised program with specially trained diving instructors.

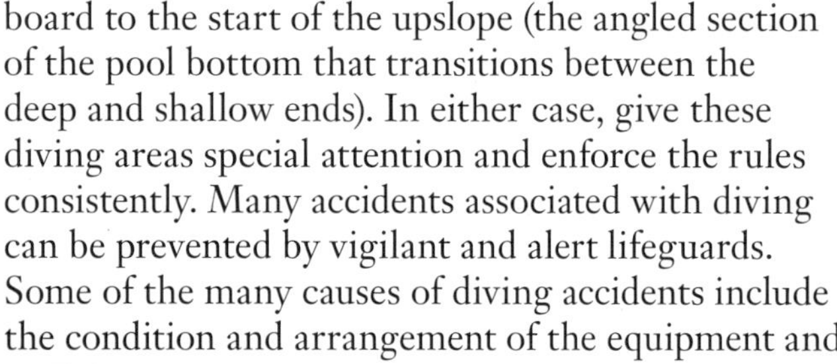

Figure 2.11 Be sure to check the area around and below your elevated lifeguard stand.

Lifeguard towers and equipment

Lifeguard towers and stands may present a hazard because they attract young swimmers, who often gather at the foot of a stand, potentially obscuring the lifeguard's view. Be sure to scan the water under and around towers in your range of vision (**figure 2.11**). Older patrons may enjoy socializing with the lifeguards. Keep your conversations brief and continue to scan your area while talking.

COMMON RULES

- Lifeguard towers shall be used only by lifeguards.
- Keep the area around the lifeguard tower clear.
- Emergency equipment is for lifeguard use only.

Ring buoys and other safety devices may attract swimmers. However, playing with safety equipment can be dangerous and can make critical rescue tools unavailable at the moment of an emergency. Emergency equipment is to be used by certified lifeguards (or under their instruction) for safety and rescue purposes only.

Wading pools and zero-depth entry pools

The reason most facilities decide to add wading pools or zero-depth entry pools (**figure 2.12**) is to provide a safe haven for nonswimmers and younger children to enjoy the water. Parents often supervise their nonswimming children in these areas, but sometimes they become involved in conversation and

Figure 2.12 With close supervision, zero-depth entry pools provide a safe area for nonswimmers to enjoy.

COMMON RULES

- Walk (do not run).
- Play safely (no rough play).
- All nonswimming children must be accompanied by an adult.
- Adults must stay within arm's reach of nonswimming children.
- No diving.

do not notice that a child is experiencing difficulty. Parents should be within arm's reach of their children; however, do not be lulled into thinking that your responsibility is covered by parents' supervision of their children. Parents may well be expecting the same thing of you.

Accidents in wading pools or zero-depth entry pools are typically the result of rough play by older children or nonswimmers who are old enough to be in the main pool. They run and splash, creating an environment where people can be knocked under the water or onto the deck; direct them to stop.

Others who frequent wading pools or zero-depth entry pools are adults who want to sit in shallow water or to watch the children play. On very hot days, such pools may become congested, and a wet deck combined with crowded conditions makes slipping and falling into the pools or on the surrounding deck a real danger.

Young children tend to spend increased time in wading pools and zero-depth entry pools. Parents should be educated to check diapers often and escort children to the restroom regularly.

Figure 2.13 Spa.

Spas and whirlpools

Spas (**figure 2.13**) add another layer of concern for lifeguards. If your facility has a spa, learn your state's codes for its maintenance and use, and add this area to your list of danger zones. Physical hazards of spas include drowning, falling, entrapment, and electrocution. Often, drownings and falls are attributed to medical conditions or to the use of alcohol in the area. Electrocutions result from the use of electrical devices in the area.

When people who are overheated from vigorous exercise or have just used a sauna get into a spa, the danger of heat-related illness increases greatly. After exercising, people should cool down properly before entering the spa, and vigorous exercise should not be allowed in the spa.

Spas may attract the elderly, individuals on blood pressure medication, and pregnant women. These persons may be at greater risk and should not use the spa. Check that management posts the rules of the whirlpool or spa prominently, and make sure you enforce the rules rigidly.

Recommended times for length of stay in spas and hot tubs:

<98°F	No limit is necessary
100–102°F	Maximum stay of 10 minutes
104°F and above	Significant element of danger, stay out of the spa

The maximum temperature for water in a spa is 102°F. Reddening skin or dizziness is a definite signal that it is time to get out of the spa no matter what the water temperature is.

Some doctors and therapists take the attitude that you will know when you have had enough and it is time to get out of the spa. This is not a good practice. Here are some more effective ways that management can promote safe spa usage:

- Post signs with suggested maximum time limits.
- On a nearby wall in clear view of all users, place clocks with numbers large enough to read from a distance.
- Place a thermometer on the wall with numbers large enough to read from a distance, or place one in the spa itself. However, if the thermometer in the spa goes missing often, an alternative is to post the water temperature on a chalk board or a dry-erase board every hour.
- YMCA of the USA recommends placing a timer on the water jets that shuts them off after 10 minutes. Locate the reset button at least 10 feet from the spa so users must physically leave the tub to turn the water jets on again.

Near the spa, posted signs are necessary that warn against overuse of the spa, including a warning that long exposure can lead to dizziness, resulting in such problems as impaired judgment and vision. Adjacent showers are important for preliminary soap showering and for cooling off after spa immersion.

Be aware that spa areas require posted rules and regulations; check with management if you have concerns about your facility's signage. For additional information about whirlpool or spa management, see chapter 14 and the *YMCA Pool Operations Manual (3rd ed.).*

Enforcing the Rules

Once rules are established, lifeguards are responsible for consistently enforcing the rules at all times. Enforcing rules is challenging. No one likes to be the bad guy, and no one likes to be corrected. But professional lifeguards are responsible for providing a safe environment where patrons can have fun in and around the water.

Discipline is necessary whenever someone's behavior

- could result in injury to the individual or others;
- could result in damage to property; or
- infringes on the comfort and enjoyment of others in the area.

COMMON RULES

For safety reasons, do not use the spa if you have any of the following conditions:

- High blood pressure
- Heart disease
- Respiratory problems
- Pregnancy
- Diabetes
- Emotional disorders
- Stress
- Epilepsy or seizure disorders

Cool down for at least 5 minutes after exercise before entering the spa.

Shower thoroughly before using the spa. No lotions, oils, and perfumes.

Use the spa only when accompanied by another person. Do not use the spa alone.

You must be 12 or older to use the spa.

Children over age 12 must be accompanied by a responsible adult.

Do not use the spa if you are using alcohol, anticoagulants, antihistamines, vasoconstrictors, vasodilators, stimulants, hypnotics, or tranquilizers.

Stay in the spa no longer than 10 minutes.

Enter the spa feetfirst. Do not dive or jump.

Food or drinks are not allowed in the spa.

Keep your head above water in the spa.

Remove your shoes before entering the spa area.

Avoid aerobic exercise in the spa.

Failure to follow these rules may result in serious or fatal injury.

Communication is the first step to enforcing the rules. In addition, keep in mind these guidelines for enforcing the rules at your facility:

- Know all rules and the procedures for enforcing them.
- Be consistent, enforcing the same rule in the same way for everyone. Do not make exceptions for friends, fellow employees, or adults. Also, enforce the rules in the same way each and every day.
- React immediately. Blow your whistle as soon as you detect a rule being broken. The patron will usually know what behavior has drawn your attention.
- Be specific. If there is a question about what behavior is prohibited, be specific in describing your concern. For example, you may say, "I saw you running on the deck. That's against the rules because it's unsafe: you might fall or knock someone down. Please walk." You have pointed out the incorrect behavior, indicated why it was a problem, and explained the proper behavior. (See Q-1-2 in chapter 1.)
- Provide alternative behaviors if you can. You might encourage the runner on the deck to take a group to the grassy recreation area, where there is room for such activities.

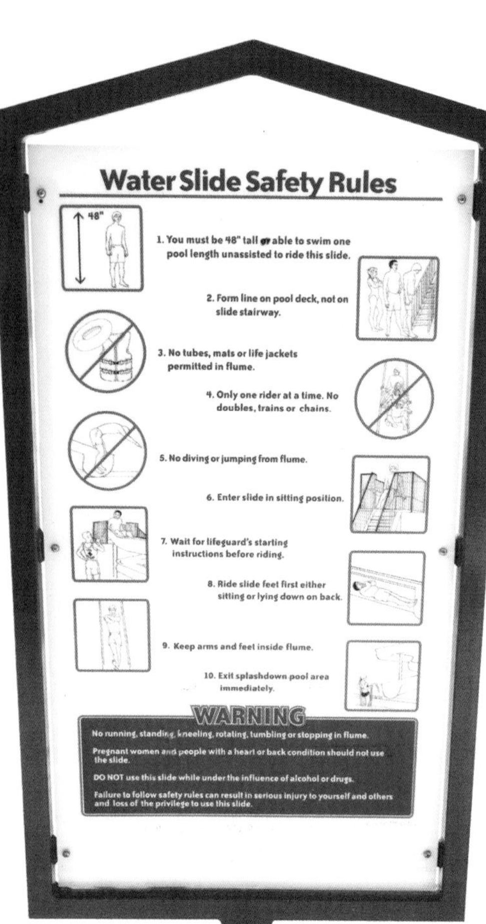

Your primary responsibility is to guard your area. Enforcing rules is just one part of that duty. It is important that you never stop scanning the water. If a rule enforcement discussion becomes lengthy or draws your attention away from your assigned area, signal for assistance.

By following these guidelines, you will earn the respect and cooperation of those who use your swimming facility. And each time you enforce the rules, you gain experience in how to deal with people successfully.

Special Situations

Although every facility has rules of conduct, some patrons inevitably try to test those rules. As an employee of a recreational facility, you are responsible for ensuring that one patron does not endanger the safety or well-being of others. This section is designed to help you handle those situations. Your management may also post emergency contact phone numbers in the pool office should you need additional assistance.

Crowd control

If an accident occurs, people might gather and create congestion. You may be put in charge of moving the patrons from the accident area. Moving the patrons will allow staff to deal with the situation without interference or gawking. Stay composed and be respectful as you move patrons to a prearranged area, such as a locker room or another part of the facility or grounds. Remind everyone to remain calm, as the situation is being taken care of by the facility's trained staff.

If you are in a single-lifeguard situation, be sure your facility has an emergency action plan (EAP) for you to obtain assistance with crowd control immediately when it is needed. Another method of helping with crowd control in single-lifeguard situations is to teach members to clear the pool when they hear one long whistle blast. Post signage to remind patrons.

Theft

Your facility's management will probably post conspicuous notices regarding responsibility for loss of personal property. However, be alert to any theft. If an incident is reported to you, notify the manager or assistant manager so he or she may contact law enforcement officials.

Do not accuse a person of theft. Present your evidence to law enforcement authorities and let them respond. You could be charged with making a false accusation if you act hastily and have no proof of your claim. Speak only of what you know to be true or what others (whom you identify to law enforcement) have stated in your presence. Make sure you fill out the appropriate incident report form and obtain statements from witnesses before they leave the scene (see chapter 10).

Sexual activity

Do not permit sexual behavior in your facility. Diplomatically control these situations from the start of the swimming season.

Indecent exposure

Exposing oneself in public is a crime in most states. If someone indecently exposes himself or herself, ask the person to cover up immediately. If your request is ignored or if the behavior is repeated, contact the management and police. Be aware that most states have laws that allow mothers to breast-feed in public places. Speak with your supervisor if you have questions.

Disregard for lifeguard authority

Anyone who disregards a lifeguard's authority is creating a risk. Summon the manager or assistant manager with a prearranged signal, such as a raised, clenched fist, to assist you if patrons ignore the rules. Repeated disregard of authority is grounds for banning a person from the facility. If necessary, management can contact local authorities to escort a person from the scene.

Working at a facility that your friends frequent can put you and them in an awkward situation. You are duty-bound to consistently enforce the rules of the facility, no matter who violates them. It may help to explain that to your friends if they are causing problems.

Conflicts or disturbances

Use your customer relations skills when situations arise. In a conflict, you can use the PACA problem-solving process (see chapter 1). When you are trying to resolve such situations, keep the following guidelines in mind:

- Keep your emotions in check and stay calm. Remember that the conflict is not about you, so do not take it personally.
- Listen actively and acknowledge what is being said. Use "I" statements and restate what the other person said to be sure you understand.
- Be respectful.
- Speak with a purpose.
- Ask all concerned to state the problem, their feelings, and what they want.
- Maintain control of the situation and the process of resolution.

If a situation arises between patrons in the pool or pool area and you cannot resolve it quickly, call for an off-duty lifeguard or your supervisor, who can either deal with the patrons or change places with you. Your facility should have a prearranged signal to alert other lifeguards or your supervisor of such situations. This way, your zone in the pool remains covered. As a last resort, you can clear the pool until proper backup arrives.

If you are having difficulty getting patrons to resolve their dispute, be sure to involve your head lifeguard or supervisor. The head lifeguard or supervisor should separate the individuals, asking them to move to different areas, and then talk with each of them separately. If the situation escalates, contact the police for assistance. Be sure to complete an incident report form after any disturbance and obtain witness statements.

Violence

The first step in dealing with violence in the pool area is to know and practice your facility's emergency plan for preventing and responding to violence. Know and practice your facility's procedures for dealing with violence as you do other emergency plans.

One key to the success of emergency plans is your professionalism. Effective lifeguards command authority, and you can promote order with your professional appearance, attitude, and behavior. Rules are also critical tools for preventing dangerous behavior. Educate patrons about your facility's rules and be sure that you can explain to them why the rules exist. Enforce all rules consistently and effectively.

If you suspect a violent act may happen, immediately notify your supervisor. If a violent act clearly is about to happen, immediately contact both your supervisor and the authorities. Follow your facility's procedures. Your priority is the safety of your patrons and yourself. Once authorities arrive, listen to and follow their instructions and let them take charge.

Following a violent incident, work with management to inform those who were involved in the violence of when, if ever, they will be allowed to return to the swimming area or facility. Be sure to complete an incident report and gather witness statements. After a violent incident, management will have to decide when it is appropriate and safe to reopen the swimming area. This includes determining whether lifeguards are mentally prepared to resume their duties or if replacement lifeguards are required to finish their shifts.

Substance abuse

Prohibit people who are abusing substances such as alcohol or other drugs from all aquatic areas; their lack of judgment and reduced physical abilities could easily endanger both them and other patrons. Be aware of signs or behavior patterns that are characteristic of substance abuse, such as these:

- Unusual tiredness or poor muscle control
- The odor of alcohol, tobacco, or other drugs
- Unsteadiness and lack of coordination
- Unusual detachment from the group
- Unusual changes in mood or attitude
- Unexplained lack of interest in normal activities
- Unusual giddiness
- Preoccupation with drug-related clothing, signs, or other paraphernalia
- Obvious slurring of words
- Public use of alcohol, tobacco, or other drugs

If you suspect that a patron in your area is under the influence of alcohol or other drugs, watch the person carefully and request that the manager or assistant manager join you. If the manager agrees that the patron is acting suspiciously, and the behavior does not appear to be caused by a medical condition, your manager can ask the patron to leave. Encourage the patron to have someone take him or her home. Your manager may authorize calling a taxi or providing other transportation assistance. If the person will not leave, contact the police. Once the person has left, document the behavior on an incident report form. The manager may inform the parents of people involved.

Concern for younger patrons

If you think you see signs of child abuse or neglect or of drug abuse in children, notify your manager or the appropriate staff member and explain what you have noticed. That staff person can then contact the child's parents and take whatever steps are deemed appropriate and necessary, including referrals to agencies and services. (See the appendix for more on preventing child abuse.)

Challenges unique to your facility

Although the section you have just read may provide some basis for your decision making, each facility has its own unique challenges and its own rules. And to a large degree, lifeguards must make their own decisions about what constitutes a potentially dangerous situation. Study the layout of your facility and the rules that govern it. If you see potential problem areas, bring them to the attention of the management. Then assist in the creative process of establishing rules that will preserve a safe and fun environment.

Review

Review Topics

Successful lifeguards are aware of the aquatic facility and its possible dangers. This chapter covered pool hazards and the rules that protect people from them. Here are some key points to know in this chapter:

1) Why rules are necessary for aquatic facilities
2) How to clearly communicate the facility's rules to patrons
3) High-risk areas in aquatic facilities and the kinds of risks they present
4) Special rules for high-risk areas
5) How to handle special situations, such as crowding, theft, and improper sexual behavior
6) How to manage conflicts

Review Questions

1. Why are rules necessary for aquatic facilities?
2. Why is consistent enforcement of the rules so important?
3. Describe how you would respond to someone who disregards your authority as a lifeguard.
4. Name six of the high-risk locations in most aquatic facilities.
5. List the rules for the high-risk locations you named in question 4.
6. Describe the risks associated with diving.
7. This chapter recommends a minimum depth that water should be before lifeguards allow anyone to dive from the deck. What is that depth?
8. List some of the risks associated with spas and whirlpools.
9. What are some guidelines for handling an incident of theft? Of violence? Of substance abuse?

CHAPTER 3

Accident Prevention

Accident prevention is a major part of the lifeguard's job. Your knowledge of the different conditions that can affect patron safety is key to your effectiveness as a lifeguard. To create a safe environment, lifeguards use a number of systems that help prevent accidents. These systems help you maintain vigilance and control of your area of responsibility at all times.

In this chapter, you will learn the following:

- Physical conditions that may affect swimmers
- Safety check systems
- Severe weather risks

3
CHAPTER
Manuel
Aquatics

Physical Conditions That May Affect Swimmers

Lifeguards must be aware of physical conditions that can cause discomfort or put swimmers at risk while swimming. Just as important, these conditions can affect lifeguards when they are in the water, whether on the job or at leisure. The ability to recognize these conditions in others and in yourself will allow you to react correctly and calmly.

Panic

Panic is an emotional state in which individuals are overcome by sudden fear and lose the ability to help themselves. Panic usually occurs when a person is faced with a seemingly life-threatening emergency. For example, someone who cramps while swimming and is unaware of the cause or treatment may panic. Regardless of what triggers it, panic can cause a person to drown.

Figure 3.1 When a cramp hits, stay calm and relaxed. Stretch and gently massage the muscle.

Cramps

While guarding, you may notice a distressed swimmer who has a cramp. The actual process of how cramps occur is not fully understood. Cramps can be triggered by dehydration, fatigue, hypothermia, or a lack of sodium (salt), calcium, potassium, or oxygen. Lack of oxygen is one of the most accepted theories for the occurrence of cramps in swimming. Reduction in oxygen results in the buildup of lactic acid in the muscle, causing the muscle to contract beyond its normal range. When enough lactic acid accumulates, the muscle fibers contract and cease functioning, resulting in considerable pain. This condition is called contracture.

Cramps were once thought to be the major cause of drowning, but they are not life threatening if the swimmer does not panic. Most cramps occur in the calf, foot, or hand because these body parts are most active in swimming (**figure 3.1**). They are also the body parts farthest from the heart, so they receive oxygenated blood last, which increases the probability of a cramp.

If you suspect a swimmer is experiencing a cramp, encourage the swimmer to stay calm and relax as much as possible. Ask the swimmer to leave the water if possible (or you may need to assist the distressed swimmer to the side); it is much easier to release a cramp on land. Follow these steps to relieve a cramp:

- First, stretch the cramping muscle. Stretching should be slow and steady, not bouncy.
- Hold the stretch as long as is comfortable. If the cramp is severe, the pain may initially get worse during the stretch but will subside over time.
- Continue to stretch the muscle as long as pain is evident.

- If the cramp occurs while in the water, bend forward as in survival floating and massage the cramped muscle gently, massaging it toward the heart, not away from it. This will increase the blood flow to the area and bring more oxygen to the muscles, relieving the cramp.
- Use a different stroke to swim and take frequent rest periods by floating on the back.
- Once the cramp has released, take a break from swimming to give the muscle time to recover. If it is warm, stay out of the water to rest the cramping muscle and drink plenty of water or a sports drink to replace lost minerals. Remember, returning to activity too soon can result in the speedy return of a cramp.

Swimming after eating

As a lifeguard, you may be asked when it is safe to go back in the water after a meal. Most everyone has heard you should not go swimming for an hour after you eat or you will get a stomach cramp. This may sound like common sense, but swimming is no different from other exercise and poses no special risk after eating. Still, an individual may consider different factors when choosing when to swim after eating:

- How much the patron ate
- What the patron ate
- The patron's physical condition
- How fatigued the patron is
- The water temperature
- How active the patron will be in the water

After eating a large meal, most people do not feel like swimming or participating in any vigorous activity for an hour or more. This is nature's way of keeping the body quiet so the digestive system can start the process of food absorption. Normally when you begin swimming, blood is diverted from your stomach to the muscles that need energy to maintain activity, which slows your digestive and absorption functions.

Tip

Because people do eat and swim, it is common for lifeguards to experience a victim vomiting. If rescue breathing is required, remember that keeping a clear airway is vital.

Breath-holding and hyperventilation

All swimmers must learn to hold their breath as they gain skills and confidence in the water; however, prolonged breath-holding and hyperventilating are dangerous! Make it a priority to prevent breath-holding activities or games of any kind.

When a person breathes normally, inhaling and exhaling regulate the level of carbon dioxide in the body. As the level of carbon dioxide in the bloodstream increases between breaths, it triggers the part of the brain that controls breathing (the medulla oblongata) and tells it to take a breath.

Hyperventilation is excessively deep, rapid breathing. Some people think if they cause themselves to hyperventilate it will increase the oxygen level in their blood and allow them to hold their breath longer and stay underwater longer. This is false. In fact, hyperventilation is very dangerous. Hyperventilation lowers the level of carbon dioxide in the bloodstream by tricking the brain and delaying the signal to take a breath. As the oxygen level in the bloodstream drops, a person can pass out before the body feels a need to breathe. If this happens to someone who is underwater, when the person finally does instinctively take a breath, water can rush in and begin the drowning process.

Prevention and education are critical when dealing with hyperventilation and breath-holding because these activities can so quickly lead to blackouts and drowning. Watch for patrons who talk about wanting to swim the length of the pool underwater. Identify people who are taking rapid, deep breaths or forcefully exhaling at the side before going underwater. Prevent anyone who is hyperventilating from swimming underwater.

Should a swimmer black out underwater, it may be difficult to observe. Sometimes swimmers continue moving erratically even after losing consciousness. Scan carefully so you do not mistake this continued motion for swimming. Be sure to note whether the patron is making forward progress. If you notice that a patron swimming underwater is not moving forward, activate the emergency action plan (EAP) and enter the water immediately to rescue the victim. (See chapter 5 for more on recognizing submerged victims.)

Another danger is swimming on top of the water without taking a breath for long periods of time. Stop these activities and explain why they are dangerous. Be aware that patrons of all ages and swimming skill levels may experiment with breath-holding.

A conscious person who hyperventilates and is breathing too fast, too slowly, noisily, or painfully may require emergency medical services' (EMS) attention to restore appropriate levels of carbon dioxide in the blood. Symptoms of hyperventilation also include tingling in the arms and around the mouth, cramps in the fingers, or sharp chest pains. Continue to watch the person for any complications that might arise. If the person is unconscious, contact EMS and monitor breathing.

Hypoxic Training

While guarding a swim team practice, you may notice the swimmers performing what is called hypoxic training. Hypoxic (low-oxygen) training is achieved by reducing the number of breaths taken while practicing swimming strokes at the surface of the water. Breathing every fifth stroke, for example, is a typical hypoxic training method.

Hypoxic training can be an acceptable way to teach competitive swimmers and other aquatic athletes how to handle the rigors of reduced oxygen in competition provided that it is used with more experienced swimmers in good physical condition and always under specific supervision.

Carefully monitor swimmers engaged in hypoxic training. Do not allow hypoxic training with hyperventilation or prolonged underwater swimming, including swimming the length of the pool underwater. Educate well-meaning but overzealous coaches or instructors about the dangers of hyperventilation and prolonged breath-holding.

Sometimes normal breathing resumes after someone hyperventilating loses consciousness. However, if breathing stops, immediately provide rescue breathing.

Hyperventilation or blackouts brought on by oxygen deprivation can also occur for other reasons, including overexertion—the most common cause of unintentional hyperventilation. During overexertion, the body uses its stored oxygen very quickly, which hastens a lack of oxygen. Overexertion also decreases the body's ability to sense the trigger to breathe. Poorly conditioned or overtaxed swimmers are especially susceptible to overexertion blackouts, so know who is at risk and monitor their behavior closely.

Physical Conditions That May Affect Lifeguards

While these conditions, ear squeeze and sinus squeeze, can be problems for any swimmer, they are of particular concern for lifeguards because they may affect the ability to effectively carry out a rescue.

Ear squeeze

Ear squeeze is pain a swimmer feels within the ear when submerged in the water. When increased water pressure is greater in the outer ear than in the middle ear, the eardrum (tympanic membrane) is stretched inward, which causes the pain. The following methods usually alleviate ear squeeze (Graver 2003):

- Close the mouth, pinch the nostrils, and blow gently.
- Close the mouth, pinch the nostrils, and swallow.

- Close the mouth and jut the jaw forward while yawning.
- Use a combination of these three methods.

These actions increase pressure in the throat, which in turn opens the eustachian tube, which connects the throat and the middle ear, increasing the pressure in the middle ear. When the pressure between the outer and middle ear are equalized, the eardrum returns to its normal position and the pain stops.

When rescuing a victim from the bottom, you will need to clear your ears early and often. Be sure to take time to equalize pressure in your ears when you descend in the water. Try equalizing pressure at every 2 to 5 feet of descent or whenever necessary to relieve discomfort or pain. Failure to equalize can rupture the eardrum, causing potential hearing loss, loss of balance or orientation, and other complications. It is not safe to swim until such an injury is fully healed. It is also unwise to swim underwater when your eustachian tube is clogged or when you have a cold or the flu. This prohibits air from moving through into the middle ear. When a eustachian tube is blocked, trying to equalize pressure increases the risk of a serious ear injury.

Sinus squeeze

When a lifeguard has nasal congestion, pressure associated with increased water depth can cause sharp pain in the sinus area (upper teeth, cheeks, and above the eyes) as well as the ears. This pain may occur within a few feet of the surface. A bad cold may cause the sinus openings (ostia) to swell shut. This makes it difficult for the body to equalize air pressure in the sinuses. When the sinuses are inflamed, they may cause severe pain and may damage sinus membranes. Nose drops or decongestants can sometimes alleviate symptoms, but these remedies can wear off or cause drowsiness. Check with your physician for remedies that will not make you drowsy.

Safety Check Systems

Most camps and youth organizations use one or more safety check systems to quickly account for all patrons. They are especially useful in lakes or river waterfronts where visibility is limited. Each of the safety systems discussed below is useful in different settings. Although management will ultimately determine the systems used, you may be asked to give input. And for any system to work, swimmers must be informed of the procedures. As a lifeguard, you will play a major role in the safety check system educational process.

Safety swim test and band system

In this type of safety system, all youth (and adults who give concern) take a swim test. An off-duty lifeguard conducts the swim test and then gives

Safety Check Systems

Any one of these safety systems will help lifeguards be aware of the number and location of swimmers in the water. Combining safety swim tests with an appropriate group-swimming safety-check system provides an even stronger accident-prevention program.

- Safety swim test and band system
- Safety swim breaks
- Multilevel safety approach
- Buddy system
- Tag board system
- Roll call system

the patron a color-coded safety band based on the results of the swim test. Wristbands and break-away necklaces are common, but bathing caps are also used. The following color coding is widely used:

- Green – advanced swimmers
- Yellow – intermediate swimmers
- Red – beginners and nonswimmers

The advantage of this system is that lifeguards, staff, and patrons can easily spot someone wearing a red or yellow band in an area reserved for advanced swimmers and act quickly to move the patron to a safer area. The system also makes clear to the swimmer what areas of the water are appropriate for him or her.

Set up lifeguard rotation to accommodate swim testing. Remember that swim tests are to be administered by lifeguards who are not in the rotation and who are not on guard duty. Posting swim test times can help manage the safety swim test system and educate parents about the safety swim test.

Figure 3.2 A patron who has passed a deep-water proficiency test receives a green band.

Green band test

For a green wristband (**figure 3.2**), a patron would pass a deep-water proficiency test such as:

- Swimming across the shallow end of the pool once.
- Jumping into water that is over the individual's head and returning to the surface.
- Swimming one length of the pool unassisted and without rest. The swimmer must maintain positive body position (that is, the legs may not drop past a 45-degree angle) for the entire distance of 25 yards. Note: Have the swimmer start at the deep end and travel to the shallow end in case the swimmer tires and needs to stand.
- Treading water for at least 1 minute, and then turning onto the back and floating briefly.
- Swimming (on front or back) to a ladder or the side of the pool and exiting the pool.

Patrons who pass this test would be allowed to swim in any area of the pool. If a swimmer could not complete all of the objectives listed above, the swimmer would be issued a yellow band after passing the shallow-water competency test.

Yellow band test

For a yellow band, a swimmer would pass a shallow-water proficiency test such as:

- Swimming 15 to 20 feet unassisted.

- Floating horizontally and moving from a facedown position to a faceup position.
- Regaining a vertical position (standing up).

Swimmers who pass the shallow-water competency test would be allowed to play in water that is armpit deep or less.

Red band nonswimmers

Those who do not pass the shallow-water proficiency test are marked with red bands and considered nonswimmers. Those who decline to take the test are also considered nonswimmers. Nonswimmers may not use the deep end of the pool at any time.

More Color-Coded Safety

Large beach areas with multiple lifeguard stands likely do not use safety bands to differentiate swimmers with different skill levels because there are simply too many swimmers to test, and there may be no control over who can use the water. However, some beaches are using the colored wristbands to help keep kids from getting lost. Here's how: Paint each lifeguard stand a different color. Give each child a colored wristband that matches the color of the nearest lifeguard stand. Instruct the children that they can swim only in the area near the stand that matches their wristband. This makes it less likely for kids to wander too far away and makes it easier for lifeguards to spot a missing child if one does wander off. This wristband system is based on a similar program developed by the United States Lifesaving Association.

Nonswimmers require active adult supervision, which means that the parent or guardian must be in the water and within arm's reach at all times. The supervising adult may not supervise more than two nonswimming children at once. Some facilities may also require nonswimmers to wear a Coast Guard–approved PFD and to stay within arm's reach of the supervising adult.

At no time may a patron with a red band or a yellow band swim in the deep end of the pool. Intentionally wearing the wrong safety band requires immediate removal from the pool. Lifeguards may retest any person who demonstrates uncertainty or discomfort in the water. Encourage swim lessons at the Y for red- and yellow-band patrons when possible.

Safety swim breaks

The widely used safety swim break system (also called the safety check system) is designed to help give swimmers a rest. On a specified signal, all swimmers must leave the water or sit on the edge of the pool. The lifeguards stay on stands and continue to scan the entire area. This provides swimmers time to use the restroom and gives parents the opportunity to check diapers, which can help reduce the number of fecal accidents in the pool.

Safety breaks are a good opportunity to take pool readings (see chapter 14). Note, however, that active guarding is required if patrons are on the deck. Do not leave patrons in the pool area without the appropriate number of lifeguards.

Be aware that safety checks can be annoying to patrons if overused. Inform swimmers that checks are performed to ensure safety and try to post checks at regular intervals. To make checks less objectionable, consider coupling them with announcements, brief swimming tips, or the beginning of special activities. During safety swim breaks, you can also educate parents and guardians about the multilevel approach to safety.

Multilevel approach to safety

In a multilevel approach to safety, parents, patrons, and lifeguards all work together to ensure aquatic safety. In this system, everyone has some responsibilities.

Parents should

- cooperate with swim testing procedures;
- stay within arm's reach of small children (**figure 3.3**) and nonswimmers;
- reinforce facility rules and promote aquatic safety; and
- support the safety swim break system, which also gives children time to rest and use the restrooms.

Patrons should

- follow posted rules;
- follow the directions of lifeguards; and
- be aware of aquatic safety and provide additional eyes and ears to look out for trouble.

Aquatic staff should

- promote accident prevention (**figure 3.4**);
- educate parents and patrons about the importance of swim lessons for everyone in the family;
- educate patrons that it is always preferable to swim with a buddy; and
- enforce the rules.

By permission from Lifesaving Society 2007.

Figure 3.3 Parents stay within arm's reach of small children.

Figure 3.4 Staff promote accident prevention.

Buddy system

In the buddy system, every swimmer is assigned a buddy of similar ability. If there is an uneven number of swimmers, have a counselor become a partner. This is preferable to forming one group of three because it is more readily apparent to a lifeguard when pairs drift apart than when a trio splits into a pair and a single. Buddies are required to stay close to each other at all times. If one buddy is having difficulty, the other buddy is responsible for signaling for help.

At a unique, predetermined signal, all swimmers must "buddy up": they stop, join hands with their buddies, raise their arms high, and remain stationary (**figure 3.5**). This positioning allows staff members to count buddy groups and account for all swimmers. After a second sounding of the signal, buddies may drop hands and continue their activities.

It is important to sound the signal often so partners remain close together. If any buddies have strayed too far apart to buddy up quickly when you give the signal, warn them that doing so again will result in time out of the water (see the Q-1-2 system in chapter 1). Consistent enforcement helps make the buddy system an effective safety check.

Figure 3.5 At the signal, buddies join hands, raise their arms, and remain still while the lifeguard counts pairs.

Tag board system

In the tag board system, each swimmer receives a name tag. Swimmers hang their tags on a pegboard as they enter the water and remove their tags when they leave the water. It is important that both events are closely monitored throughout the swim period by an extra lifeguard or staff member.

A variation of this system uses color-coded tags with a different color on each side (**figure 3.6**). One color indicates the swimmer is in the water; the other color indicates the swimmer is out of the water. At the end of each swimming period, the group leader can easily check to see that all swimmers have left the water.

If a tag is unaccounted for, an immediate in-water search is initiated. For the safety of all swimmers, the group leader must enforce the rule that each individual is responsible for her or his own tag. Spot-checking swimmers is a good way to test whether they are following the rules and using their tags correctly. Identify a swimmer and then check to see that his or her tag is displayed appropriately. If not, summon the swimmer and reinforce the rules.

Roll call system

The roll call system (**figure 3.7**) checks attendance before and after the swimming session and requires no special equipment. The group leader simply takes attendance by calling names aloud before swimmers enter the water and immediately after they exit. If a swimmer does not respond, an in-water search is initiated immediately. One drawback of the roll call system is it does not provide a way to check on swimmers while they are in the water.

Figure 3.6 Different colored tags indicate swimmers who are in or out of the water.

Figure 3.7 In the roll call system, the leader checks swimmers in and out of the water.

Severe Weather

Preventive action is the key to the YMCA Lifeguard course. Prevention can extend well beyond the confines of the pool, however. Severe weather can affect the safety of patrons, even in indoor facilities, so be aware of changing weather conditions.

Because pools are connected to plumbing and electrical equipment, lightning poses an electrocution risk even in indoor pools. All pools should be cleared when lightning is within 10 miles of the facility. Likewise, tornadoes and waterspouts pose a danger for patrons in any aquatic environment, indoors or outdoors. In the event of a tornado, follow your facility's emergency guidelines. For more information on severe weather, see chapter 13.

Track It!

There are two useful devices to help management and lifeguards stay aware of changing weather conditions.

Weather alert radios provide notifications of approaching weather conditions such as severe thunderstorms, tornadoes, hurricanes, floods, and blizzards and of civil problems such as Amber alerts and even terrorist attacks. Most are programmable to receive notifications for a specific county or counties.

A **lightning detector** is a device that detects and warns about the approach of severe thunderstorms, giving you time to clear the pool and locker room wet areas. There are portable models and versions that provide data to a computer. You can be warned of a storm's approach by an audible tone or a visual display.

Review

Review Topics

As a lifeguard, you are responsible for promoting accident prevention in and around the water. In this chapter, you learned about dangerous physical conditions and how to prevent them. Here are some key points to know in this chapter:

1) Conditions that may affect swimmers
2) Dangers of breath-holding and hyperventilation
3) Conditions that may affect lifeguards and how they can be relieved
4) The importance of safety swim checks and why facilities should test patrons' swimming ability
5) Types of safety swim check systems and how to use them
6) Dangerous weather conditions and when a pool should be cleared for weather reasons

Review Questions

1. What emotional state can lead to drowning? What causes this emotional state?
2. How do you relieve a cramp?
3. Ear and sinus squeeze are two conditions that can affect a lifeguard attempting a rescue. What can you do to alleviate these conditions?
4. How are hyperventilation, breath-holding, and hypoxic training alike? How are they different?
5. Name and briefly describe three safety swim check systems.
6. Describe the swimming abilities associated with green, yellow, and red wristbands.
7. Certain weather conditions require that the pool be cleared. What are these conditions?

RECOGNIZE

CHAPTER 4

Scanning and Recognizing Potential Victims

Accident prevention is a major component of lifeguarding, but sometimes swimmers do get into trouble. Effective lifeguards quickly recognize this because they know how to scan and what to look for when scanning. Preventing dangerous situations means being alert, actively scanning for potential victims, and recognizing signs of trouble.

In this chapter, you will learn the following:

- Scanning techniques and guidelines
- Maintaining vigilance and fighting fatigue
- Types of victims
- Signs of trouble

4
CHAPTER

Scanning

Scanning is the cornerstone of accident prevention in the YMCA Lifeguard course. Scanning is a system of visual observation in which lifeguards perform systematic visual sweeps of the facility, its patrons, and their activity. Proper scanning consists of repeatedly sweeping the entire zone, vigilantly watching, moving your head, and moving your eyes. When scanning a pool, look at the bottom of the pool, the middle of the water, and top of the water while covering the entire zone. When scanning in an open water area, you may not be able to scan from bottom to top. Generally, you will be unable to see below the water, so concentrate your efforts on the surface.

Make every effort to practice scanning. Have a supervisor stand behind you to watch and provide feedback.

Scanning techniques

Proper scanning requires you to observe, mentally record, and assess the condition of each swimmer in your zone. Make sure your scanning is constant, vigilant, and systematic.

When scanning, swivel your head from side to side and make a pronounced downward sweep. Move your head and eyes to look directly at each area (**figure 4.1**). Because studies have shown that visual acuity (sharpness) is best in the center of your vision (Fenner et al. 1999), as you scan, stop your eyes momentarily every 10 to 15 degrees to detect details. If you see movements in your peripheral vision, look directly at them to evaluate. Do not fix your stare on one single swimmer. These techniques are especially important when patrons are similar in appearance because it may take longer to identify potential drowning victims.

Figure 4.1 While scanning, swivel your head and look directly at each area.

A

B

C

D

Practice developing and improving your perception skills. As you scan, note patrons' sizes, swimming proficiency, comfort, and facial expressions. Watch all the people in your zone for any potential danger signs. Be alert to changes in body position. Most people swim in a horizontal position, so if you notice that any swimmers change body position, drop their legs, or lose stroke efficiency, check their progress frequently. Ask yourself, "Is the swimmer's stroke deteriorating? Is the kick weak? Is there hair in the swimmer's eyes? Is the swimmer getting tired or struggling? Is the swimmer moving through the water or staying in one spot?" In addition to these signs of drowning risk, also watch for patrons who are doing things such as these:

- Swimming long distances or many widths underwater (Stop this activity immediately—see chapter 3 about breath-holding)
- Having breath-holding contests (Stop this activity immediately—see chapter 3 about breath-holding)
- Doing what appears to be the jellyfish float (limply floating on the surface)
- Thrashing at the surface
- Appearing panicked
- Violating rules
- Behaving unusually
- Engaging in horseplay

As discussed in chapter 1, be aware of aspects of your facility and your assigned zone that affect your sight lines and the quality of your scanning. Management may change zone assignments as necessary, so review the posted diagram of your facility's zone coverage system and learn the limits of each zone and any accompanying high-risk areas or blind spots (see chapter 2 on high-risk areas). Report blind spots to your supervisor and ask if you may adjust your position to improve visibility. If that is not possible, request that management arrange for additional lifeguards.

Scanning methods

Use whatever scanning method is effective and comfortable for you. There are many different patterns: horizontal, diagonal, vertical, circular, triangular. Be sure to scan below and above the surface of the water, including the bottom and the middle of the pool and the top of the water, each time you scan your zone.

Scanning and the Senses

Use your senses to monitor what is happening and to anticipate and spot trouble:

- **Sight**. Watch the flow of activity, monitor the position of other lifeguards, and look for changing weather conditions.
- **Hearing**. Listen for unusual sounds such as people arguing, equipment breaking, or sounds made by occurrences outside your field of view (such as thunder). Also listen for signals from other lifeguards or patrons. Swimmers who become fatigued, suffer a cramp, or become injured may call for help.
- **Smell**. Notice if you can smell liquor on patrons' breath, chemicals from spills or leaks, or smoke from a fire.
- **Touch**. Feel the sun's heat, the roughness or suppleness of surfaces, drops of rain, or strong winds.

By permission from Lifesaving Society 2007.

Scanning Guidelines

- Scan your zone continuously. If a patron asks you a question, continue to scan your zone while responding; if it appears that the conversation will be lengthy, summon help to address the patron's concerns.
- Constantly assess the state of each patron in your zone.
- Position yourself to have a clear, unobstructed view of your zone at all times. Move your position to offset any glare or if you cannot see something because someone or something is blocking your view.
- In pools, scan the bottom, middle, and top of the pool. In open water, scan the water surface.
- Know every lifeguard zone in the facility and the zone variations used for peak or high-risk periods.
- Start and end each scan with a visual check of the adjacent lifeguard and zone boundary.
- When replacing another lifeguard, ask if there are any special areas or swimmers you should know about.
- Stay focused and vigilant.
- Scan directly under your stand or tower. This high-risk area is sometimes difficult to monitor. Always position your elevated lifeguard chair at the pool's edge. When walking or standing, position yourself at the pool's edge or waterside.
- Change your body posture every few minutes to help stay focused and vigilant.
- When in doubt, check it out. A victim on the bottom of the pool (pictured) may look like a blur or a slightly discolored object.
- Do not hesitate! If you are unsure, enter the water yourself. Never send someone else to check on a swimmer on the bottom.
- Remember to pay extra attention
    - to high-risk patrons;
    - to high-risk areas (see chapter 2) such as ladders, gutters, lifelines, slides, diving boards, and recreation attractions;
    - during high-risk times, such as with large groups or camps or when groups rent the facility; and
    - when there is a lot going on: distractions such as frequent rule violations can interrupt the scanning process and may decrease scanning performance.

Be sure to look at the lifeguard in the adjacent station at the beginning and end of each scanning sweep, which helps you both feel confident help is nearby. Lifeguards can help one another keep track of potential problems, assess patrons' conditions, and get another angle or second opinion about a situation.

Here are some additional strategies you can use to organize and sort your observations of swimmer characteristics, behavior, and signs of trouble, which are discussed later in this chapter:

- **Head counting**. Notice changes as you count the swimmers in your zone during each scan.
- **Grouping**. Group swimmers by age, gender, risk potential, or some combination of these categories. Monitor changes and be aware of those who are on the fringes.
- **Mental filing**. On each sweep, build swimmer profiles based on their abilities, skills, or activities. Track changes in behavior or activity on each scan.
- **Risk-profile matching**. Measure what you see against characteristics of types of victims (discussed later in this chapter).
- **Tracking**. Track progress of patrons who have submerged (from the diving board or surface) and those who fit a high-risk profile.
- **Counting seconds**. If visibility is poor, count 20 seconds whenever you see a swimmer go underwater: If the swimmer does not surface after 10 seconds, stand up in your chair or tower and count 10 seconds more. If the swimmer still does not appear, activate the emergency plan and enter the water. When in doubt, check it out!
- **Sorting while scanning**. Sort swimmers based on their abilities and potential needs. Who is at high risk and who is at low risk? Who might need your help the most? Someone swimming along the bottom of the pool could potentially need your care more than a child running on the deck.
- **Scanning systematically**. Scan the bottom, middle, and surface of the pool. Scan the high-risk areas and the people at high risk.

By permission from Lifesaving Society 2007

Maintaining vigilance and focus

Efficient scanning requires vigilance and focus (**figure 4.2**). Vigilance is "a state of readiness to detect and respond to certain specified small changes occurring at random time intervals in the environment" (Mackworth 1957). Being vigilant is one of the most important characteristics for you to develop as a lifeguard. Each time you get on the stand, think to yourself, "It could happen to me. I may need to make a rescue on this rotation, on this shift. I need to stay focused."

Figure 4.2 Vigilance is one of the most important characteristics of a lifeguard.

A variety of techniques will help you maintain vigilance and stay focused on your zone:

Constantly check that you can see all the patrons and the bottom of the pool in your zone. The best station for lifeguarding is on a corner so you can scan a 90-degree zone directly in front of you; however, zones should be no wider than 180 degrees. While scanning, turn your head and remember to make the downward sweep you need to actively watch your zone.

Talk to yourself. You do not have to be loud about it; just say to yourself who and what you see. "I see the young family near the corner. I see the two siblings racing across the pool. I see the older adult lap swimming." Speaking to yourself in this way can help you remain alert and vigilant (Smith 2006).

Figure 4.3 Drink plenty of water to help you stay alert.

Limit distractions. While scanning, lifeguards should have no duties other than to focus on scanning and preventing accidents. Never stop scanning, even when speaking with a patron or supervisor. Even a brief distraction can cause you to miss important information that might prevent an accident or aid a victim.

Mentally rehearse rescues. What would you do if swimmer X were in trouble? Choose a swimmer and rehearse your emergency action plan in your mind.

Get a good night's sleep every night. Studies show that sleep deprivation reduces vigilance and the ability to pay attention, and it has effects similar to those of alcohol intoxication (Williamson and Feyer 2000). The effects of sleep deprivation may last more than one day. So, even if you get a full night's sleep before your shift, you could still be affected by sleep deprivation that occurred two nights before your shift.

Fatigue busters

The work of lifeguarding can be repetitive and exhausting. According to Fenner et al. (1999), fatigue can cause your scanning ability to deteriorate. Many conditions contribute to lifeguarding fatigue, including dehydration, lack of sleep, eyestrain, hunger, and exposure to sun and wind. Come to work well rested and avoid medications (prescription and nonprescription) that affect your alertness. Fatigue reduces vigilance and slows the senses, resulting in failure to respond to warning signals, clouded reasoning ability, impaired judgment, increased panic in an emergency situation, and failure to follow emergency procedures. It is your responsibility to know how to help prevent fatigue and whom to notify when you are feeling fatigued on duty.

A lifeguard's environment can contribute to fatigue. Research analysis by Ballard (1996) states that vigilant performance decreases when a person is exposed to temperatures greater than 90°F. Additional studies indicate that increased wind and glare also decrease vigilance. This decrease in performance can happen in as little as 30 minutes.

Follow these tips to help maintain alertness:

- Be prepared for work: be well rested, be well hydrated, and eat a nutritious meal.
- Drink plenty of water (**figure 4.3**).
- Maintain good posture when standing or sitting in an elevated lifeguard chair.
- Use adequate protection against sun and wind.
- Use UVA and UVB protection umbrellas.
- Rotate tasks or areas.
- Take sufficient breaks.
- Periodically change body positions.

- Adjust your position to offset glare (both indoors and outdoors) and obstructions.
- Wear polarized sunglasses that allow clear peripheral vision.
- Perform moderate exercise between rotations.

Make sure you receive the support you need to stay alert and know whom to notify when you are feeling fatigued. When guarding, you should receive regular breaks every 20 to 30 minutes, even in single-lifeguard facilities where you are not able to rotate your position. (Recall that you will also need another two or three staff members trained in emergency assistance to effectively manage a serious emergency procedure.)

Recognizing Potential Victims

Victim recognition begins the moment patrons enter the aquatic environment. Preventing accidents requires you to know the visual and behavioral signs that people exhibit when they are at risk of drowning. As patrons arrive, you can evaluate their physical and mental state, their comfort in and familiarity with the environment, and other cues to identify potential victims before they enter the water. Once swimmers are in the water, know the early warning signs they may exhibit before they become distressed, so you can recognize and take action before an accident occurs. Recognizing the signs of a distressed swimmer is critical to taking quick action to prevent drowning.

Types of victims

Identifying potential victims early is key to your success as a lifeguard. According to the Lifesaving Society (2007), people who become victims may be in many different physical, mental, emotional, or medical conditions.

Inattentional Blindness

Inattentional blindness is a term used to describe when you fail to notice something happen in front of you because you are focused intensely on something else in front of you. You may have heard of the 1999 experiment by Daniel J. Simons and Christopher Chabris in which participants were asked to watch a video and count the number of times people in the video passed a basketball. About half of the participants were so focused on counting passes that they did not see an actor dressed in a gorilla suit walk right through the scene.

What are the implications of inattentional blindness for lifeguards? As you scan the bottom, middle, and surface of the water, be careful to avoid focusing on only a certain task or watching for one certain type of behavior. The YMCA Lifeguard course equips you with several early warning signs, ways to recognize potential victims, and many ways to stay focused and vigilant to prevent accidents—use all of them. A lifeguard who is aware of the hazards of inattentional blindness will avoid looking for just one type of victim or one type of distress signal. Do not try to count or tally how many swimmers come into the pool on your shift; you may become focused on counting and miss someone in distress (note that this is different from the effective technique of head counting (discussed earlier in this chapter), which you may use while scanning to keep track of the swimmers in your zone).

They may be exhausted, injured, panicked, unconscious, not breathing, or vomiting. They may even be calm but unable to help themselves due to trauma, cramps, or poor swimming skills. No matter the cause, your task is to recognize and help victims by removing them from danger and preventing further harm.

Visual and behavioral signs

Observe patrons as they arrive for signs of their swimming ability and familiarity with the water (Richardson 1997). Closely monitor patrons who fall into the following categories. These visual and behavioral cues may indicate a person's increased risk of becoming a victim:

- People of extreme ages—the very young and the very old
- People of extreme weights—very thin or very heavy
- People who appear to be unfamiliar or uncomfortable with the environment—pallor (paleness), timidity, or awkwardness may signal a lack of experience with aquatic activities
- Parents holding children—they may not have the strength to support both themselves and the child
- Unstable or intoxicated individuals—their movement and behavior patterns may be impaired
- People using flotation devices—use of such aids may signal lack of comfort in the water
- Physical impairment—disabilities may signal limited ability to maneuver in and around the water
- Improper dress or equipment—may mean they are unfamiliar with the environment

These categories help lifeguards identify patrons who might have problems, but categorizing is not foolproof. Monitor patrons' behavior in the water to confirm or negate your assumptions.

Signs of trouble

At any time, you may have to decide how to react to a potential victim, so learn to recognize signs of trouble. In addition to observing swimmers before they enter the water, watch for other signs from swimmers in the water to help identify potential victims.

Drowning Demographics

USA Swimming, in partnership with the University of Memphis, conducted a national research study (Irwin et al. 2010) to examine the demographics of swimming, with a focus on the high drowning rates among children of ethnic minority backgrounds.

- Nearly 14 percent of African-American and 7 percent of Hispanic/Latino children do not know how to swim, compared to less than 6 percent of their white counterparts.
- About 69 percent of African-American and 58 percent of Hispanic/Latino children consider themselves to be "low swimming," compared to 42 percent of white children.
- Socioeconomic status and swimming ability may be related: 66 percent of students receiving free or reduced school lunch have low swimming skills.

Early warning signs

Swimmers at risk of becoming drowning victims tend to display a number of early warning signs:

- Weak stroke (head held high out of the water, low over-arm recovery, or a weak kick)—demonstrates a lack of ability
- Hair in the eyes—swimmer may be too concerned with keeping his or her head out of the water to push the hair back, or the energy spent constantly pushing hair from the eyes may tire the swimmer
- Glassy, empty, anxious-looking eyes—the facial expression preceding exhaustion
- Two heads together—indicates a possible double-drowning situation
- Hand waving—a potential signal for help, may be a sign swimmer is caught in a current
- Moving toward rocks or a pier—swimmer may be caught in a current
- Erratic behavior—any activity out of the ordinary
- Clinging to objects for security—swimmer may be too tired to swim to safety
- Neutral to negative buoyancy (swimmer bobbing up and down or struggling to stay above the surface of the water)—may indicate exhaustion or poor swimming ability and may exhaust the swimmer
- Inability to respond verbally—may indicate struggling to stay afloat

Your ability to identify swimmers who may be at risk of drowning is critical to your preventing an accident. Knowing the early warning signs of troubled swimmers enables you to scan your zone more effectively. While these signs do not guarantee that a swimmer will become a drowning victim, they are keys to determining if a swimmer is at risk and needs your attention. Remember, when in doubt, check it out. If a swimmer is not making progress, quickly identify the situation, determine why, and if it is because the swimmer is in trouble, take immediate action to prevent an accident.

Distressed swimmers

A distressed swimmer is someone who is struggling to stay on the surface of the water. These visual and behavioral signs may help you recognize distressed swimmers:

- Kicking to try to maintain an upright position, with the kick providing no forward progress
- Being vertical in the water—changing from a horizontal to a vertical position, with the legs dropping past 45 degrees toward 90 degrees
- Tilting the head back to aid with breathing
- Holding the arms out to the side
- Trying to reach toward safety
- Facing the side of the pool or toward the waterfront—looking toward safety
- Trying to wave or shout for assistance, if they have the strength

Distressed swimmers can assist themselves and the lifeguard in a rescue by following instructions, grabbing an extended rescue tube or other piece of equipment, keeping afloat, and kicking.

Drownings happen quickly. When the victim slips under the water, there may be no sound or water disturbance because the strength to call out or wave for help is gone. When guarding, lifeguards are to remain vigilant and aggressively scan the water because a person can move very quickly and quietly from being a distressed swimmer to a drowning victim.

Who Is Most at Risk?

Males. In 2007, males were 3.7 times more likely than females to die from unintentional drowning in the United States.

Children. In 2007, of all children 1 to 4 years old who died from an unintentional injury, almost 30 percent died from drowning. Although drowning rates have slowly declined, fatal drowning remains the second-leading cause of unintentional, injury-related death for children ages 1 to 14 years.

Minorities:

- Between 2000 and 2007, the fatal unintentional drowning rate for African-Americans across all ages was 1.2 times that of whites. For American Indians and Alaska Natives, this rate was 1.7 times that of whites.
- Rates of fatal drowning are notably higher among these populations in certain age groups. The fatal drowning rate of African-American children ages 5 to 14 is 3.1 times that of white children in the same age range. For American Indian and Alaska Native children, the fatal drowning rate is 2.2 times higher than for white children.
- Factors such as the physical environment (for example, access to swimming pools) and a combination of social and cultural norms (for example, valuing swimming skills and choosing recreational water-related activities) may contribute to the racial differences in drowning rates. If minorities participate less in water-related activities than whites, their drowning rates (per exposure) may be higher than currently reported.

CDC 2010a.

Review

Review Topics

An important part of being a lifeguard is being able to tell when a person is having trouble in the water. This chapter covered scanning, staying alert, and how to tell when a patron is in danger. Here are some key points to know in this chapter:

1) Scanning techniques, methods, and guidelines
2) How to stay vigilant and reduce fatigue
3) Hazardous behaviors in and near the water
4) How to recognize potential victims both in and out of the water

Review Questions

1. Define scanning in your own words and explain why it is important.
2. List and explain some of the methods you can use to mentally organize the information you take in as you scan.
3. What are some things that can cause you to lose focus or become fatigued?
4. What is inattentional blindness? List some things you can do to avoid it.
5. There are many ways to maintain alertness while you are lifeguarding. List at least five things you can do to stay alert and vigilant.
6. What groups of people are at an increased risk for drowning?
7. Name some characteristics of a swimmer who is in trouble in the water.

CHAPTER 5

Drowning Victims

Despite your best efforts to prevent an emergency, you may face a situation in which a patron becomes a drowning victim. A person can transition from distressed swimmer to drowning victim very quickly, and a drowning victim can slip below the surface in as little as 20 seconds. For these reasons, it is essential that you understand how to recognize drowning victims. In addition, understanding how the drowning process works—what happens and how quickly—enables you to take the right steps at the right time to help save a victim's life.

In this chapter, you will learn the following:

- The definition of drowning
- Recognizing drowning victims
- The stages of the drowning process

CHAPTER 5

Definition of Drowning

According to an international conference on drowning in 2002, "Drowning is the process of experiencing respiratory impairment from submersion/immersion in liquid" (van Beeck et al. 2005).

The conference and related efforts in the 2000s focused on global cooperation to better track and prevent drowning as a major public health problem. Experts agreed further: "The victim may live or die after this [drowning] process, but whatever the outcome, he or she has been involved in a drowning incident" (Idris et al. 2003).

In the past, drownings were described as active or passive. Passive, or silent, drownings were thought to occur when the victim did not struggle on the surface. However, medical science has determined that in so-called passive drownings the victims simply were not witnessed as they went through the process of drowning. Therefore, these terms are no longer used to describe drownings or drowning victims (Idris et al. 2003).

Recognizing Drowning Victims

It is critical to identify a drowning victim quickly—it takes as little as 20 to 60 seconds for a person to slip below the surface. An adult may struggle for up to 60 seconds, but a child may submerge in as few as 20 seconds. Both will slip quietly below the surface.

Drowning victims, who are usually nonswimmers or exhausted swimmers, are more difficult to spot than distressed swimmers (see chapter 4) because they cannot call attention to themselves. They tend not to cry for help because their survival instinct tells them to hold on to the air in their lungs to stay afloat. Victims further along in the process use all of their energy trying to keep their heads above water in order to breathe.

Characteristics of drowning victims

When scanning the surface, look for these characteristics of drowning victims:

- An inability to call for help and a panicked facial expression
- Head back and body low in the water
- Arms extended out from the sides and moving up and down ineffectively in an attempt to keep the face above water to breathe
- Little or no support from the kick
- An upright (vertical) position facing the nearest source of assistance

Submerged victims

It can be difficult to see a victim under the water, and wind and water movement can blur the site of a person who is submerged (**figure 5.1**) or partially submerged (**figure 5.2**) underwater. Cloudy or murky water can also make it difficult to see a body underwater. You will have to scan the bottom and middle of the pool vigilantly and know the status of everyone in your zone.

When a victim is underwater, fast response is critical. "Underwater cameras have shown that even victims who are apparently motionless to observers at the surface usually make some movement underwater" (Idris et al. 2003). If the person has been swimming underwater and you notice that the swimmer is not making forward progress, enter the water immediately to rescue the victim. When in doubt, check it out. Keep in mind that the victim will likely be unconscious and unable to assist in the rescue.

In many instances, you will have no warning. This is why it is so important to stay alert. Assume that any individual who is floating facedown or sinking to the bottom and has made little or no motion for 20 seconds is an unconscious victim. Remember: When in doubt, check it out. Immediately take action by personally getting in the water and determining the condition of the potential victim. Do not send a patron to check on a potential victim—every second counts in an emergency.

Underlying conditions that may contribute to drowning

Drowning is not always linked to poor swimming ability or exhaustion—even strong swimmers can drown. A variety of situations and physical conditions can lead to drowning:

- Epilepsy or other types of seizures
- Heart attack or cardiac arrest
- Head injury
- Water blackout (due to hyperventilation or extended breath-holding)
- Alcohol or drug use
- Hypothermia or hyperthermia (see chapter 9)

Different age groups may be at higher risk of drowning from certain conditions. A study of the characteristics of drowning deaths by age group in certain counties in Washington state (Quan and Cummings 2003), for example, noted that some conditions may be more prevalent in certain age groups.

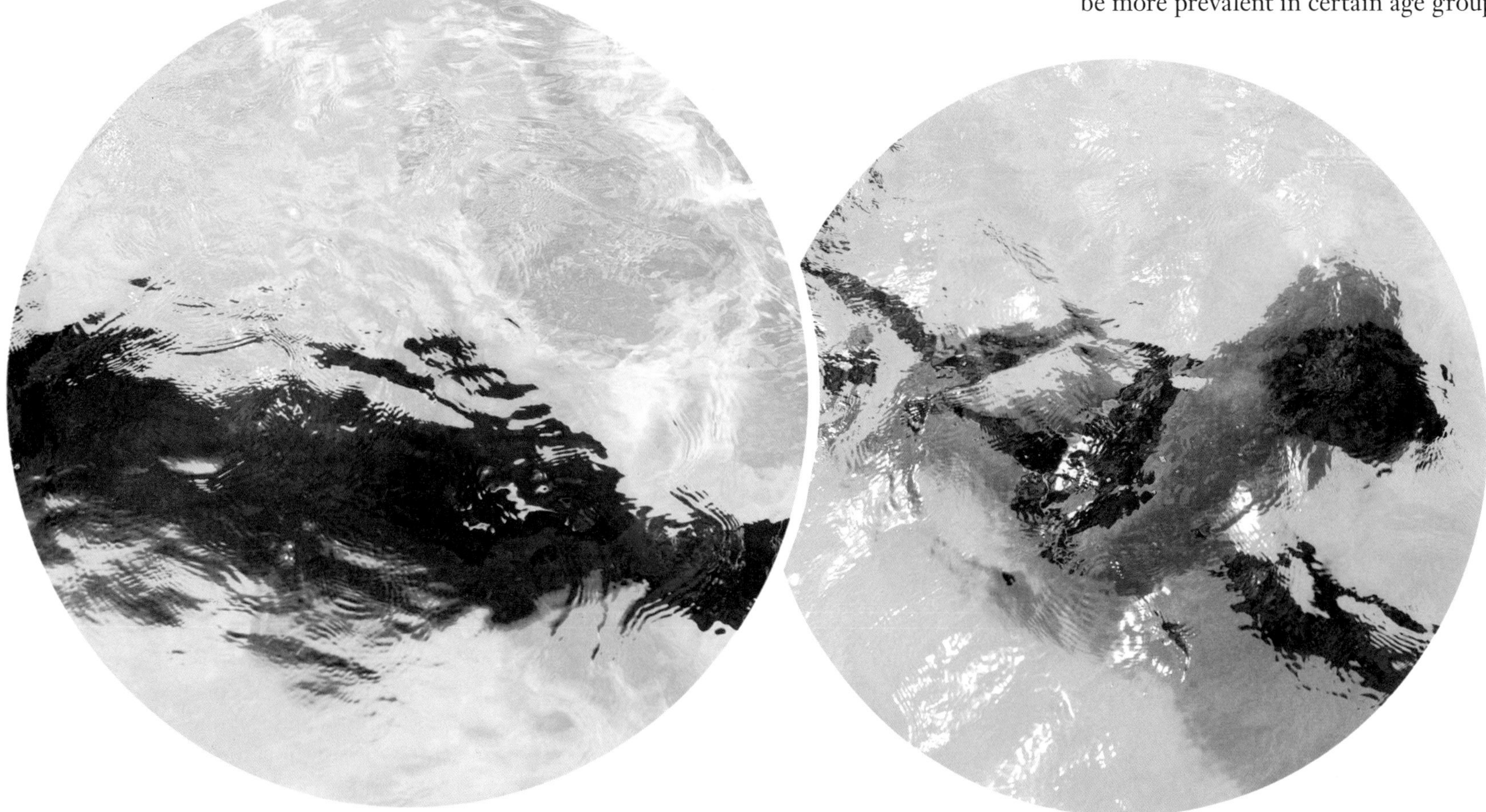

Figure 5.1 Submerged victim at the bottom of the pool.

Figure 5.2 Partially submerged victim.

Among victims 35 years and older, medical histories indicated that the victims had psychiatric conditions (22 percent), heart disease (10 percent), and diabetes (4 percent). Among victims 65 years and older, 84 percent had known heart disease. The study also showed that positive blood alcohol levels were most prevalent in two age groups, those 35 through 64 years old (35 percent) and those 20 through 34 years old (33 percent). Note that it is not always possible to determine whether the cause of death was drowning or another event. For example, in older adults, drowning may cause a heart attack, or a heart attack may bring about drowning (Idris et al. 2003).

The Stages of Drowning

In 2003, a modification to the definition of drowning was published to further explain the drowning process as being a "continuum that begins when the victim's airway lies below the surface of the liquid, usually water ..." (Idris et al. 2003). People who are drowning usually progress through four defined stages in the continuum. Although others may give the stages different names, the concept of each stage is basically the same.

Before examining the specific stages of the drowning process, here is a brief look at the anatomy involved. In the normal throat (**figure 5.3**), the **glottis** is the top edge of the beginning of the **trachea** (also known as the windpipe) that connects to the lower part of the throat. The glottis is covered by the **epiglottis,** a piece of elastic cartilage that acts as a barrier to prevent solids and liquids from entering the trachea, which carries air from the throat into the lungs. The **esophagus,** which is next to the trachea, carries food and liquids from the throat to the stomach.

The **reflex closure of the glottis** is the involuntary, or automatic, process of swallowing (i.e., the swallow reflex). As food or water enters the mouth, the tongue blocks the back of the throat and the epiglottis closes over the glottis, blocking the entry to the trachea. The tongue then drops and the water passes over the epiglottis and enters the esophagus to the stomach.

Stage I: Initial apnea

Apnea (**ap**-nee-uh) means the temporary absence of breathing, or breath-holding. In drowning, the glottis is closed by a reflex action, but—unlike during eating or drinking, when the air supply is resumed immediately once the food or drink passes the glottis—the water stays in the mouth and throat, cutting off all air to the lungs. The victim is unable to inhale air and cannot exhale carbon dioxide. However, no water enters the lungs in this stage. During this stage, the victim's panic increases. While a distressed swimmer may signal for help at this point, a person further along in the drowning process who is struggling to get air may not signal for help.

The duration of the first stage varies significantly, from seconds to a few minutes. During initial apnea, the following occur:

- The blood pressure rises and the adrenaline flow increases due to panic and the self-preservation instinct.
- The victim begins to struggle in an attempt to keep the head above water.
- The victim swallows water into the stomach and has difficulty filling the lungs with air, causing a decrease in buoyancy.
- The victim gradually sinks. Each attempt to raise the head above water is less successful because of fatigue and the inability to inhale properly to inflate the lungs.
- The brain does not get enough oxygen to function properly. This condition is called ***hypoxia*** (hih-**pok**-see-uh).

- The lack of oxygen causes an excess of carbon dioxide in the blood, a condition called ***hypercapnia*** (hy-per-**cap**-nee-uh). This makes the blood more acidic, a condition called ***acidosis*** (a-sih-**doh**-sis), and causes muscles to fatigue and stop functioning.

Stage II: Dyspnea

Dyspnea (**dis**-nee-uh) is difficulty breathing. In this stage, the glottis begins to relax partially. Air and water begin to enter the trachea. Because the victim has swallowed water into the stomach and is growing weak from struggling, the body and head will be lower in the water and more water will be swallowed.

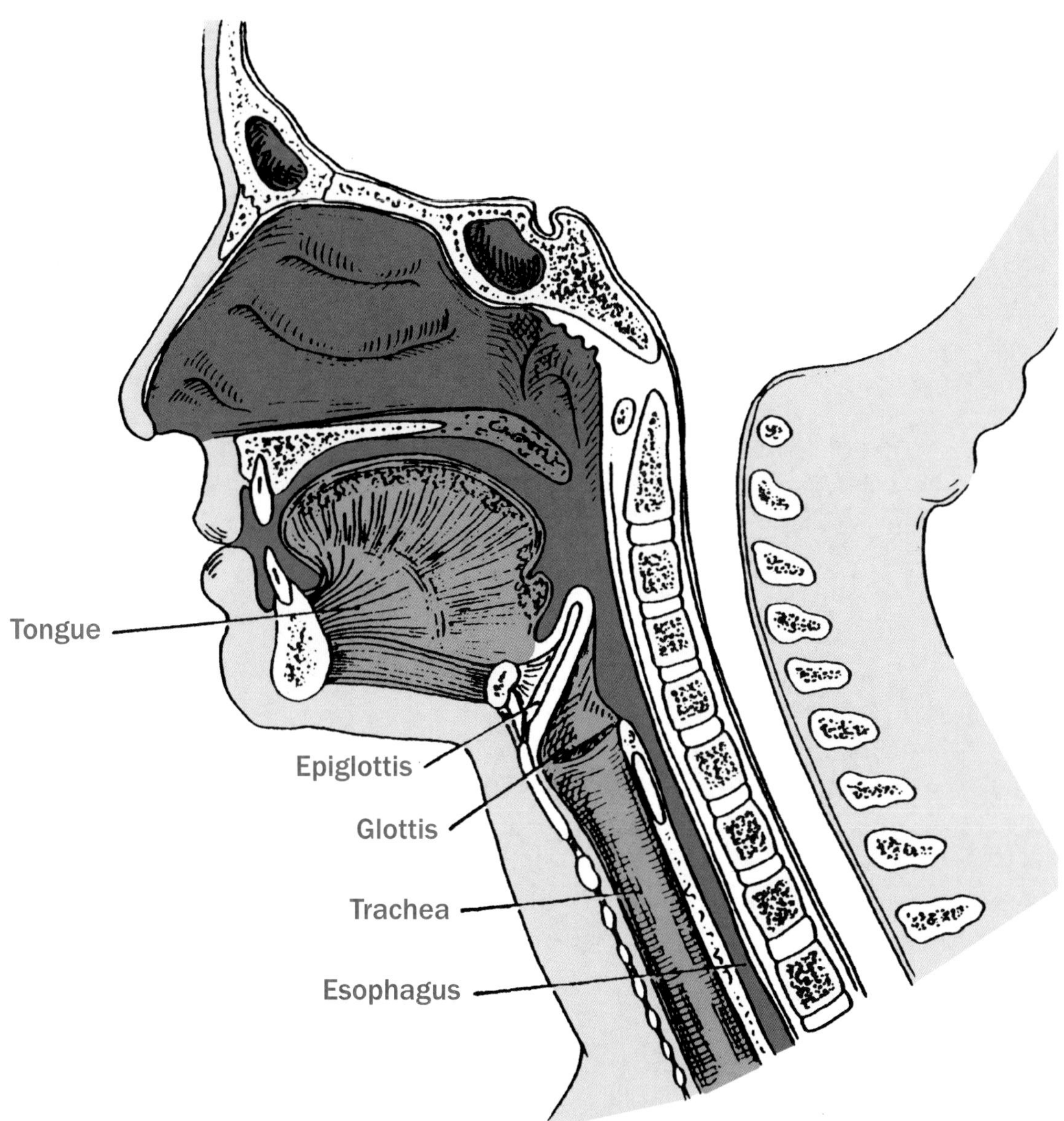

Figure 5.3 Anatomy of the throat.

This time, however, water also flows down the trachea into the lungs. If rescued during this stage, the victim usually suffers from a condition called **aspiration pneumonia,** caused by breathing water into the lungs.

The surface of every air sac (alveolus) in the lungs is covered with a substance known as surfactant (**figure 5.4**). The surfactant reduces the surface tension of the fluid that covers the membrane of the alveolus, which allows for the easy exchange of oxygen to and carbon dioxide from the blood. When water is aspirated into the lungs, it washes away the surfactant, making the exchange of gases more difficult and creating another complication to resuscitation. Although many alveoli may survive (there are an estimated 300 million in the lungs) to help exchange gases as long as they are exposed to air, the health risks to someone who aspirates water are severe. Resuscitation of victims in this stage may be difficult because of the decreased exchange of oxygen and carbon dioxide. Furthermore, and

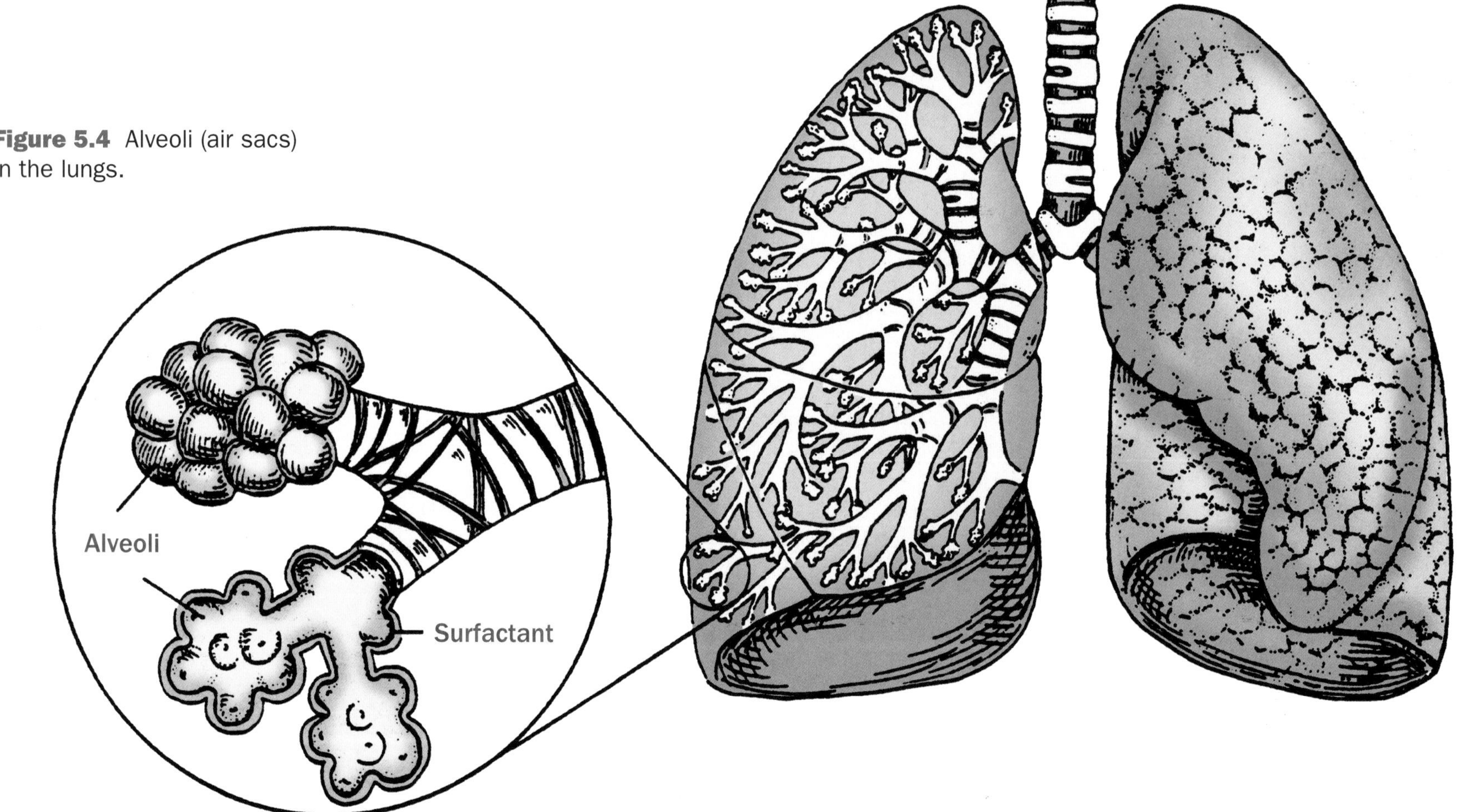

Figure 5.4 Alveoli (air sacs) in the lungs.

even in cases of resuscitation, it is important that any person who is suspected of having aspirated water be evaluated by professional medical personnel.

During dyspnea, the following occur:

- The failure of the swallow reflex causes the aspiration of water into the lungs. Although normally no one can intentionally take water into the lungs, by this stage the body's protective mechanism has failed.
- Convulsive coughing will occur as the victim attempts to expel water from the lungs, which can cause lung tissues to tear and produce a froth in the mouth. The influx of water into the stomach and lungs may cause vomiting. It is critical for a lifeguard to use a resuscitation mask during rescue breathing to prevent contact with the victim's blood and body fluids.
- Frothing may also occur in the mouth because of the mixture of surfactant and water from the lungs.
- Cerebral (brain) hypoxia continues, and very little rationality remains.
- Acidosis continues to lower the blood pH.

Stage III: Terminal apnea

As soon as the victim becomes unconscious and stops breathing, he or she has entered the third stage. Terminal apnea is respiratory arrest, in which breathing ceases. Water will be present in the lungs, making air exchange during resuscitation efforts very difficult.

During this stage the following occur:

- Brain hypoxia continues.
- Acidosis continues.
- In some cases, lack of oxygen to the brain causes convulsions in which the entire body becomes rigid and the victim jerks violently and involuntarily.
- In some cases, the sphincter muscles will relax, and the victim will urinate, defecate, or both.

Stage IV: Cardiac arrest

Cardiac arrest occurs when the heart ceases to function and pump blood. Depending on the circumstances, the third and fourth stages of drowning may occur simultaneously, with the heart and lungs stopping together. But because the heart can continue to beat up to 5 minutes after breathing has stopped, rescue breathing alone can revive victims who have been underwater for a short time. That is why the YMCA Lifeguard course stresses that it is critical for lifeguards to begin rescue breathing while the victim is still in the water. Once the heart has stopped, CPR is necessary to revive the victim.

Drowning victims experience two types of death: clinical death and biological death. **Clinical death** occurs first and is defined as the point at which both breathing and pulse have stopped and the body is in respiratory and cardiac arrest. Clinical death is generally considered to last about 4 minutes from the time the heart stops beating. The lack of oxygen causes the pupils of the eyes to dilate (widen) and the skin to become cyanotic (blue). This blue color is especially noticeable in the lips and the beds of the fingernails. If you begin CPR within these 4 minutes, it may be possible to avoid irreversible brain damage.

Figure 5.5 Timeline showing stages of drowning.

Progression of Stages

Initial Apnea (10–60 seconds)

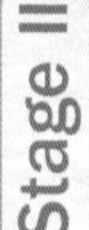

Temporary absence of breathing. Glottis is closed by reflex. Water in mouth and throat cuts off air to the lungs. Oxygen to the brain decreases. Victim's panic increases; struggles to keep head above water. Swallows water. May or may not signal for help. Victim begins to sink.

Dyspnea (60–90 seconds)

Difficulty breathing. Glottis begins to partially relax. Body and head lower in water; more water swallowed. Water begins to enter lungs. Coughing and vomiting may occur. Victim grows weaker from struggle and sinks lower in the water. Lack of oxygen to brain continues.

Terminal Apnea (90 seconds–3 minutes)

Stage III

Victim becomes unconscious and stops breathing. Water is present in the lungs. Lack of oxygen to brain may cause convulsions. Possible evacuation of the bladder and/or bowels.

Cardiac Arrest (3–5 minutes)

Heart ceases to function and pump blood. Eyes dilate and skin turns blue. Without CPR, lack of oxygen will cause irreversible brain damage.
Stages III and IV may occur simultaneously.

0–3 Minutes
Unless a preexisting medical event led to the drowning, individuals in whom effective ventilation and circulation is restored within 3 minutes of submersion will have an excellent chance for normal survival (Modell 1997).

3–5 minutes
Survival may be likely, but the longer the time period, the more probable it is that permanent neurological damage will occur.

5 minutes
Normal recovery is uncommon unless water temperature is below 70°F.

Biological death is the point at which irreversible brain damage begins and the most sensitive parts of the brain start to die. Without oxygen, brain cells begin to die within 4 to 6 minutes. Longer periods of oxygen deprivation result in the loss of more and more brain cells. Dead brain cells cannot regenerate like skin and bone; once dead, they are gone.

You can see why it is critical to reach a drowning victim, open the airway, provide rescue breathing, and then begin CPR as soon as possible. CPR maintains minimal circulation and respiration in order to sustain life until advanced medical care can begin.

In cold water, bodily functions are slowed significantly and blood is withdrawn from the extremities and pooled near the brain, lungs, and other vital organs. As a result, less oxygen is needed to maintain vital body functions. Because of the slowed depletion of oxygen, cold-water drowning victims may experience a delayed onset of biological death.

Progression of stages

Figure 5.5 summarizes the stages of drowning and provides an approximate timeline for their occurrence.

The following factors affect how much time can pass between submersion and resuscitation before permanent neurological damage or death occurs (Modell 1997):

- Whether the victims entered the water with lungs maximally deflated or maximally inflated
- Whether the victims had preexisting diseases that limit resuscitation

- What water temperature victims experienced
- Whether the victims were mentally or physically impaired

Other factors that may be involved include the use of drugs or alcohol, age, level of swimming ability, fatigue, and physical conditioning.

If no one saw the victim's initial submersion, it may be difficult to determine how long the victim was drowning before resuscitation or what caused the submersion to occur.

Delayed effects of drowning

A person who has been the victim of a drowning incident—that is, again, someone who has experienced "respiratory impairment from submersion/immersion in liquid"—may experience a delay in the physiological effects of drowning. This may seem counterintuitive because it means a person may be resuscitated or not need resuscitation and appear normal after an incident and then later experience serious effects of drowning, including death. This delay in the drowning process is one of the most important reasons why anyone who experiences a significant submersion or immersion needs to be evaluated by a medical professional and receive close observation after the incident.

Buoyancy of a Drowned Body

Many people mistakenly think that a drowned body will always float and that the word buoyancy is synonymous with floating; however, buoyancy can be positive (floating), negative (sinking), or neutral (hovering between floating and sinking) (**figure 5.6**).

Buoyancy refers to the tendency of a body to float or sink and the upward force exerted by a fluid on an object submerged in it. Whether a drowned body will float or sink depends on the victim's original buoyancy and on the amount of water taken into the lungs and stomach. Positively buoyant victims will float; negatively buoyant victims will sink. If the victim originally has neutral buoyancy, the amount of air in the lungs—the vital capacity—may change the body's ability to float. As the body descends, the lungs are squeezed, forcing the air out of the lungs, causing the body to descend faster as it goes deeper. Air bubbles from the victim may appear on the surface for some time.

Now that you understand what happens during and after the drowning process, you will be more aware of how critical your quick and proper action are to an effective rescue response.

Figure 5.6 Neutral buoyancy: The body hovers between floating and sinking.

Review

Review Topics

As a lifeguard, you may face a situation that involves drowning. From this chapter, you learned about the drowning process and how quickly it can happen. Here are some key points to know from this chapter:

1) Definition and signs of drowning
2) Risk factors associated with drowning
3) Why it is important to identify drowning victims quickly
4) What happens at each of the four stages of drowning and how long each stage lasts
5) The difference between clinical death and biological death and why this is important
6) Why it is important that anyone who experiences a significant submersion or immersion needs to be evaluated by a medical professional

Review Questions

1. Define drowning in your own words. Explain why it is important to understand that a drowning victim may live or die after a drowning incident.
2. What are some health-related risk factors that may lead to drowning?
3. How is a drowning swimmer different from a distressed swimmer, and what are the signs of a drowning swimmer?
4. Name the four stages of drowning and describe what happens at each stage and how long each stage lasts.
5. About how long does it take to progress through all four stages?
6. Any drowning victim who has aspirated (inhaled) water into the lungs requires professional medical attention. Describe how you would explain this to a patron who is hesitant to seek medical attention after a drowning incident.
7. Explain what “delayed effects of drowning” means and its importance in the medical care a person receives after a drowning incident.
8. Define buoyancy. Tell how it relates to drowning victims.

ACTIVATE EAP

CHAPTER 

Emergency Action Plans

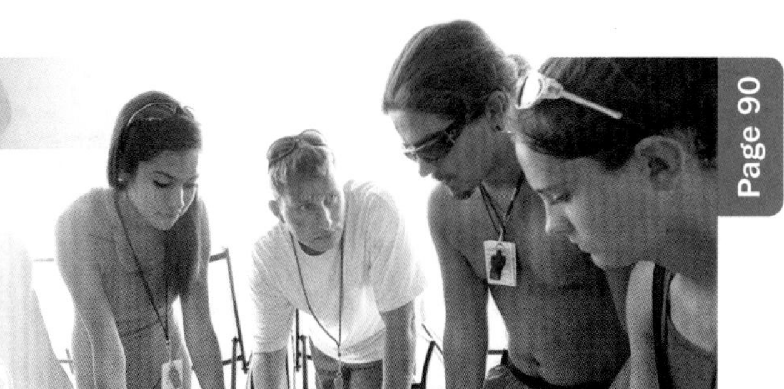
Page 90

CHAPTER 6

Emergency Action Plans

Emergency action plans (EAPs) help lifeguards and other key staff understand their roles and responsibilities during an emergency so they can make sound decisions and take the necessary steps to help the victim while protecting all patrons' safety. Having an effective EAP helps the entire response team provide critical support during and after an emergency. Knowing and practicing EAPs helps you eliminate guesswork and can reduce the amount of stress you experience in an emergency, making you a more effective and confident team member.

In this chapter, you will learn the following:

- Preparing for emergencies
- Guidelines for emergency action plans
- Types of emergencies
- Sample plans

CHAPTER
6

Preparing for Emergencies

Solid teamwork between the aquatic staff and the facility staff is essential to a successful emergency response. This collaboration reduces the risks for both lifeguards and patrons and increases the speed and efficiency of the response. All facilities should have in place emergency action plans (EAPs) and an in-service training program for handling the variety of emergencies that might reasonably be expected to occur.

Your emergency team includes fellow lifeguards, staff trained to assist lifeguards, law enforcement officials, fire department personnel, emergency medical staff, civil defense officials, and the members of a variety of other local organizations. The involvement of each group makes EAPs more efficient and effective.

Setting up emergency plans

It is important that all facilities develop and document emergency plans well before any emergency occurs. Having trained, knowledgeable staff will enhance the quality and safety of an aquatic program. If you work for a facility that does not have these plans documented, strongly encourage the management to take these steps to develop an emergency action plan:

- Specify an emergency team leader and define this leader's responsibilities and limitations.
- Specify the staff who are to be involved in an emergency response and assign them specific duties.
- Specify a chain of command (a list of the people in charge, where each person is accountable to the person above him or her on the list), so that lines of authority are clear.
- Establish a sequence of emergency steps.
- Post emergency phone numbers.
- Prepare a written script for calling in emergencies and post it by the phone.
- Define the procedures for moving and transporting victims.
- Instruct lifeguards in the importance of and procedures for completing accident and incident reports (described in chapter 10).
- Schedule regular emergency procedure training and practice sessions.
- Select one spokesperson for the facility and direct all questions from outside persons to that person.

It is essential that the emergency procedures be practiced frequently and systematically. Only through practice will reactions be refined and procedures fully understood. Practice also makes the emergency situation less stressful as all team members are familiar with their responsibilities. The more comfortable team members are when performing their duties during an emergency, the more effective and efficient they will be. Effective supervisors evaluate staff performance after an emergency or training to help staff identify hazards, refine their responses, improve the EAP, and celebrate successes (**figure 6.1**). You can also evaluate your own performance and identify areas for improvement.

Emergency Action Plan Guidelines

The purpose of having an EAP is for all employees to know their roles and be able to respond quickly and efficiently. It is extremely important that all staff members stick to their assigned roles during an emergency response. The lifeguard is the sole authority of the pool or waterfront. Swim instructors, swim coaches, and nonaquatic staff assist the lifeguard during an emergency; they all need to know and practice their roles.

Lifeguards' roles

Most of the incidents and accidents you encounter as a professional lifeguard will be minor; however, you must be prepared for both minor and major emergencies in your role. Responding to emergencies can require split-second decision making, so repeatedly practicing EAPs will help you handle real emergencies more effectively.

When an incident happens, what is your role as a lifeguard?

- To make sure the patrons in and around your aquatic environment are safe
- To serve as a team member with other lifeguards in executing the EAP and safety procedures
- To assist in managing an accident scene

To help you understand how emergency roles work, this chapter provides several examples of emergency action plans and the roles involved. The following lists outline the primary EAP roles and their responsibilities when responding to an in-water incident.

Lifeguard #1 is the staff member who recognizes the victim and therefore leads the rescue response as follows:

- **activates the EAP**;
- **determines the appropriate action to reach the victim**: a nonswimming or a swimming rescue;
- **rescues** the victim and, if necessary, begins rescue breathing;
- **removes** the victim from the water;
- **provides emergency care**, giving first aid as needed; and
- **reports** and documents the incident or accident.

The other lifeguards in the EAP all follow the emergency coverage plan for their zones until the pool is cleared or until another lifeguard takes over their zone. Each lifeguard has a unique responsibility in the EAP and may assist Lifeguard #1 as necessary:

- **Lifeguard #2's** EAP responsibility is to direct and monitor patrons. In a major emergency, Lifeguard #2 clears the pool and sends patrons to the locker rooms.
- **Lifeguard #3's** EAP responsibility is to EMS and crisis communications. This person ensures that EMS is called, met at the entrance, and brought to the victim following the best route for EMS. After EMS is called, Lifeguard #3 activates the crisis communication plan.
- **Lifeguard #4's** EAP responsibility is to manage the emergency equipment and assist Lifeguard #1 in providing emergency care.

How do you know if you are Lifeguard #2, #3, or #4? Part of your role as a professional lifeguard is to understand the roles and responsibilities of your facility's EAPs and know your role at all times while on duty. If your EAP is not detailed or you are unsure of your role, check with your supervisor.

Figure 6.1 Supervisors review team performance after training.

One common method for assigning responsibilities is proximity to the incident, for example:

- Lifeguard #1 is the one who identifies the victim, activates the EAP, and begins the rescue.
- Lifeguard #2 is the lifeguard closest to the incident/rescue.
- Lifeguard #3 is the next closest lifeguard.
- Lifeguard #4 is the farthest from the incident.

If there are additional lifeguards and staff available to monitor patrons in the locker room, have male staff go to the men's locker room and female staff to the women's locker room. However, care is required by staff stationed in locker rooms in how they respond to patrons' questions. Follow these guidelines:

- Acknowledge that there has been an emergency.
- Explain that the facility's emergency procedures are being followed and the pool is being cleared so the emergency response team can give aid.
- Refrain from giving details or guessing what is happening on the pool deck.
- Inform patrons in classes that the facility will communicate with them about their next class.
- Thank patrons for their patience during the emergency.

Regular practice is critical to the success of a facility's EAPs, including rehearsing the EAP for each type of emergency and holding in-service trainings once a month. Recognize that each facility you work in will be different. It will be important for you to understand the facility's guidelines and EAPs, so be sure to ask your supervisors any questions you have to make sure you will be an effective team member in the event of an emergency.

Exposure Control Plan

The Occupational Safety and Health Administration (OSHA), part of the U.S. Department of Labor, requires that all employers whose employees might be exposed to blood or other infectious materials have a written exposure control plan that outlines how the employer will prevent or minimize employee exposure. The exposure control plan must be available for employees and explain specifically what employees need to do to prevent the spread of infectious diseases. OSHA regulations state: "When there is occupational exposure, the employer shall provide, at no cost to the employee, appropriate personal protective equipment such as, but not limited to, gloves, gowns, laboratory coats, face shields or masks and eye protection, and mouthpieces, resuscitation bags, pocket masks, or other ventilation devices." (OSHA 1992)

Facility layout

Another key to a quick and successful emergency response is knowing the layout of your facility. That may sound simple enough, but knowing the easiest way for medical personnel to reach each area is critical in an emergency. Your facility should plan for emergency access and not leave to chance finding the best route for emergency personnel. The shortest and safest routes for paramedics to reach all locations at your facility should be determined ahead of time. The best entrance may be through

Calling 911 or Emergency Medical Services

When you call 911 for emergency assistance (pictured), follow these steps:

- Tell the operator that you are a lifeguard and provide the name of your facility and its street address.
- Explain what type of accident has occurred, what types of injuries have been sustained, what the victim's status is, and what medical aid is being provided.
- Answer honestly any questions asked of you. If you do not know an answer, say so.
- Provide a callback number and your extension, if any. You want the operator to be able to reach you if there are questions or problems.
- Tell the operator the best way to access the facility for emergency responders and, if possible, that there will be someone waiting for them at that location to guide them to the accident location.

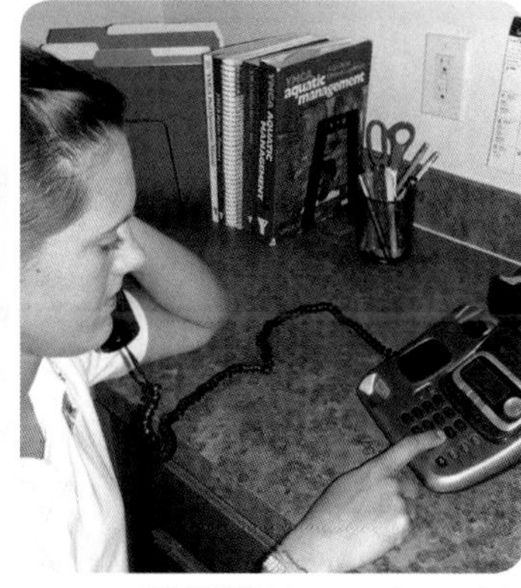

- Wait for the EMS operator to tell you to hang up the phone; then wait until the operator has disconnected before you hang up.
- Have someone wait by the phone, if at all possible, to handle a callback.

an exterior emergency exit door. If so, the facility should clearly mark that door as the emergency entrance for the pool.

When determining the best access routes for emergency personnel, management considers the following factors:

- The length and width of the backboard and ambulance gurney
- Stairs
- Sharp corners and narrow hallways
- Locked doors or other obstacles

Once the shortest and safest access routes for emergency personnel are determined, make sure these routes are kept clear at all times. The excitement of an emergency may make clearing the routes difficult when it is most important.

Your facility should arrange in-service training sessions with outside emergency personnel to practice procedures. During these practice sessions, the team can evaluate the access routes. Those routes, along with the locations of fire alarms, fire extinguishers, telephones, first-aid areas, and tornado shelter areas, should be posted for all staff and patrons.

Emergency medical services

It is critical that all staff understand the needs and procedures of emergency responders. Work with EMS staff during in-service training to plan, practice, and document how to best work together.

For example, determine whether EMS will enter the water to help remove a victim with injuries. Ignorance or misunderstanding may increase danger for the injured person and expose the facility to increased legal liability.

Equipment Assessment

Examine your equipment and supplies every day as part of your opening procedure. Every facility should have a variety of lifeguarding and emergency medical equipment, including an adequate supply of the following:

- Rescue tubes or rescue buoys
- Backboards, straps, and head immobilizers
- Manual suction device
- Bag-valve mask
- AED
- Oxygen
- Personal protective equipment (PPE)
- Rescue pack including resuscitation mask and disposable gloves
- Telephones and posted emergency telephone numbers
- First-aid kits including personal protective equipment for blood-borne pathogens
- Blankets
- Weather radio
- Lightning detector
- Shepherd's crooks or reaching poles
- Ring buoys and attached lines

Every locale has a code specifying the emergency equipment requirements for recreational facilities. Management should contact your state, county, and local health departments for lists of the equipment they require.

Safety equipment that is broken, in poor repair, or locked in a room is of little use in an emergency. Equipment is valuable only if all staff members know where it is stored and how to use it. Managers should ensure that regular in-service training sessions are held so that lifeguards can react effectively to a variety of emergency situations.

Water-Activated and Wireless Alarm Systems

Having to notify other lifeguards of an emergency by pressing an alarm button on the wall may slow a lifeguard's response to an emergency. A wireless or water-activated alarm, when combined with appropriate rescue protocols, can save time during an emergency. Water-activated and wireless alarms are portable aquatic-emergency summoning devices that take the place of a hard-wired emergency button. These devices allow the lifeguard to respond almost immediately to an aquatic emergency rather than having to travel to an emergency call button before responding to a distressed swimmer. When the wireless sensor button is pressed or the water-activated alarm gets wet, a loud alarm instantly sounds at the base station. The alarm continues to sound until it is reset. The sensors come with a clip for permanent mounting, a neck chain, or a stand.

Types of Emergencies

Eight specific groups of emergencies are presented in this section:

- Medical emergencies
- Water emergencies
- Missing persons
- Environmental (weather) emergencies
- Chemical emergencies
- Mechanical emergencies
- Facility emergencies
- Extreme violence

As you read this section and the rest of this chapter, consider how you and your facility would handle various emergency situations. Your facility should have an EAP for each category of emergency. If your facility does not have a plan for each type of emergency, suggest that management create one following the information in this chapter and in the manual *YMCA Aquatic Management*. For information on emergency equipment, see chapter 7. For more on providing first aid, see chapter 9.

Medical emergencies

In an aquatic setting, there can be a wide variety of medical emergencies, from life threatening to minor. Serious emergencies require first aid (for example, CPR) and transportation to a medical facility. A medical emergency can change quickly depending on the health of the victim and the situation. A lesser level of emergency can become a higher level of emergency that requires urgent care (for example, paramedic response). Some medical emergencies might require a doctor's care, but not urgently (for example, the victim requires stitches but presents no other medical problems). Minor cases can be treated on site (for example, small cuts and scrapes).

As a lifeguard in a medical emergency, you will rely on the training you have received in first aid, CPR Pro/AED, and oxygen administration to determine the level of response required to help the victim.

Types of medical emergencies

Following are some of the medical emergencies you might face as a lifeguard. Discuss with your supervisor and other staff how to handle these and other medical emergencies at your facility.

- Cardiac arrest (the heart suddenly and unexpectedly stops beating)
- Heart attack (blockage of blood flow to a section of the heart) or angina (chest pain)
- Uncontrolled bleeding
- Drowning
- Cessation of breathing (breathing stops)
- Obstructed airway or respiratory emergency
- Seizure
- Poisoning
- Allergic reaction
- Spinal injury
- Asthma attack
- Loss of consciousness
- Diabetes or insulin shock
- Fracture
- Cut or laceration
- Reaction to extreme heat or cold

Water emergencies

By the time you finish this lifeguarding course, you will have the skills to handle a wide variety of water emergencies. Through in-service training, the lifeguards and staff at your facility should practice the EAPs that are specific to your facility so you can respond effectively and efficiently to water emergencies, including these:

- Drownings
- Severe injury in the water, including spinal injury
- Cardiac or respiratory emergencies in the water

Missing persons

If a missing person is believed to be in the water, the situation is life threatening. If the missing person is believed to be out of the water, the situation is unlikely life threatening but may still be critical. In either instance, help locate the missing person and confirm that the person is not in the water. See the sample EAP later in this chapter for steps to take when a person is missing. See chapter 12 for additional discussion of search and rescue techniques for waterfront situations.

Figure 6.2 Examples of emergency hazard signs.

Environmental (weather) emergencies

It is important that facility staff know the policies and procedures for a variety of weather-related situations, including these:

- Thunderstorms and lightning
- Hurricanes
- Tornadoes and high winds
- Heavy rain and hailstorms
- High and low temperatures
- Reduced visibility (due to fog, haze, dust, blowing debris, or other causes)
- Earth tremors or earthquakes

Chapter 13 provides information about storms and signs of approaching bad weather. It is important, for example, to clear even indoor pools and wet areas of locker rooms once you hear thunder.

Chemical emergencies

Pool operators must be very careful when handling the chemicals used to keep the water chemistry properly balanced. Unfortunately, accidents sometimes occur that can create potentially hazardous conditions. It is important for lifeguards to read about and understand the chemicals used at their facility and to know the safety and emergency procedures for working with these chemicals, including signage (**figure 6.2**). Each facility should have procedures for handling a variety of chemical emergencies:

- Chlorine exposure due to tank ruptures, leaks, or spills resulting in serious or fatal injuries
- Acid spills resulting in caustic vapors and skin irritations
- Explosion of flammable chemicals (for example, chlorinated granulates or bromine)

- Imbalance in water chemistry (for example, cloudiness or improper pH or chlorine level that irritates swimmers' skin or eyes)

The EAP should list evacuation sites that your facility has previously secured, including more than one option so you can send patrons to a site upwind.

For chemical spills, remember these steps:

- Protect yourself and others.
- Evacuate the facility if necessary to protect safety.
- Control the spill if you can do so safely.
- Contain the spill if you can do so safely.
- Clean up the spill if you can do so safely.
- Report the spill to management and regulatory agencies.

It is important that your facility has these emergency phone numbers prominently posted. Check and update them regularly:

- CHEMTREC Operations Center 800-424-9300
- National Response Center 800-424-8802

These agencies provide 24-hour call-in service to answer questions about chemical spills.

To ensure chemical safety in the workplace, OSHA's Hazard Communication Standard requires that information be available to employers and employees about the identities and hazards of chemicals used in the workplace. Every facility should keep copies of material safety data sheets (MSDS) in the pool office and filter room and place a copy in its master emergency response document. Your facility management should ensure that you are trained on all chemicals used in your facility before your first assignment. Be sure you have read the MSDS. For more information on pool chemistry, see chapter 14.

Mechanical emergencies

Various potential mechanical hazards may exist at your facility. Procedures should be in place for handling these issues:

- Structural failure
- Filtration system failure
- Lighting failure
- Equipment malfunctions (slides, wave pool, diving boards)

Facility emergencies

Not all emergency situations that affect your facility will occur within the pool area. Be sure you know your facility's provisions for handling a variety of emergency situations:

- Fire on the grounds
- Electrical outage
- Chemical explosion on the grounds or nearby, presenting danger from fire or fumes
- Fire near the facility, presenting danger from flames or smoke

Extreme violence

An act of violence in the workplace might involve gun violence, a bomb threat, an armed intruder, robbery, assault, child abduction, or major damage to or loss of control of the building. Many employers have emergency response plans detailing what to do in case of workplace violence. If you are not aware of such plans, ask your supervisor. Practice drills will help everyone act calmly and efficiently in the event of an actual incident of extreme violence.

Treat all threats as though they are real. Keep in mind that safety of the patrons and staff is of utmost importance.

Tip

Many facilities use one long whistle blast to signal an emergency and initiate emergency procedures. That whistle blast serves a second purpose: it allows the lifeguard to see if the victim is responsive.

Sample Emergency Action Plans

EAPs usually include five fundamental steps:

1. Initial recognition of a victim and activation of the EAP.
2. Secondary response by other team members to resolve the emergency (including clearing the pool and monitoring patrons, working with EMS, and preparing emergency equipment and assisting with first aid).
3. Notification of designated staff as specified in the crisis communication plan. (Only designated staff will comment on the emergency situation to any witness, bystander, or reporter. Only those specified in the chain of command are to be given information.) Management notification of the victim's emergency contact.
4. Rescuers complete the necessary incident or accident report.
5. Investigation of the incident.

The manner in which each of these steps is completed varies with the specific situation. **Figure 6.3** is a sample of an emergency action plan for a multi-lifeguard facility.

The sample plans provided in this chapter, meant only as a guide, are for multi-lifeguard facilities. Each facility will determine which lifeguards perform which duties. Single-lifeguard facilities will establish a procedure for the lone lifeguard to signal for immediate assistance from other trained facility staff. Responsibilities for the lifeguard, staff assistants, and supervisor under those circumstances must be carefully defined.

It is important that your facility has written procedures for handling emergencies. Be sure you are familiar with the procedures and your responsibilities. Your in-service training and practice sessions will help you feel comfortable in responding. When your staff practices, time how fast your team can respond and give aid. Record and log your times, striving to be quicker and more efficient with each drill. Make sure that safety is not compromised in an effort to be faster. Do not make this a race in which someone might be injured. You are aiming to be expeditious, efficient, and safe.

Sample pool evacuation plan

Each facility should have a plan for evacuating the pool area. In all emergencies, quick and organized action is important. The following plan is appropriate for a weather emergency:

1. Signal other lifeguards to initiate the evacuation plan.
2. Direct swimmers to clear the pool.
3. Remain on post until all swimmers have left the pool area.
4. Lock and secure the pool.
5. Assist other staff in directing patrons to a shelter or designated safe area.
6. Reassure patrons of their safety.
7. Report to management for further instruction or assignment.
8. Assist as necessary.
9. Assist in completing the incident report form.

Note that in some evacuations, such as for chemical emergencies, patrons may have to exit outside. Check that the EAP has a cold weather plan, such as providing towels and foot coverings. If it is necessary to evacuate the entire facility, direct patrons to the site designated by management.

Sample emergency action plan for a medical emergency

This sample EAP outlines a procedure for providing first aid for a heart attack victim who requires prompt attention:

1. Activate the EAP by hitting your remote alarm button, and then signal another lifeguard to cover your area.
2. Assess the situation; direct the staff members who respond to your alarm to call for EMS assistance; provide first aid.
3. Lifeguard who called EMS notifies the chain of command.
4. Complete an accident report and file it with the appropriate person before returning to duty.
5. Review your actions with the manager.

Figure 6.3 Sample emergency action plan.

Sample Emergency Action Plan Roles

Time	Lifeguard #1	Lifeguard #2	Lifeguard #3	Lifeguard #4
	Recognize victim			
5 sec	Activate EAP	Take over Lifeguard #1's and Lifeguard #3's zones; begin to clear pool and send patrons to locker rooms	Call EMS Allow Lifeguard #2 to take over zone and clear the pool	Clear zone or instruct another lifeguard to take over clearing zone
10–60 sec	Perform rescue Extricate and position victim	Continue to clear pool Send additional staff to monitor locker rooms	Activate crisis communication plan	**Bring/prep emergency equipment** (AED, O2, first-aid kit, gloves, towels, backboard) Help remove/position victim
1–3 min	Begin emergency care; provide CPR, if needed; apply AED, if needed	Secure pool area and assist Lifeguard #1 as needed	Meet EMS	Help Lifeguard #1; prepare victim for AED
4 min	Continue emergency care and monitor AED	Assist Lifeguard #1 as needed	Bring EMS to victim	Continue emergency care and monitor AED
EMS takes over				
Complete and file the necessary incident or accident report				
Return to duty as soon as fit to do so				

Sample emergency action plan for a drowning at a pool

This is a sample procedure for a water rescue at a multi-lifeguard facility.

1. Signal other lifeguards to initiate emergency procedures. Hit the remote alarm button. (See 6 for the duties the other lifeguards perform simultaneously.)
2. Assess the situation and determine what action or rescue skills and equipment are necessary.
3. Perform the rescue.
4. Remove the victim from the water.
5. Begin any necessary first aid and continue until EMS arrives.
6. During steps 2–5, the other lifeguards or trained staff perform these duties:
    a. Lifeguard #2 assists Lifeguard #1 if needed; continues scanning and takes over the zone of Lifeguard #1 (and others if needed); clears the pool; sends patrons to the locker room; and monitors patrons in the locker room.
    b. Lifeguard #3 (or qualified staff) assists Lifeguard #1 if needed; calls EMS; activates the crisis communication system; meets EMS; and brings EMS to the pool (following the best route for EMS).
    c. Lifeguard #4 brings backboard (for speed board exit) and emergency equipment (AED, emergency oxygen, BVM, suction, and first-aid kit); prepares the equipment; assists Lifeguard #1 with removing the victim from the water; assists Lifeguard #1 with positioning the victim; and prepares the victim (for example, places pads and readies for shock) or otherwise aids Lifeguard #1 as requested. If AED and oxygen equipment are not stored in the pool area, a system should be in place to bring AED and oxygen equipment to the pool immediately when the EAP alarm is activated.
7. Calmly notify those in the chain of command about the accident; they in turn should notify emergency contacts (relatives or other designated individuals).
8. Complete and file the necessary report.
9. Return to duty as soon as you are fit to do so.
10. Complete the investigation.

Sample emergency action plan for a missing person at a pool

It is essential to have and practice an EAP for finding a missing person. A variety of different search and rescue techniques can be used for open water areas (see chapter 12). When searching for a missing person at a pool, follow these steps:

1. Signal the other lifeguards to initiate emergency procedures.
2. Signal an immediate pool check. Clear the pool and have patrons sit well away from the pool.
3. If the missing person has become a drowning victim, complete the rescue and begin emergency first aid immediately. Arrange for EMS assistance.
4. Complete the necessary accident or incident report.
5. Return to duty as soon as you are fit to do so.

If it is determined that the missing person is not in the pool and is not a drowning victim, follow these steps, making sure not to leave the pool unguarded:

1. Designate a search coordinator. Determine the identity of the missing person.
2. Get an accurate description of the missing person that includes the person's age, skin color, height, weight, hair and eye color, clothing, and, if it is a child who is missing, type of shoes (often an abductor will change a child's clothing but find it difficult to switch the shoes) and where he or she was last seen. Relay this information to the search coordinator. Keep the person who provided the description nearby in case other information is needed.
3. Make an announcement over the PA system for the missing person to report to a central location, and ask anyone who has seen the missing person to report to a staff member.
4. Use the designated communication system as instructed by the search coordinator while sweeping the building and grounds.

If the missing person is a child, follow these additional steps:

1. Post staff at all facility exits to watch all children who exit the building. Depending on the size of the facility and the number of exits, the facility may be locked down while the child is missing.
2. Have someone wait for a parent or relative at the front desk.
3. Call 911 if the child is not found within 10 minutes.
4. If the child is found with an abductor, do not allow them to leave; however, do not use force. Instead, call 911. (If a call has already been made to 911, call again with updated information.) Turn the incident over to the police.
5. If the child is found injured from an accident, provide care and follow first-aid procedures.
6. If the child is found unharmed, cancel the search and contact 911. Return the child safely to the parent or guardian.
7. Complete the necessary accident or incident report.
8. Return to duty as soon as possible.

If it is determined that the missing person is not a drowning victim, swimmers may return to the water if there are enough lifeguards to guard the pool while other staff search for the missing person. Follow these steps when searching for a missing person:

1. Check all facilities, including washrooms, locker rooms, gymnasiums, storage closets, and any related facility on the grounds.
2. Check the missing person's home by phone.
3. If the person is not found, notify those in the chain of command, who should in turn notify emergency contacts.
4. Notify law enforcement officials. This is the duty of the manager or the head lifeguard.
5. Complete the necessary accident or incident report.
6. Return to duty as soon as possible.

Review

Review Topics

Every lifeguard has a role in emergency action plans (EAPs) defined by an aquatics facility. In this chapter, you have learned about EAPs and how they are critical in an emergency. Here are some key points to know from this chapter:

1) Why an emergency action plan is important
2) Why it is important for aquatic teams to practice for emergency situations
3) The responsibilities of each role in your facility's EAPs
4) Why you should know your facility's layout
5) Why is it important to work with your local EMS unit to prepare for emergencies
6) The major types of emergencies to expect and how to handle them
7) Five basic steps common to most EAPs

Review Questions

1. Why is teamwork critical in an emergency?
2. What does "chain of command" mean and why is it important in an emergency?
3. What are the primary responsibilities of each of the four lifeguard roles in an EAP?
4. Why is it important to know the layout of your facility?
5. How often should you examine your emergency equipment and supplies?
6. Why is it important to be aware of the different types of emergencies that may occur in an aquatic facility?
7. List and describe four of the eight types of emergencies discussed in this chapter.

RESCUE

CHAPTER 7

Rescue Strokes, Equipment, and Assists

Page 106

Rescue Procedures

Page 124

CHAPTER 7

Rescue Strokes, Equipment, and Assists

Your swimming skills and the types of lifeguarding equipment you use are critical components of your ability to make quick, effective rescues. Using what you learn from this lifeguarding course and on-the-job experience, you will be able to make sound decisions and take the appropriate action.

In this chapter, you will learn the following:

- Lifeguard approach strokes and techniques
- Types of personal and rescue equipment
- Nonswimming rescues

7
CHAPTER

Staying Afloat

Aquatic activities are popular forms of recreation, but they do include a degree of danger. Because accidents in the water do happen, even to good swimmers, be sure you know how to take care of yourself and others. Everyone who works or plays on or in the water should know certain essential skills such as how to stay afloat in deep water for an extended period. The resting stroke and treading water are two essential skills for both lifeguards and swimmers.

Resting stroke or survival float

The resting stroke, also called the survival float, is recommended for swimmers who are in warm water and not wearing a personal flotation device (PFD). The resting stroke lets a swimmer float in a relaxed position for long periods of time, even without the use of the legs and arms. The most common procedure is illustrated in **figure 7.1**.

After taking a breath, let your body submerge with your arms and legs relaxed and hanging down. Keep your back near the surface. This position will be easy to assume because the air in your lungs will lift your back.

Hold your breath only as long as you feel comfortable, then begin to exhale. There is no need to wait until you desperately need a breath. When you are ready to breathe, bring your arms close to the surface, separate your legs as you would when starting a scissors kick, and finish exhaling. Press down on the water with your hands, complete the scissors kick, and lift your head above the water to inhale. Make sure that only your face comes out of

Figure 7.1 Resting stroke.

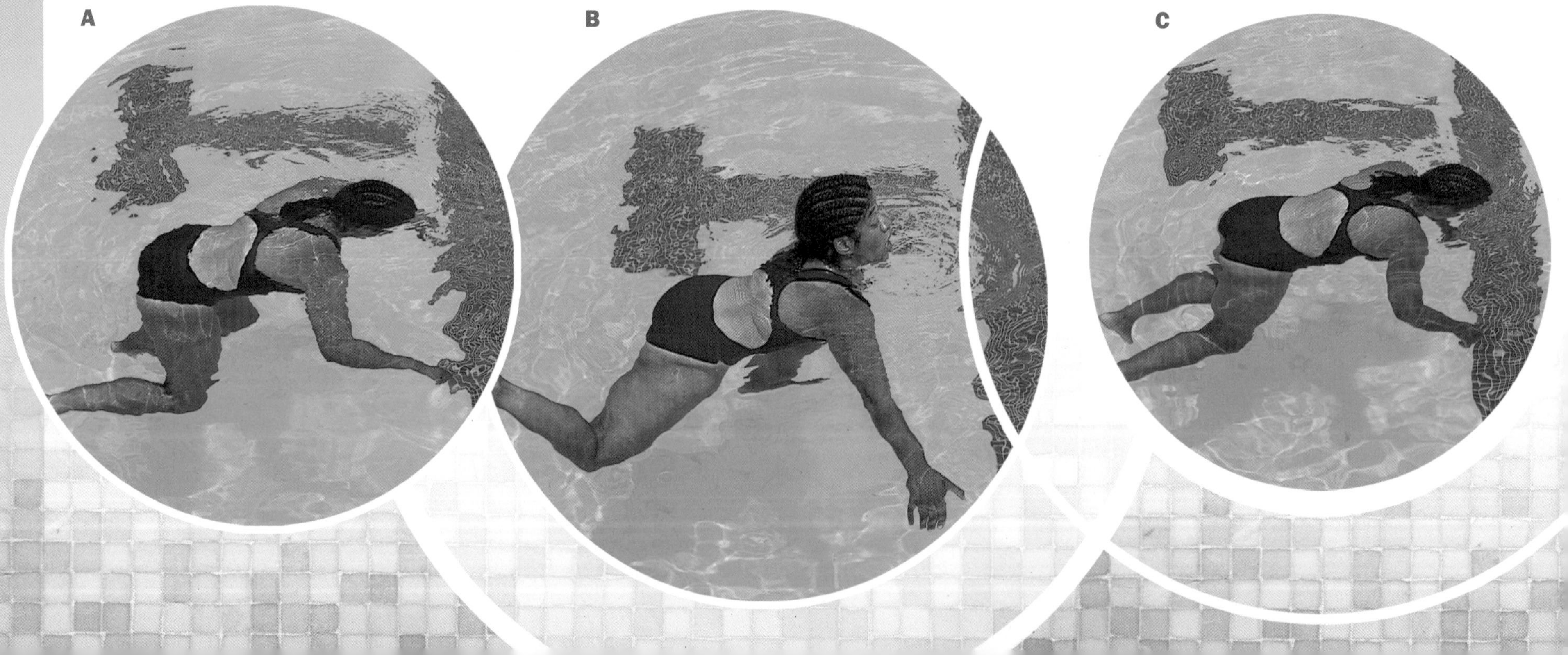

A

B

C

the water. Take a quick breath and return to the relaxed starting position.

Because your head is submerged in the floating position, you will lose body heat while doing the resting stroke. In cold water and cold air temperatures, this heat loss can lead to hypothermia (discussed in chapter 9) and can be reduced by using the heat escape lessening position described in chapter 12. Heat loss is less of a concern if the water and surrounding air are warm.

Treading water

Treading water is an important survival skill for everyone to master. When treading water, your arms move in a wide in-and-out motion with the palms turned down at a 30- to 35-degree angle. This movement keeps constant water pressure against the hands and lets your body maintain its position in the water.

Different kicks can be used in treading water:

- The **scissors kick** (**figure 7.2**) provides a strong upward lift by having one leg move forward and the other leg move backward and then bringing the legs together. For the **single scissors kick**, one leg always moves forward and the other backward. For the **double scissors kick**, also called the **flutter kick**, the legs alternate moving forward and backward.
- The **breaststroke kick** is performed vertically with the legs moving simultaneously.
- The **eggbeater, or rotary, kick** (**figure 7.3**) provides the most consistent support of all the kicks, although it may be the most difficult for some people to perform. This kick is similar to the breaststroke kick, but the legs work alternately rather than both at once. To do the eggbeater kick, pull one heel toward your seat, turn your toes to the outside, and kick your leg around and to the front. Repeat with the other leg and continue alternating.

Figure 7.2 Treading water using a scissors kick.

Figure 7.3 Treading water using an eggbeater, or rotary, kick.

Strokes for Survival Situations

Lifeguards who work in open-water settings may be a long distance from swimmers. These lifeguards need to know swimming strokes that can carry a person a great distance without causing exhaustion. More often, they will use this knowledge to coach swimmers who are a long way from shore but who are not in imminent danger. These survival strokes help swimmers reach the shore while conserving energy.

Elementary backstroke

The elementary backstroke (**figure 7.4**) is a very comfortable stroke for most swimmers. Because this stroke keeps the face out of the water, it is recommended for long distances.

To swim the elementary backstroke, initiate the kick by bending your knees, pulling your heels toward your seat, and turning your toes out. As your knees bend, pull your arms up along your sides with the elbows down and the palms toward the body. Stretch your arms outward slightly above your shoulders. Then kick by whipping your legs out, around, and then together. At the same time, pull the arms back to your sides. Use the following cues to coordinate the stroke: up, out, together.

Breaststroke

The breaststroke (**figure 7.5**) is a useful survival stroke in either calm or choppy water. It is initiated from a front glide position in which the arms and legs are fully extended. When doing the breaststroke in a survival situation, you may want to keep your head out of the water and look forward. Keeping the elbows high, press your hands outward and downward, moving in a motion that resembles half of a heart. At the end of the pull, press your elbows toward your sides, bring your hands together in front of your chest, and reach again to the front.

Figure 7.4 Elementary backstroke.

A

B

C

D

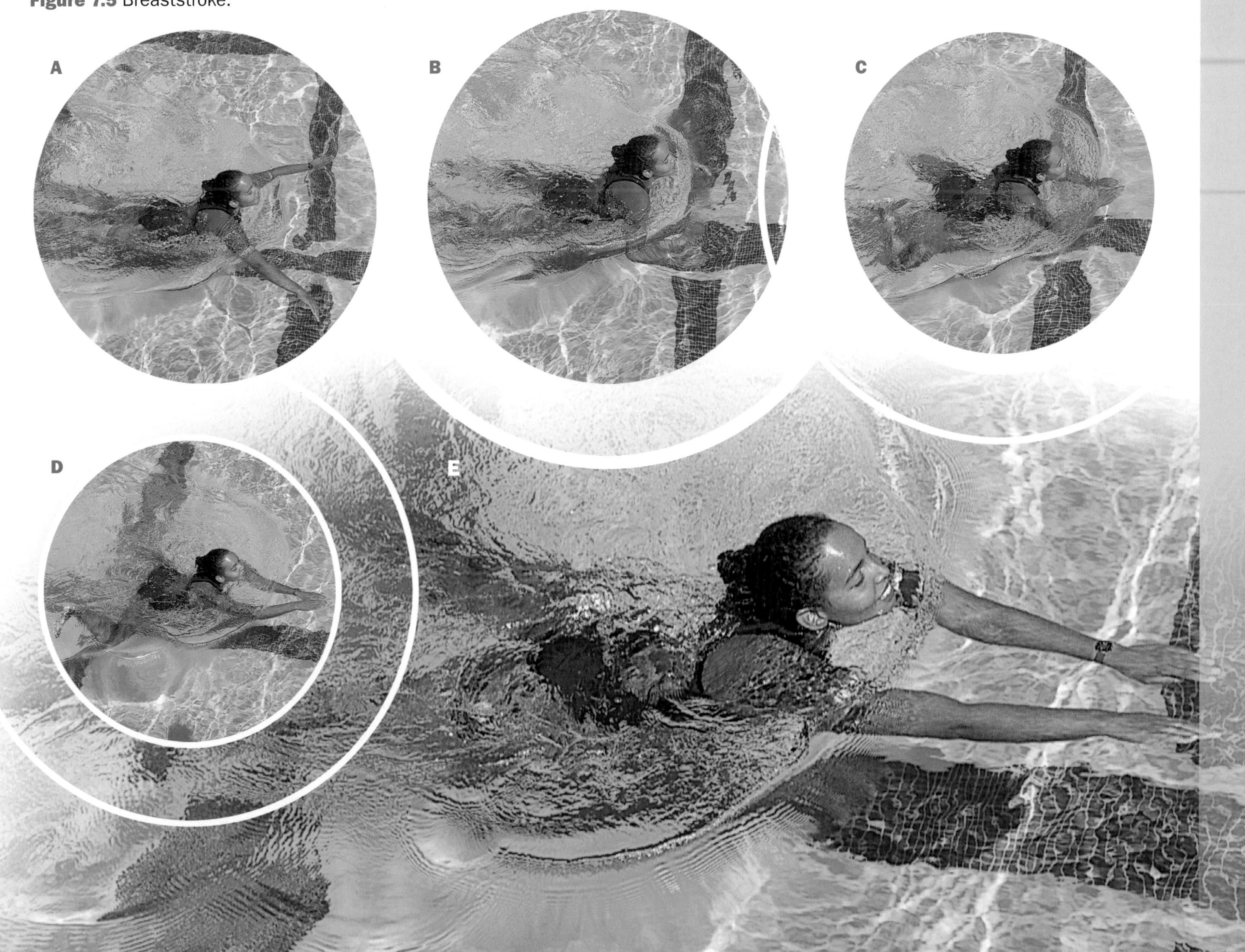

Figure 7.5 Breaststroke.

To kick in the breaststroke, pull your heels toward your seat and turn the toes out to the sides. Kick the legs outward and then together in a circular motion. The coordination of the stroke is to pull with the arms and recover the legs and then kick and extend the arms forward and glide.

Sidestroke

In a survival situation, do the sidestroke (**figure 7.6**). To begin, assume a glide position on your side, with the bottom arm stretched above your head in the water and the top arm along your side. Lean your head to the side with your ear in the water.

For the stroke, pull your bottom arm (the arm extended overhead) back toward you, bending the elbow and pulling the water toward your chest, and then return it to the extended position overhead. Bend the elbow of the top arm (the arm near your side), reach the hand toward the opposite shoulder, and then push the water toward your feet. The arms work in opposition: while one is stroking, the other is recovering. Both arms move toward the chest and then return to the glide position at the same time.

The kick follows the top arm (the arm along your side). As the top arm recovers, moving toward the shoulder, the legs recover, pulling up to your seat; as the top arm strokes, the legs kick. To kick, begin with your heels pulled near your seat. Stretch your top leg in front of you and your bottom leg behind you, and then kick outward and bring both legs straight together again.

When towing a victim, reverse the direction of the legs by bringing your top leg back and your bottom leg forward. This is called a rescue kick. It is important to move the top leg back because it prevents you from kicking the victim.

Figure 7.6 Sidestroke.

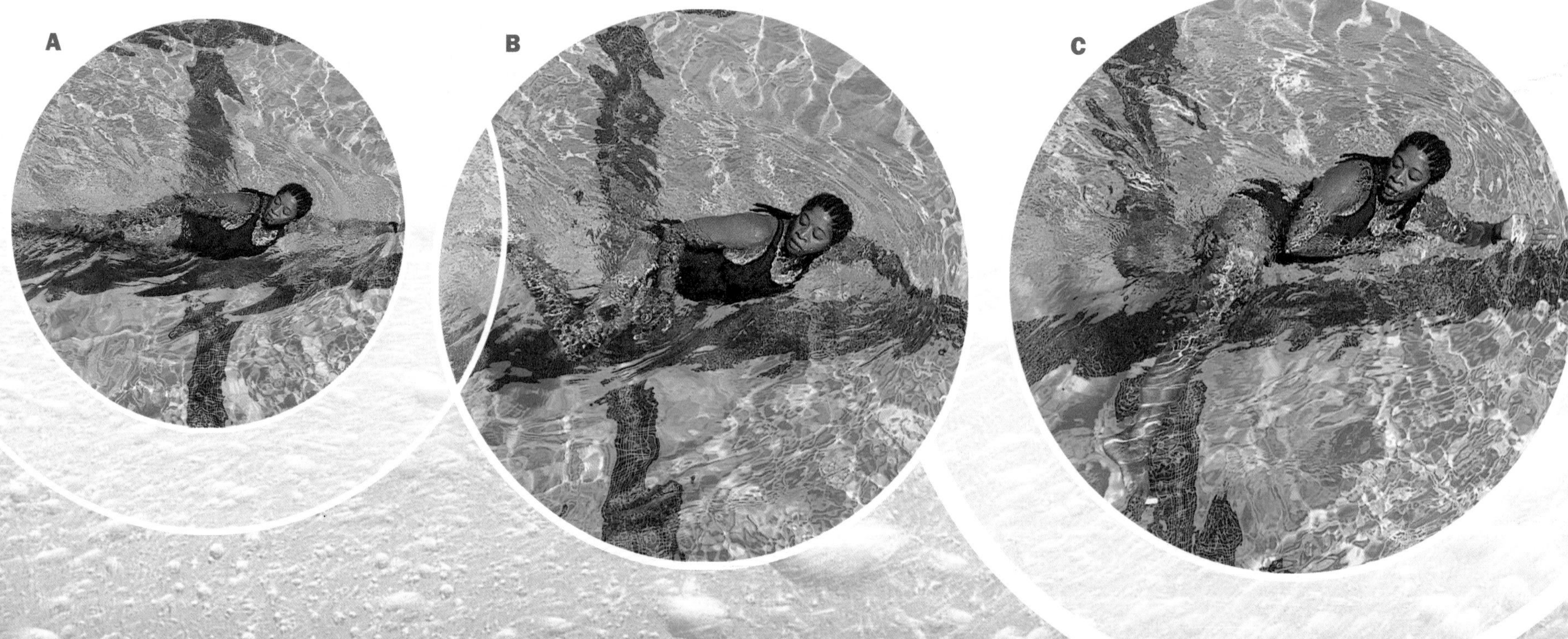

Surface Dives

While in the water, you may need to use a surface dive to get below the surface and recover a victim. This can be either a feetfirst dive or an arm-over-arm dive. A feetfirst dive is best used when you are not sure of the water depth or the presence of debris. If you strike something, the feetfirst dive is less likely to cause injury than a headfirst (arm-over-arm) dive.

Whenever you perform a surface dive, be sure to equalize your ears regularly and often. Equalize your ears at the surface and every 2 to 5 feet during descent.

Feetfirst surface dive

Follow these procedures to execute a feetfirst surface dive (**figure 7.7**):

1. Begin from a vertical position.
2. Stretch one leg forward and one back. With one large scissors kick, snap your legs together and push down on the water as you bring your arms down to your sides. This should bring you up out of the water, and then begin a downward decent. Keep your body streamlined.
3. Keeping your arms straight, pull them out and up from your sides with palms facing up and bring them together above your head.
4. If you need to go deeper, slide your arms back down along your sides and repeat the upward lift.

Figure 7.7 Feetfirst surface dive.

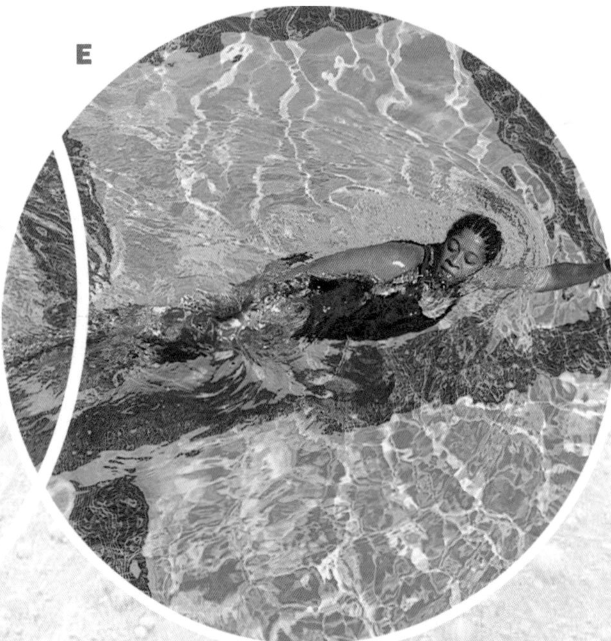

Arm-over-arm surface dive

The arm-over-arm surface dive allows you to perform a headfirst dive in a continuous motion. Depending on your ability and strength, you can do this dive in either a tuck or a pike position. The tuck position requires less strength because it shortens the distance between the hips and feet. The pike position (**figure 7.8**) allows the legs to go higher out of the water, which speeds the rate of descent. Follow these steps:

1. As your left arm recovers from a crawl stroke, keep your right hand next to your right leg.
2. Reach down toward the bottom of the pool with your right hand while simultaneously ducking your head.
3. Pull your left hand back toward your left thigh.
4. Turning your palms down, sweep both hands toward your chest. This will lift your legs out of the water and pull your head toward the bottom. Your hands and arms will be below your head, closest to the pool bottom.
5. Pull with your arms (a breaststroke or modified pull) for faster descent.

Personal Equipment

As a lifeguard, you require certain equipment to carry out your duty and be comfortable while on the guard. Some examples are picture in **figure 7.9**. Your employer may provide some of it, but you must take the initiative to have appropriate lifeguarding equipment with you at all times while on duty.

Always report for work properly attired. Wear a **swimsuit** that is comfortable and practical. An **identifiable shirt or assigned uniform** is important

Figure 7.8 Arm-over-arm surface dive from a pike position.

Checklist of Personal Equipment

Every lifeguard

- _____ Appropriate swimsuit
- _____ Identifiable shirt or uniform
- _____ Towel
- _____ Whistle
- _____ Water bottle
- _____ Rescue pack containing personal protective equipment (resuscitation mask and gloves)
- _____ Rescue tube or buoy
- _____ Swim fins, mask, and snorkel (for deep pools and waterfront lifeguarding)
- _____ Inflatable rescue tube for multiple rescues, waterfronts, and boats
- _____ Aquatic shoes (optional)

Outdoor facility lifeguard

- _____ Wide-brimmed hat or visor
- _____ Polarized sunglasses
- _____ Sunscreen
- _____ Cold weather gear
- _____ Rain gear
- _____ Insect repellent (for areas where insects are a problem)

Open-water lifeguard

- _____ Binoculars
- _____ Swim fins, mask, and snorkel
- _____ PFDs (when in a boat or small craft)

so patrons can recognize you as a lifeguard. A shirt is also necessary to help protect you from the sun.

The well-prepared lifeguard also has a **towel** at the station. You may need to towel off after being in the water, or you may need a towel as a rescue aid. (Your towel can also reduce the embarrassment of a patron who loses a suit after diving or going down the water slide.) And a towel can even help pad the seat on your lifeguard stand.

Every lifeguard must have a **whistle**, preferably kept close at hand on a wrist strap or on a breakaway lanyard around your neck. Your whistle is your prime communication tool. You may even want to have extra whistles at your disposal. Test your whistle before you go on duty to make sure it is working properly. Do not use other lifeguards' whistles because it can lead to the transmission of germs and viruses.

Always be prepared to provide emergency first aid. Your **rescue pack** should include basic first-aid supplies and necessary **personal protective equipment (PPE)**, which prevents transmission of blood-borne pathogens (see chapter 9). PPE should include at least a one-way resuscitation mask and disposable (single-use) gloves. Other PPE items in your rescue pack may include protective eyewear and breathing barriers. Consider putting these items in a fanny pack to keep them close at hand while on land. During water rescues, be sure to have your **resuscitation mask and gloves**.

While on duty, always carry a **rescue flotation device (RFD)**, either a **rescue tube or buoy**. An essential tool for any water rescue, an RFD is a flotation aid with a strap that keeps it secured to you. Hold the extra line from the rescue tube in

Figure 7.9 Examples of personal equipment.

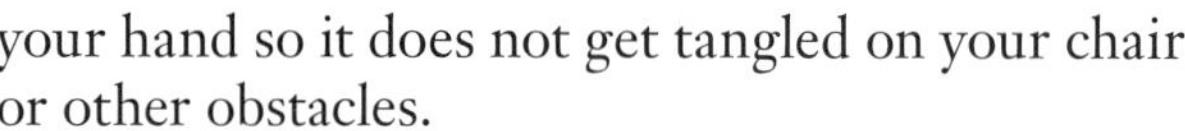

your hand so it does not get tangled on your chair or other obstacles.

Stay hydrated by keeping a **water bottle** nearby at all times. You will be sitting or standing for a period of time in a location without access to drinking water. Research shows that drinking beverages with high sugar content has a negative impact on long-term vigilance (Anderson and Horne 2006). So water is the smartest way to stay hydrated.

Many lifeguards choose to work in **aquatic shoes**, which can be worn both in and out of the water. There are a variety of aquatic shoes available today. On the deck, aquatic shoes help protect your feet from hot and irregular surfaces and from scrapes, cuts, and stones. They also provide additional traction on slippery surfaces. In the water, aquatic shoes will not interfere with your ability to swim, and in open water they can protect your feet from unseen dangers. If you cannot easily swim in aquatic shoes, choose a pair that you can easily slip off or will fall off once you are in the water.

If you are an outdoor lifeguard, you will be exposed to the harmful effects of the sun. Excessive exposure to the sun can cause skin cancer. Be sure to protect yourself as follows:

- Wear a wide-brimmed **hat or visor** to protect your face from direct sunlight and from glare off the water.
- Wear **polarized sunglasses** to reduce glare and protect your eyes from ultraviolet ray damage. (Use sunglasses indoors if glare is a factor.)
- Use **sunscreen** (**figure 7.10**). The American Academy of Dermatology recommends sunscreen with a sun protection factor (SPF) rating of 30 or higher. (Although SPF ratings go up to 100 or more, the amount of additional protection provided gets smaller as the SPF increases. For example, SPF 15 filters out about 93 percent of UVB rays, SPF 30 about 97 percent, and SPF 50 about 98 percent.) Be sure to reapply sunscreen regularly—at least every two hours. (AAD 2010)
- Use **sun-screening clothes and umbrellas**.

Figure 7.10 Apply sunscreen at least every two hours.

Also see Sunburn Precautions in chapter 13 for more on protecting yourself from the sun.

Other days will not be bright or sunny. Cool temperatures, wind, and rain can make an unprepared lifeguard miserable. Have a breakaway (snap or Velcro) lifeguard parka and breakaway pants available for very cold days or drape a blanket or towel over your legs for warmth. Come prepared for rainy days with a breakaway (snap or Velcro) slicker or rain suit with breakaway pants (**figure 7.11**).

Remember, you may have to shed clothing quickly. Do not wear sweatshirts or sweat pants when guarding, as they take too long to remove. Instead, use **breakaway clothing** that can easily and quickly be removed, such as a parka draped over the shoulders (do not put your arms through the sleeves) or held together by snaps or Velcro. During in-service training, practice with the equipment and clothing you will be wearing to see how much time it takes to slip out of a parka and rip off pants. You must be able to do this fast so you can reach a victim as quickly as possible.

Insect repellent should also be a part of your equipment in areas where biting insects are a problem. Using repellent may help you avoid the discomfort of multiple insect bites and swarming gnats or mosquitoes. Do not let pests interfere with your ability to concentrate and monitor your assigned swimming area.

Have **binoculars** on hand if you are lifeguarding on the open water—a river, lake, or ocean—because you will need to clearly see and evaluate possible emergencies at greater distances. Binoculars are not effective for routine scanning because your field of vision is limited (binoculars narrow your field of vision and eliminate peripheral vision entirely). However, if you spot a potential problem some distance away with your naked eye, you can use binoculars to get a close-up view.

If you guard open water or deep water, necessary equipment includes a **mask, fins, and snorkel** for use in searching for underwater victims. If rescue is required, swim fins will also cut down on the time it takes to reach a victim. (Fins also help speed underwater rescue in pools with deep water or diving wells.) If you will be using swim fins, practice putting them on quickly; taking too long can eliminate the value of the extra speed they give you in the water. Wear a **personal flotation device (PFD)** if you are required to use a boat for patrolling or rescuing (you may choose to remove the PFD before the rescue, depending on the situation).

Effective lifeguards have a dedicated bag for their lifeguarding equipment. Having this equipment together and ready will make you well prepared for duty.

Do not wear sharp or loose jewelry when lifeguarding; this includes jewelry for body piercings. If you have to rescue someone, such jewelry poses a danger to you and the victim. And remember, no shoes (except water shoes), no cell phones or texting, and no personal music players while on duty.

Figure 7.11 Breakaway clothing provides protection from the elements while allowing a quick response.

A

B

C

D

Rescue Equipment

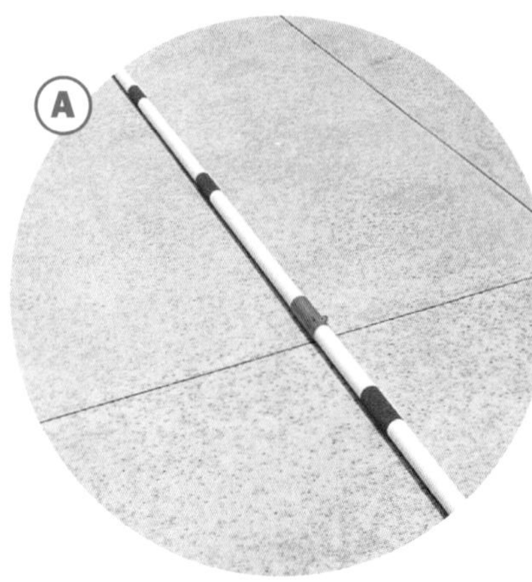

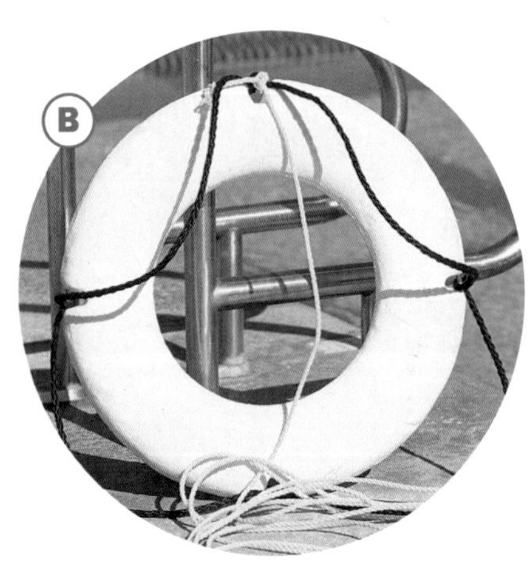

Figure 7.12 Rescue equipment: (**A**) Reaching pole; (**B**) Ring buoy; (**C**) Throw bag; (**D**) Rescue tube; (**E**) Rescue buoy; (**F**) Inflatable rescue tube.

You will learn how to make a variety of rescues in this lifeguarding course. In each one, you will use a piece of rescue equipment. Using rescue equipment reduces the risk of harm to you and the victim. The equipment provides support, conserves your energy, and makes it easier to tow the victim to safety.

The most common pieces of rescue equipment are pictured in **figure 7.12** and described here:

Shepherd's crook and reaching pole. The shepherd's crook and reaching pole are lightweight wood, aluminum, or fiberglass poles 10 to 15 feet long. The shepherd's crook has a blunt hook on one end that is large enough to place around an unconscious victim. Both the shepherd's crook and reaching pole can be used to assist a conscious victim. State codes commonly require that a shepherd's crook and a reaching pole be available for use by nonlifeguards to provide a means of rescue without having to enter the water.

Ring buoy. The buoyant ring buoy usually weighs no more than 2.5 pounds and is used primarily on lakefronts and in pools. The ring buoy is attached to a 40- to 50-foot line for use in throwing assists. Most state bathing codes require the presence of a ring buoy to provide nonlifeguards a way to rescue a distressed swimmer who is out of reach of a shepherd's crook or reaching pole. A ring buoy is generally effective only for helping a distressed swimmer who can grab it. An advantage is that you can throw it. Disadvantages are that you might not throw it close enough or might throw it so close that you strike the distressed swimmer. Remember to hold the end of the line, usually by standing on it, so that you can pull the ring buoy back.

Throw bag. The throw bag is a self-contained throwing device consisting of a 75-foot rope coiled inside a bag. Because of its weight and compact size, the throw bag can quickly reach a victim at distances far beyond the reach of a ring buoy. It is used most frequently in moving water, such as for rescues on waterfront locations or from small craft (for example, canoes, sailboats, rowboats, and kayaks) when boaters or fishers have fallen overboard. The throw bag does not provide flotation, so only a conscious victim who can stay afloat without extra buoyancy will benefit. It requires practice to use a throw bag efficiently and accurately. Recovering the rope takes time and making a second throw can be challenging (see Throwing assists later in this chapter).

Rescue tube. A rescue tube is one of the most versatile pieces of lifeguarding equipment. It can be used to extend to a struggling victim, tow a distressed or unresponsive victim, support a victim during in-water rescue breathing, and support a rescuer when needed. Although sizes and shapes vary, a typical rescue tube is made of buoyant molded foam and measures 3.5 inches by 5.5 inches by 40 to 54 inches. Rescue tubes have a clasp or fastener and a line with a loop, which is called the tail, attached to one end. The line may vary in length depending on the depth of the water in which it will be used. A special rescue tube made for the YMCA has a slot in it to hold a resuscitation mask so the mask will be immediately available to the lifeguard for in-water rescue breathing. To learn how to wear a rescue tube, see chapter 8.

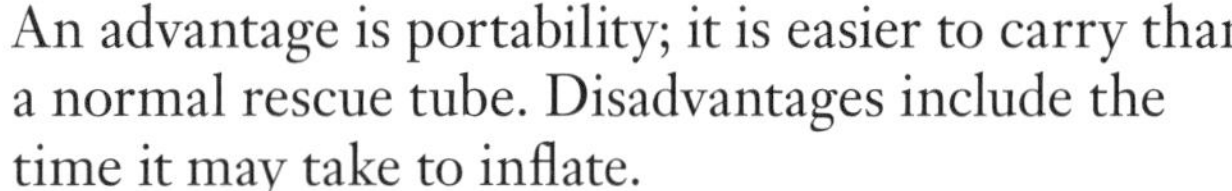

Rescue buoy. The rescue buoy is made of a lightweight, hard plastic. It is hollow and very buoyant. It has molded handles along the sides and the end, and like the rescue tube, has a towrope attached to one end. The buoy can be used in a reaching assist, as a buoyancy aid for victims, and for in-water rescue breathing. You cannot, however, use it to support an unconscious victim without maintaining contact with the buoy and victim. The buoy is used predominantly in waterfront and surf rescues. It can be used to rescue multiple victims due to its high degree of buoyancy and the handles on it.

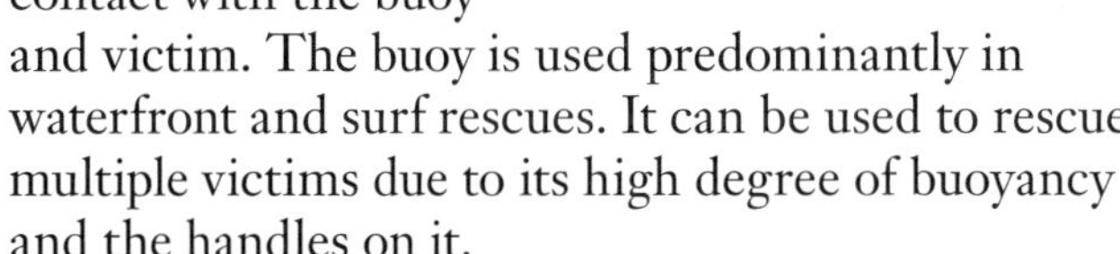

Inflatable rescue tube. An inflatable rescue tube may be used for water rescue when people are camping, backpacking, canoeing, or engaging in other outdoor aquatic activities. The tube can be inflated and deflated either manually or with an automatic CO_2 inflator. An advantage is portability; it is easier to carry than a normal rescue tube. Disadvantages include the time it may take to inflate.

Paddleboards. Paddleboards, also known as rescue boards or rescue surfboards, are versatile. Because of their buoyancy, they can be used as floating lifeguard stands or for quick transportation to reach a victim in light to moderate surf. They can be used to carry a victim back to shore, and their flat surfaces make it easier to perform in-water rescue breathing. See chapter 12 for more about the use of paddleboards on the waterfront. While you can learn basic paddleboard skills in a pool, practice paddleboard skills in the environment where you will be lifeguarding, whether ocean, lake, or river.

Emergency care equipment. The facility should have a first-aid station stocked with a first-aid kit and emergency care equipment such as a manual suction device, an AED, bag-valve masks, and emergency oxygen. See chapter 9 to learn more about this equipment.

Nonswimming Rescues

Recall the keys to lifeguarding: prevent, recognize, activate EAP, rescue, emergency care, and report. Now, imagine you are on duty and scanning your zone—scanning the bottom, middle, and surface of the pool—and noting any people or areas that give concern. While scanning, you notice someone in trouble near the side of the pool. You activate the EAP by signaling to another lifeguard that you are going to make the rescue and the lifeguard you signal takes over scanning your zone.

In this scenario, a safe way to perform a rescue is to use one of several nonswimming assists made from a stable position. These include reaching, extension, and throwing assists performed from the pool deck or pier and wading assists done in water no higher than chest deep.

Sharpen Skills With In-Service Training

In-service training is ongoing training that gives professional lifeguards a chance to regularly practice skills, test their knowledge, and practice rescue scenarios to ensure peak performance in the event of an emergency. It is important that in-service includes training and practice in these areas:

- Prevention
- Decision making
- Scanning and victim recognition
- Emergency action plans (EAPs)
- Rescues and removal
- Emergency care
- Physical conditioning
- Records and reports
- CPR Pro/AED, first aid, and oxygen administration

Reaching and extension assists

Reaching assists play an important role in lifeguarding and may be your best choice for rescuing a distressed swimmer. If the patron is near enough to reach from the side of the pool or dock, you can perform the rescue while staying secure, which may be faster and safer for both of you.

To perform a reaching assist without entering the water, lie on the pool deck or dock to establish a stable position. Spread your legs apart to increase stability, keeping your center of gravity over a wide base. If available, have another person on shore hold on to you. Extend *one arm only* over the water. Your goal is to grasp the swimmer's wrist or upper arm.

Reaching rescues can also be made in the water. While maintaining eye contact with and distance from the distressed swimmer, slip into the water. Establish a firm grasp on a ladder, the side of the pool, or a dock support. Then extend your other arm or a leg to the distressed swimmer while telling him or her to hold on to you and that you are there to help. When extending the arm, be sure you grab the swimmer before he or she grabs you. If you are caught off guard, you may be pulled away from your anchor and become a victim yourself.

If a distressed swimmer is too far away to use a reaching assist, consider an extension assist (**figure 7.13**). Traditional lifeguard equipment or a towel or piece of clothing can be used for a quick extension rescue. Remember to establish a firm base of support with your legs spread and your weight low and away from the victim so you are not pulled into the water. Distressed victims can grab the extended equipment (although they may not do so). Be prepared for a sharp tug at the object. Continue to talk to the victim as you bring him or her to safety.

As you learned in chapter 5, a drowning victim will probably not grasp the extended reaching pole or assisting device. In this instance, keep the object within reach of the victim, slide it under the victim's armpit, or press it against the victim's side. This will generally cause the victim to grab the object. Do not try to jab the victim with the object; it may cause additional injury.

Once the victim has a firm grasp of the object, maintain your position with your weight shifted away from the victim; pull the victim in slowly, hand over hand. Communicate with and reassure the victim as you bring him or her to safety.

Extension assists can also be made in the water (**figure 7.14**). While maintaining eye contact with and distance from the victim,

Figure 7.13 Extension assist from the deck.

Figure 7.14 Extension assist in the water.

slip into the water. Firmly grasp a ladder, the side of the pool, or a dock for support and then extend the object to the victim.

Throwing assists

If the distance to a distressed swimmer is beyond the range of an extension assist, and if the necessary equipment is available, the next option is the throwing assist. The key to success is throwing accuracy, and the key to accuracy is preparation and practice. A rescue bag, a ring buoy with a line, and a heaving line (a line with a weighted knot on the end) are all acceptable throwing devices.

To perform a throwing assist, as illustrated in **figure 7.15**, follow these steps:

1. Hold the neatly coiled rope in your open hand with the throwing device in your throwing hand. Be sure the coils lie side by side to avoid any tangling. Step on the rope with your forward foot. Secure the rope by standing on it with the knot snug against the side of your foot to stop the rope from slipping through.
2. Throw the rescue device underhand and let the rope feed freely from your open hand. Throw the device past the swimmer's head, and then pull it to the swimmer.
3. Instruct the swimmer to grab the device and then pull him or her to safety.

If you are on a river, throw upstream from the swimmer and allow the current to carry the device downstream to the victim. If the wind is strong, compensate for it in aiming your throw.

If your throw is unsuccessful and the device moves away from the swimmer, plant your feet and pull in the rope, letting it drop on the ground in front of you. Do not recoil the line; that wastes precious time. Simply throw the device again as soon as possible. Always be careful to avoid rocks, branches, or anything else that could tangle the line.

If you are using a throw bag, remove the knotted end and leave the rest of the rope coiled inside the bag. Do not stand on the rope. Rather, hold the knot with your

Figure 7.15 Throwing assist.

Nonswimming Rescue Guidelines

In making any nonswimming rescue, let the following principles guide you:

- React calmly and quickly, following your emergency action plan (see chapter 6).
- Maintain visual contact with the victim at all times.
- Find a piece of rescue equipment appropriate for the situation. Almost any object can be used as an aid for reaching, extension, and wading assists.
- Establish a firm base for your rescue. Keep your weight low and away from the victim to avoid being pulled into the water or the victim's grasp (if you are already in the water).
- Establish communication with the victim. You may get the victim to assist in the rescue, and you may reduce the victim's anxiety.
- Bring the victim to safety. Ask whether the victim is injured and, if so, where. Keeping possible injuries in mind, help the victim exit the water.
- Provide any necessary first aid or call for assistance.
- Complete the appropriate accident or incident reports.

If you keep these principles in mind, you will find nonswimming assists safe and valuable tools.

non-throwing hand. Be sure to leave 4 to 6 feet of slack. The rest of the throwing procedures are the same. If your first throw is inaccurate, do not restuff the bag. The water gathered in the bag as you tow it back to shore will provide the necessary weight to guide your second toss.

Wading assists

A wading assist (**figure 7.16**) is more dangerous than other nonswimming rescues because you must enter the water. Use a wading assist when the victim is too far away for a reaching or extension assist, is too close to warrant a throwing assist, and is in water that allows you to go no farther than chest-high water. Safe wading assists follow these steps:

1. As you enter the water, take a rescue tube or buoy to extend toward the victim.
2. Move into water no deeper than your chest.
3. Assume a stable position with one foot forward and one foot back and your weight shifted away from the victim.
4. Extend the nose end of the rescue device to the victim or, if the victim is farther away, push the buoy or tube toward the victim while holding the harness.
5. After the victim has grabbed the device, slowly walk to safety, holding on to the tail end (the harness end). Reassure the victim as you bring the victim to safety.

Figure 7.16 Wading assist.

A

B

Review

Review Topics

As a lifeguard candidate, you already have strong swimming skills. Chapter 7 taught you how swimming skills and equipment can be used to help others. Here are some key points to know from this chapter:

1) How to conserve your energy while floating or swimming
2) Three strokes you can use to move safely with minimal use of energy
3) Different surface dives and how and when to use them
4) Personal equipment and its uses
5) Rescue equipment and its uses
6) Different kinds of nonswimming rescues and when they are used
7) Objects that can be used as an extension assist
8) How to use a ring buoy and a throw bag

Review Questions

1. Why are the resting stroke and treading water important skills for a lifeguard?
2. Name the three swimming strokes you can use when you need to conserve energy.
3. Describe two ways to reach a submerged victim when you are on the surface of the water.
4. Lifeguards should always have certain equipment when they are on the guard. List five things you should have for any lifeguarding assignment, indoors or out.
5. Describe three pieces of rescue equipment and how they are used.
6. When would you perform a reaching or extension assist?
7. When would you use a throwing assist? What pieces of rescue equipment would you use?
8. Why should you keep your weight shifted back when performing an assist?
9. When would you use a wading assist?

CHAPTER 8

Rescue Procedures

Despite your best preventive efforts, there may come a time when you see someone in immediate distress and you must activate the emergency action plan and perform a rescue. Different rescue situations call for different combinations of skills and techniques. This chapter examines procedures for rescuing distressed swimmers and drowning victims in a variety of scenarios. Studies by Porter (1997) and Leclerc (1997) found that the rescue techniques taught in YMCA Lifeguard are particularly efficient.

In this chapter, you will learn the following:

- Water entries
- Approach strokes
- In-water rescues
- Rescues for spinal-injury victims
- Victim removals from the water
- Rescues when off duty

4 FT 3 IN
CHAPTER
8

Water Entries

In the previous chapter, we examined a scenario in which scanning led you to recognize a victim near the pool's edge, which required you to perform a nonswimming assist. Now we explore a new scenario. Once again, you are scanning your zone, bottom to top, and paying close attention to anyone who is at risk and to high-risk areas. You notice someone needs your help, but this time the patron is located in the middle of the pool.

When a nonswimming rescue is not possible, you will enter the water and swim to the victim. Any time you enter the water, take a rescue flotation device—either a rescue tube or, sometimes for open water, a rescue buoy—with the shoulder strap secured to you. A rescue flotation device helps you protect yourself while supporting a victim during a rescue.

Before you enter the water, activate the emergency action plan (EAP) by blowing your whistle, using an air horn, or activating the pool alarm to indicate the beginning of a rescue procedure and to summon backup. Then, double-check that the strap of your rescue tube or buoy is secure. Make sure you take your personal protective equipment (PPE), which includes a resuscitation mask and gloves, with you in case in-water rescue breathing becomes necessary. (See the section on in-water rescue breathing later in this chapter.)

You have several choices for entering the water. In a given situation, determine which of the methods described here is most appropriate. Whatever method you use, make every effort to maintain eye contact and communicate with the victim. Practice the different types of entries regularly so you are prepared to select the most appropriate entry when an emergency occurs.

Figure 8.1 Touch-and-go entry.

A B C D

Touch-and-go entry

You can use a touch-and-go water entry (**figure 8.1**) for all depths of water:

1. Look to make sure it is safe to enter the water. Then, keeping your eyes on the victim, place one hand on the edge of the pool or dock and hold the rescue tube or buoy in your other hand.
2. Jump or step into the water. The hand on the edge controls your speed while the other hand holds tightly to the rescue tube.
3. Once in the water, begin to approach the victim.

Compact jump entry

The compact jump (**figure 8.2**) is typically used when entering water from a height, such as from an elevated lifeguard stand or a dock. Check that the water is at least 5 feet deep, and then do the following:

1. Hold the rescue tube or buoy horizontally under your arms and against your chest.
2. Jump into the water with both feet parallel to the water surface and your knees bent. Hold the excess line in your hand.
3. As you hit the water, bend your knees slightly to absorb the shock. Allow the rescue tube or buoy to lift you to the surface.

Keep in mind that you will lose sight of the victim when you go underwater. If possible, note a fixed landmark over the head of the victim. If for some reason you cannot locate the victim when you surface, aim toward that landmark or the last point at which you remember seeing the victim. Move the tube or buoy to one hand or drop it and begin to approach the victim.

Stride jump entry

In water more than 5 feet deep and from a height of not more than 3 feet, you can enter the water quickly and maintain eye contact using a stride jump (**figure 8.3**, next page). Where you hold the rescue tube during the entry depends on the rescue conditions, including how close the victim is and how many people are in the water.

If the victim is far away, follow these steps:

1. Hold your arms out from your sides, hands slightly above your shoulders, holding the rescue tube in one hand.
2. Lean forward with your chest ahead of your hips and step out away from the edge, with your legs wide apart in a giant A-shaped

> **Wearing Your Rescue Tube**
>
> Wear the shoulder strap so that it hangs from your left shoulder to your right hip, if you are right-handed. (Reverse that placement if you are left-handed.) If the tube has a long line, or tail, hold a coil or two in the hand you use to grip the tube—the line should not interfere during a rescue.

Figure 8.2 Compact jump entry.

A

B

stride. While over the water and clear of the edge, drop the rescue tube to the side and behind you.

3. As your body enters the water, force your legs together using a scissors kick. As your arms touch the water, bring your arms forward to slow your downward motion and keep your head above water.

If the victim is a short distance away, follow these steps:

1. Hold the rescue tube horizontally against your chest and under your arms.
2. Lean forward with your chest ahead of your hips and step out away from the edge, with your legs wide apart in a giant A-shaped stride.
3. As your body enters the water, force your legs together using a scissors kick.
4. When you begin your approach stroke, move the rescue tube from under your chest and to the side, keeping it in one hand.

Note: Regardless of your distance to the victim, if you plan to use the stride jump to enter water where many people are located, hold the rescue tube to you, either at your side or against your chest, rather than dropping it.

Practice is particularly important for the stride jump to learn whether you can perform this entry safely,

Figure 8.3 Stride jump entry.

A

B

C

quickly, and efficiently in 5-foot-deep water given your body size and type.

Shallow dive entry

When time and speed are crucial, a shallow dive might be the most appropriate entry. In this entry, you sacrifice visual contact momentarily for greater momentum. Before deciding to use the shallow dive entry, be sure you know the water depth so you will not be injured. YMCA of the USA recommends that only rescuers trained to do shallow dives use this dive and only if the water is at least 5 feet deep. Also check the water conditions before diving. In open water, marine life, seaweed, floating debris, rocky terrain, and pollution may make a shallow dive dangerous and inappropriate. You might not see a fixed object in murky water that could injure you.

Once you have determined it is safe to perform a shallow dive, check that your rescue tube or buoy is secured to you by the shoulder strap and the line will not become caught on any obstruction as you enter the water. Execute a shallow dive (**figure 8.4**) and propel yourself to the surface by steering up with your arms and head. Reestablish visual contact with the victim as quickly as possible. Approach the victim while letting the rescue tube or buoy trail behind you.

Waveless entry

When you have reason to suspect the victim may have a spinal injury and the victim is within 10 feet of your entry point, use a waveless entry. Waves created by jumping or diving into the water too close to a spinal-injury victim may cause additional injury.

The waveless entry for shallow water (**figure 8.5**, next page), uses these steps:

1. Move to a location close to the victim.
2. Working quickly, sit on the side of the pool or dock. Put your rescue flotation device on the deck or in the water next to where you will enter.

Figure 8.4 Shallow dive entry.

Recognizing Spinal Injuries

Most injuries to the head, neck, and back occur in shallow water. Suspect a spinal injury when you

- witness a potential head or neck injury (e.g., a dive into shallow water, a fall from a height);
- are told of a suspected injury ("Help, he just fell and hit his head");
- observe signs of injury (pain, deformity, etc.); or
- observe signs of a clear mechanism of injury (e.g., a large young male victim motionless in shallow water).

In any of these instances, a serious injury to the spinal cord may have occurred. Because victims with spinal injuries require special care, be aware of the signs of spinal injury.

Injuries to the spine include fractures and dislocations of the vertebrae, sprained ligaments, and compressed or displaced intervertebral discs. Any of these injuries can cause injury to the spinal cord that may result in paralysis or death.

A victim of a spinal injury may exhibit any of the following signs:

- Pain at the site of the injury
- Loss of movement in the extremities
- Loss of movement below the site of the injury
- Tingling or loss of sensation in the extremities
- Disorientation
- Deformity in the neck or back
- Visible bruising over an area of the spinal column
- Difficulty breathing
- Head injury
- Blood or fluid (other than water) in the ears or nose
- Unconsciousness

Victims with spinal injuries will not necessarily be paralyzed after impact with the bottom of the pool or the diving board. They may be able to swim or walk. Spinal-injury victims sometimes exhibit signs similar to those of victims in the process of drowning. They might struggle at the surface momentarily and then sink to the bottom. They might swim to the side of the pool or shallow water. They might even climb out of the water or sit on the edge of the pool.

It will be important for you to identify the cause of the injury to assess if damage to the spine may have occurred. If a victim in the water exhibits any of the signs of spinal injury, regardless of water depth, or has hit the diving board, provide in-line stabilization (using the head-splint technique) and perform the backboarding procedures described later in this chapter. If a victim is out of the water, follow the first-aid procedures for injuries to the back and neck described in chapter 9.

3. Support your weight equally on your hands and slide forward into the water, maintaining visual contact with the victim.
4. Retrieve your rescue tube or buoy.
5. Once you are in the water, wade toward the victim to avoid creating waves.

A waveless entry for deep water (**figure 8.6**, next page), or an alternative waveless entry for shallow water, when the victim is within 10 feet calls for the following steps:

1. Moving quickly, sit on the edge of the deck. Put your rescue flotation device on the deck or in the water.
2. Place one hand on the deck near your leg.
3. Reach across your body with the other hand and place it on the deck or on the lip of the pool gutter.
4. As you lower yourself into the water, try to keep visual contact with the victim. You will be turning 180 degrees to face the side of the

Figure 8.5 Waveless entry into shallow water.

A

B

C

pool. If visual contact with the victim was briefly lost, reestablish it as soon as possible.

5. Retrieve your rescue tube or buoy.
6. Swim toward the victim using a waveless, underwater stroke, such as the breaststroke.

Surf entry

Use this surf entry (USLA 2003) to enter the water quickly and efficiently from the shore. Have your rescue equipment on you and ready for use.

- From the shoreline, run in to the water using high-stepping strides. Run as far as possible before beginning to swim. Allow your rescue tube or buoy to trail behind you, unless there is a chance of it becoming caught.
- As much as possible, jump over the waves. As the waves get higher, use porpoise dives (small dives over short incoming waves) or surface dives (small dives under tall incoming waves too large to jump over) to reach swimming depth. Remember to keep your arms up at ear level and extended to the front to protect your head and neck when you dive.

Regardless of whether the slope of the beach is steep or gradual, running and porpoise or surface diving are the quickest ways to approach a victim until the water depth allows for fast, effective swimming. Be

Figure 8.6 Waveless entry into deep water.

A

B

C

aware of the water depth and do not dive forward if you are uncertain what lies beneath the water; be familiar with the shoreline you are guarding.

Approach Strokes

Your goal when selecting an approach stroke is to reach the victim as quickly as possible with enough reserve energy to rescue and tow the victim to safety.

Choosing the most appropriate stroke to reach a victim can save critical time and help reduce further injury to the victim. You will either use an approach crawl or a breaststroke to reach the victim. Consider these five factors when deciding which stroke to use:

- The distance from the victim
- The number of people in the swimming area
- The concentration of people between you and the victim
- The condition of the victim
- Your strength and condition

In all cases, have your rescue pack and your rescue flotation device, either a rescue tube or buoy, with you and ready for use.

Depending on your distance from the victim and the presence of potential obstacles in the water, you will approach with the rescue tube or buoy either in your hand or trailing behind you (**figure 8.7**, next page). If the victim is near or if there are people or obstacles between you and the victim, swim with the rescue tube or buoy in your hand, as follows:

- Turn the rescue tube on edge and place your hand at the center on top. (If using a rescue buoy, grasp the long side handle.)
- Point the nose of the tube or buoy in the direction you are swimming, keeping it in front of you and its line end (the tail) pointed toward your feet.
- Swim to the victim using a single-arm-pull breaststroke, a modified crawl stroke, or a combined stroke using the breaststroke kick and a single-arm crawl.

This will allow you to manipulate the tube or buoy, move relatively quickly, and swim around patrons in a crowded pool. This technique has been found more efficient than holding the tube or buoy across the chest while approaching a victim (Leclerc 1997).

Approaching a Victim When You Suspect a Spinal Injury

Whether you are in shallow or deep water, as you approach a victim whom you suspect may have a spinal injury, make as little water disturbance as possible. If you are in shallow water, walk toward the victim. If you are in deeper water, use the breaststroke or a modified crawl stroke with an underwater arm recovery.

Remember that your first priority is the victim's breathing. If the victim's face is submerged, you must use your judgment and skill to balance the need for speed with the effort to not disturb the water. Practice your approaches so you can move swiftly and smoothly in the water should you have to rescue a spinal-injury victim.

Figure 8.7 Approach strokes: (**A**) Single-arm crawl; (**B**) Single-arm breaststroke; (**C**) Crawl with rescue tube trailing; (**D**) Breaststroke with rescue tube trailing.

A

B

For longer distances, unless there is a possibility that your rescue tube or buoy could become caught on something behind you, allow the line to trail behind you as you approach the victim.

If lane lines are between you and the victim, hold the tube or buoy in one hand and stroke over the lane line, pushing the lane line down as you go over it (**figure 8.8**).

The crawl stroke allows the quickest approach. If you are at a distance from the victim, you may place your face in the water to swim faster. Turn your head to the side to breathe, and then rotate your head forward to look at the victim before putting your face in the water again. Once you are within 15 feet of the victim, keep your head up and your eyes on the victim.

Regardless of whether you hold your rescue flotation device in your hand or let it trail behind you, if you suspect a victim has a spinal injury, approach in a way that creates as few waves as possible as you near the victim.

C

D

Figure 8.8 Approach stroke going over lane lines.

Your Practice Will See You Through

As you learn these rescue skills and techniques, know that with regular practice you will be able to manage an emergency when the time comes. Performing a rescue can be a frightening experience. It is distressing to see any person in harm's way, especially a child. The victim may be bleeding or have a visible injury; other patrons may become very upset.

If you have regularly practiced the correct skills and procedures, be assured that you can trust that your knowledge and skills will kick in—along with your body's natural defense system—to help you focus and perform your duty.

When rescuing a victim, do not become distracted by other patrons' reactions, the victim's appearance or behavior (such as vomiting), or other dramatic occurrences. Stay focused on your priorities:

- Keeping the victim breathing
- Keeping the victim afloat with the face above water
- Avoiding further injury to the victim
- Moving the victim to safety
- Providing first aid

Activate the emergency action plan so your fellow team members can assist you, and then do what you are trained to do. Remember, most rescues are successful.

Rescues

As noted earlier, any time you enter the water, take your rescue pack and your rescue tube (or rescue buoy) secured to you by a shoulder strap. The rescue tube or buoy serves as a flotation aid to assist you in performing the rescue, protects you from a panicked victim who might otherwise grab you, and helps in positioning the victim for in-water rescue breathing.

This section describes rescuing the following types of victims:

- Distressed swimmers
  - Conscious victim from front
  - Conscious victim from rear
  - Conscious victim just below the surface
  - Injured, conscious victim on the surface
- Unresponsive victims
  - Unresponsive victim from front
  - Unresponsive victim from rear
  - Unresponsive victim just below the surface
- Submerged victim
- Multiple victims
- Victims with suspected spinal injuries
  - Spinal-injury victim in shallow water
    - Victim faceup
    - Victim facedown
  - Spinal-injury victim in deep water
    - Victim on surface
  - Submerged victim

The following rescues are written for right-handed individuals. If you are left-handed, please reverse the instructions accordingly. Note that the instructions for rescuing distressed swimmers, drowning victims, and multiple victims are for use when you have no reason to suspect that the victim has a spinal injury. Different procedures for rescuing spinal-injury victims are presented later in this chapter. For information on when to suspect a spinal injury and how to approach the victim, see the sections earlier in this chapter.

Before performing a rescue, remember always to activate the emergency action plan: blow your whistle, use an air horn, or activate the pool alarm to indicate the beginning of a rescue procedure and summon backup.

Distressed swimmers

Conscious victim from front

After activating the EAP and approaching a conscious victim from the front (**figure 8.9**), you may have the tube or buoy in one hand or trailing behind you, depending on the type of approach you used. If the tube or buoy is behind you, tread water and grab the tail of the line, pulling the device to you as you continue to look at the victim.

Always keep the rescue device between you and the victim during a rescue. This allows you to present the device to the victim so that he or she grabs it and is supported by it. Along with your reassurance, this helps protect you by avoiding contact with a panicked victim and provides a chance for the victim to calm down.

1. If you are using a rescue tube, bring it in front of you and turn it on edge.

Figure 8.9 Rescuing a conscious victim from the front using a rescue tube.

Figure 8.10 Rescuing a conscious victim from the rear using a rescue tube.

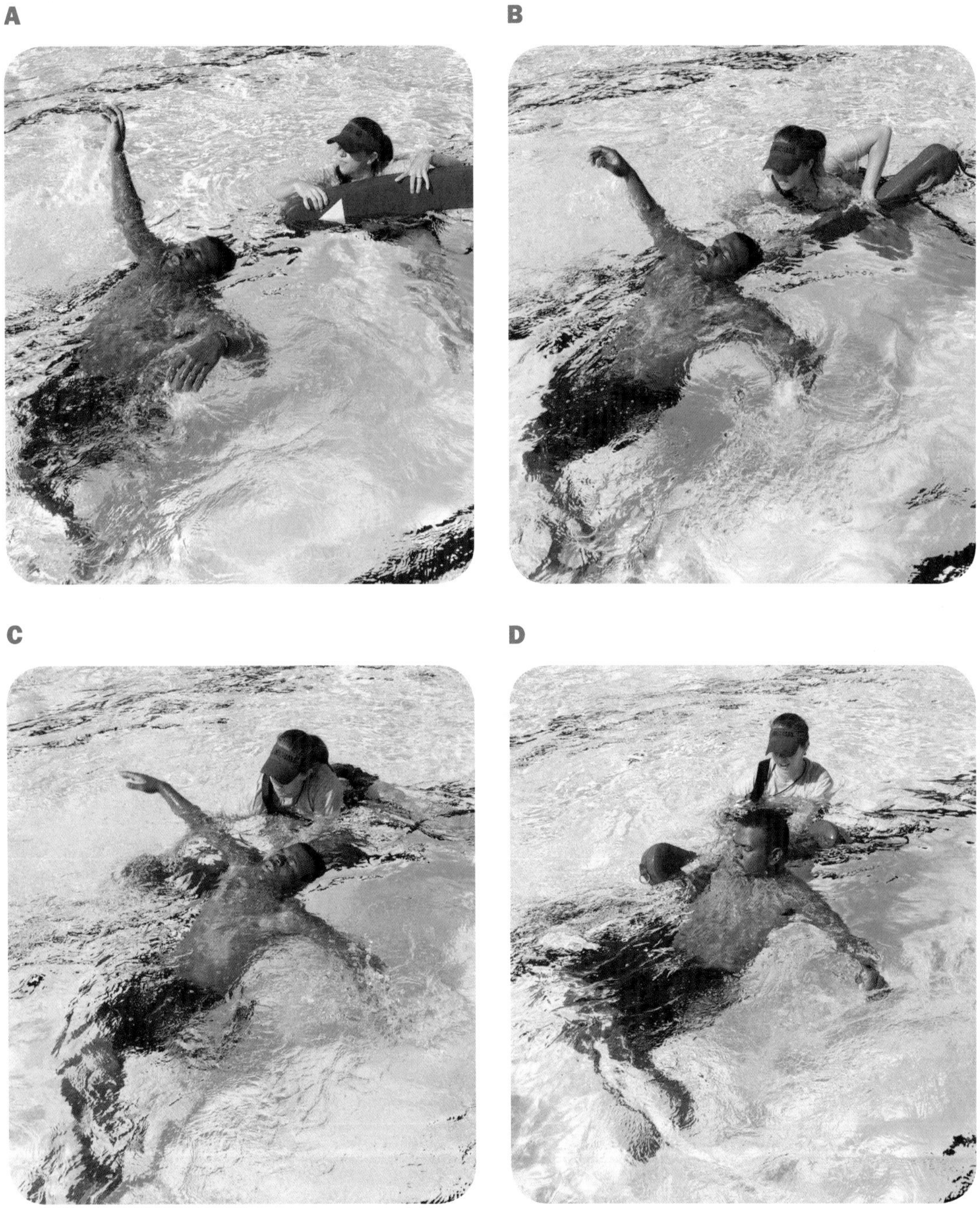

A

B

C

D

Hold the rescue tube with one hand at the nose and the other hand in the center. If you are using a rescue buoy, turn it on edge and hold it with one hand on the top handle and the other hand on the nose.

2. To extend the tube or buoy to the victim, press the nose across the front of the victim and under one arm.
3. Push the victim's arm down on the rescue device to help him or her hold it by trapping it under the victim's arm. Once the victim grabs the device, continue to give reassurance.
4. If the victim does not grab the rescue tube or buoy, help the victim hold on by quickly pushing the victim's arm down, trapping the device under the victim's arm. You may have to remind the victim to hold on, or you may have to continue to press the victim's arm around the device yourself.
5. As you hold the victim's arm and the rescue tube or buoy, use a rescue kick (as in the sidestroke) to move the victim to safety. Continue to reassure the victim.

Conscious victim from rear

Rescuing a conscious victim from the rear (**figure 8.10**) uses the same technique as rescuing from the front.

1. Approach the victim from the rear.
2. Push the nose of the tube or buoy across the victim's back and underneath the victim's arm.
3. Take your hand off the nose and place it on the victim's upper arm.
4. Press the victim's arm down, trapping the rescue tube or buoy.
5. Tow the victim to safety.

Remember to always keep the tube or buoy between you and the victim.

Conscious victim just below the surface

To rescue a conscious victim who is not suspected of having a spinal injury and who is just below the surface (**figure 8.11**), do the following:

1. Approach from the front or rear and slightly to the side of the victim.
2. Place the rescue tube or buoy so it is between you and the victim.
3. Reach over the tube or buoy and grasp the victim's wrist or forearm.
4. Pull that arm up and over the rescue tube or buoy to keep the victim afloat on the surface.

Figure 8.11 Rescuing a conscious victim just below the surface using a rescue tube.

Safety Tip

If the victim grabs you in a way that places you at risk, use the submerge defense (pictured). Take a quick breath and submerge, pushing the rescue tube or buoy up and into the victim. Swim away underwater. When you surface, reassess the situation and make another approach if necessary.

A

B

C

Always activate the emergency action plan before making a rescue.

5. Follow all other procedures for rescuing a conscious victim.

Remember to keep the rescue device between you and the victim at all times.

Injured, conscious victim on the surface

When a victim has an injury, remember that your primary goal is to keep the victim afloat and breathing. Your secondary goal is to avoid further injury due to movement, so modify your rescue methods as necessary to suit the victim's condition.

Begin by trying to identify what area of the victim's body has been injured; how the injury occurred and how the victim moves in the water after the accident can give you clues. In any situation in which you do not know the extent of an injury, perform the rescue that will provide the most support to the victim and reduce the victim's overall movement. As always, have your personal protective equipment with you in your rescue pack and ready for use.

After a traumatic injury to an upper or lower extremity, conscious victims may be dazed, disoriented, incoherent, and unable to move efficiently. They may be able to support themselves fairly well, or they may have a great deal of difficulty staying afloat, perhaps struggling to stay at the surface or alternating between surfacing and submerging. If such a victim is having difficulty swimming to safety, perform an in-water rescue. For your protection, always keep the rescue flotation device between you and the victim. If you suspect a spinal injury, perform the appropriate rescue for a spinal-injury victim detailed later in this chapter. For nonspinal injuries that involve upper or lower extremities, use the following rescue procedures.

Upper extremity injury

An upper extremity injury could be an injury to the shoulder, upper arm, elbow, lower arm, wrist, or hand. Perform a conscious victim rescue from either the front or rear. It is best to keep the injured extremity as motionless as possible, so determine which body part is injured and place the rescue tube or buoy under the victim's armpit on the opposite side of the injury. Hold on to the rescue tube or buoy

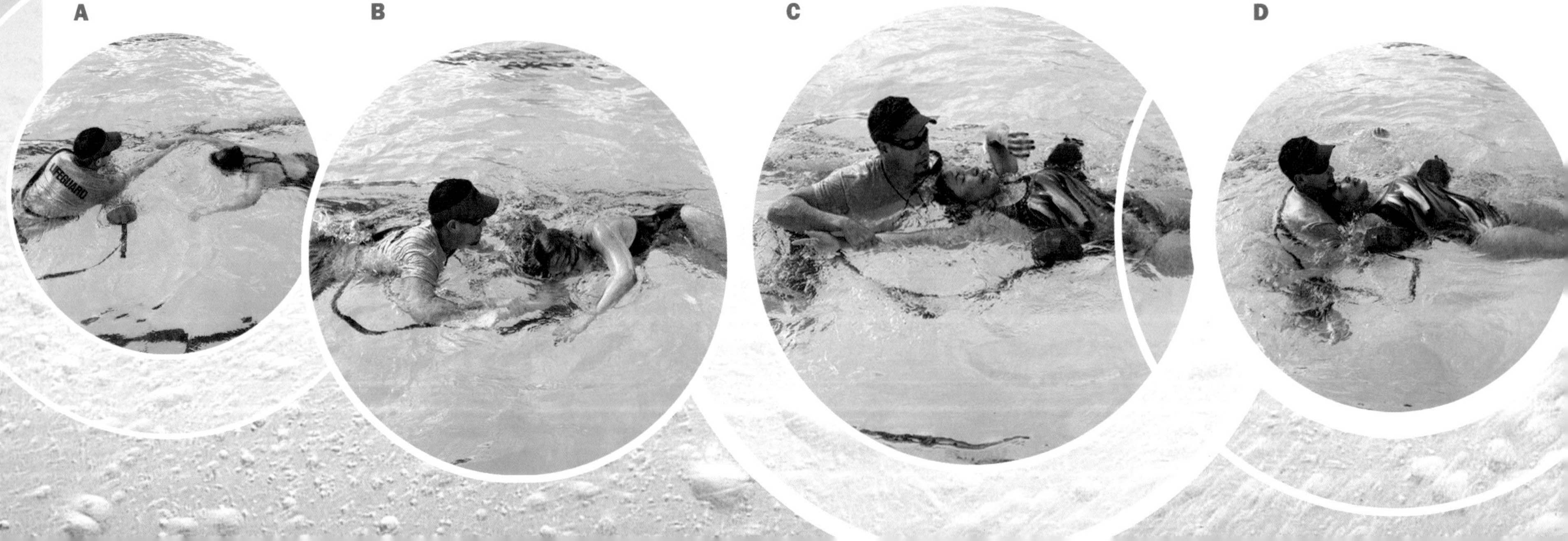

Figure 8.12 Rescuing an unresponsive victim from the front using a rescue tube.

A B C D

and tow the victim to safety. This procedure provides good flotation for the victim and allows the victim to avoid moving the injured limb.

Lower extremity injury

A lower extremity injury could be to the hip, upper leg, knee, lower leg, ankle, or foot. A victim with an injury to a lower extremity may be able to stroke with the arms but may have difficulty kicking. Because of the water's resistance, any leg movement may be extremely painful.

Perform a conscious victim rescue from either the front or rear. If the victim is unable to hold the rescue tube or buoy and you are a short distance to shore, press and hold the victim's arm over the rescue tube or buoy and tow the victim to safety. To secure a rescue tube for towing a farther distance or to simply provide more stability for the victim, swim to the rear of the victim, place the rescue tube under the victim's shoulder blades, hold an end of the tube's fastener in each hand, and reach under the victim's armpits to fasten the ends of the tube together to form a ring around the victim. Support the victim in a comfortable position and swim the victim to safety.

Unresponsive victims

Unresponsive victim from front (tube)

In this situation, the victim is not struggling and is floating facedown, and you have determined there are no signs of spinal injury. Swim with your rescue tube and your rescue pack, including resuscitation mask and gloves, while keeping the victim in sight. When you approach the victim, quickly bring the rescue equipment to your side.

To perform this rescue with a rescue tube, take the following steps (**figure 8.12**):

Do-si-do Method

The do-si-do method allows you to use one arm to keep the victim afloat and in position for rescue breathing as you tow the victim to safety. This allows you to use your other hand to hold the resuscitation mask in place. Once the victim is faceup and supported on the rescue tube, perform the do-si-do method following these steps:

1. Position yourself to the side of the victim's head.
2. Reach your arm over the victim's upper arm and down (between the victim's upper arm and chest), so the victim's arm is secured under your armpit.
3. Reach your hand under the victim to support the victim's back, if necessary.
4. Check for breathing. If the victim is not breathing, use your free hand to grab your resuscitation mask. Place the mask securely over the victim's nose and mouth, and then begin in-water rescue breathing.

E F

In-Water Rescue Breathing

When a victim who is not breathing is found in the water, the YMCA Lifeguard program places the highest priority on getting air into the victim through rescue breathing. This means beginning rescue breathing in the water and continuing to provide air to the victim as much as possible while removing the victim and beginning emergency care on the deck or shore. Exhaled air contains about 17 percent oxygen. During rescue breathing, the oxygen concentration from the rescuer's exhaled breath is enough to temporarily support life.

To determine whether a victim is breathing, level the victim, and then tread water hard enough so you can place your ear close to the victim's mouth to listen for breathing and to see if the chest is rising and falling. Do not submerge the victim's head or turn it toward you. If the victim is breathing, move toward safety.

If the victim is not breathing, while moving toward safety and as conditions allow, follow these steps to provide rescue breathing for a victim who shows no signs of spinal injury (see later in this chapter for rescue breathing procedures for those suspected of having spinal injuries):

1. Take out your resuscitation mask and be sure the dome is pushed out and the one-way valve is attached to the mask. Shake the mask to remove excess water.
2. Position the resuscitation mask over the victim's nose and mouth, making sure you maintain a good seal. Hold the resuscitation mask in place with your thumb and middle finger as you tow. Tilt the victim's head back to open the airway. Bend the valve toward you with your index finger and begin rescue breathing (exhaling air into the victim's lungs through the mask).
3. You should be able to feel the air move into the victim's lungs. If not, reposition the victim's head or the resuscitation mask and try again.
4. Vomiting is very common during resuscitation; expect it to occur. If vomiting occurs, move slightly toward the top of the victim's head, turn the victim's head toward you, wipe the vomitus away from the victim's mouth, and resume rescue breathing with the mask. If the vomitus is watery froth, continue to give breaths and blow through the froth. The mask's one-way valve will protect you from exposure.
5. Tow the victim to safety and exit the water.

Continue rescue breathing until emergency personnel arrive on the scene to relieve you. Any person who experiences a significant immersion or submersion requires professional medical attention.

Practice performing rescue breathing in the water often. It is a difficult but important skill to master. Keep your resuscitation mask with you at all times so you have it when you respond to an emergency.

1. Place the tube between you and the victim so that it crosses the front of your body. Place your left hand on the center of the tube.
2. Reach over the tube with your right hand while submerging the tube slightly with your left hand. Reach your right hand to the underside of the victim's right wrist (as if you were shaking hands with the victim's wrist). Grasp the victim's wrist with your thumb on top.
3. Turn the victim faceup by pulling the arm down and then back up toward the surface (in other words, draw a *U* with the victim's arm). Simultaneously, push down with your left hand to submerge the tube while pulling the victim's wrist just past your ear to bring the victim onto the tube. With your left hand, push the tube until it reaches a position below the victim's shoulder blades.
4. Once the tube is under the victim's back, release your hold on the victim's wrist. Moving to the victim's right side, place your right arm between the victim's upper arm and chest, so the victim's arm is in your armpit. (Do not drape your arm over the tube.) This is known as the do-si-do method. Pull your left hand from under the victim. (Note: If you are in choppy water or far from safety, grab an end of the tube's fastener in each hand and secure the tube together around the victim. If you are in calm water and close to safety, it is not necessary to secure the tube. Use your judgment.) Move the victim toward safety.

Figure 8.13 Rescuing an unresponsive victim from the front using a rescue buoy.

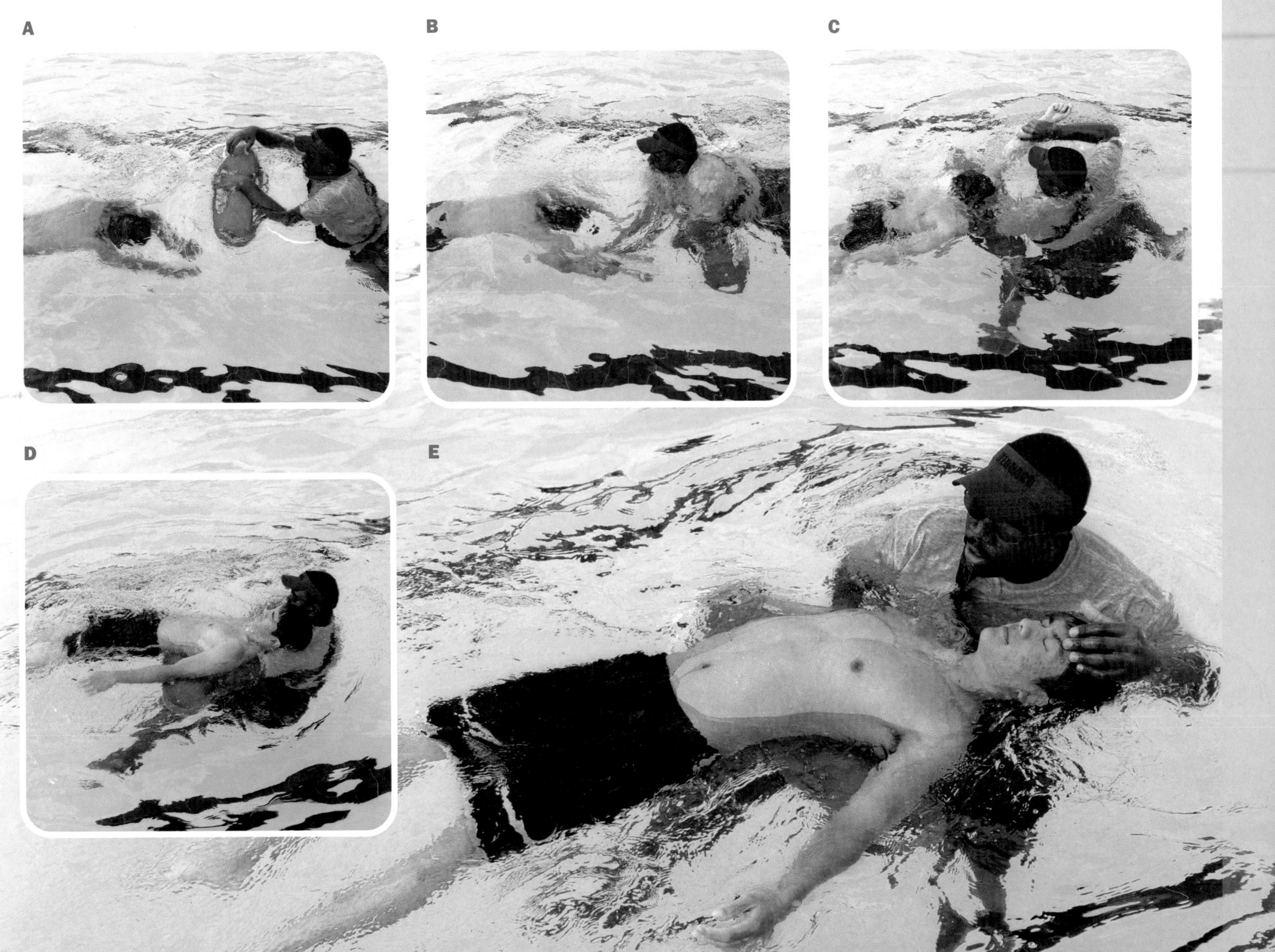

5. Move to the right side of the victim's head and get your resuscitation mask ready to use. Place your left hand on the victim's forehead and tilt it back to check the airway and breathing as you continue to move to safety. If the victim is not breathing, use your resuscitation mask to perform in-water rescue breathing.
6. Tow the victim to safety.

Unresponsive victim from front (buoy)

The rescue buoy is used primarily when guarding open water. As always, have your rescue pack with you at all times. If there are signs of spinal injury, follow the procedures described later in this chapter. Otherwise, follow these steps to use a rescue buoy for this rescue (**figure 8.13**, previous page):

1. With your right hand, bring the buoy nose-end-first to a position between you and the victim. Then, place your left hand over the buoy, grasping the handle with your fingers on the outside and thumb inside.
2. Reach over the buoy and grasp the underside of the victim's right wrist with your right hand (as if you were shaking hands with the victim's wrist). Grasp the victim's wrist with your thumb on top.
3. Turn the victim faceup by pulling the arm down and then back up toward the surface (in other words, draw a U with the victim's arm). Simultaneously, push down with your left hand to submerge the buoy while pulling the victim's wrist past your ear to bring the victim onto the buoy.
4. When the buoy is under the victim, release the victim's wrist, move to the right side of the victim's head, and place your right arm over the victim's right arm and down (between the victim's arm and chest). Grab

Figure 8.14 Rescuing an unresponsive victim from the rear using a rescue tube.

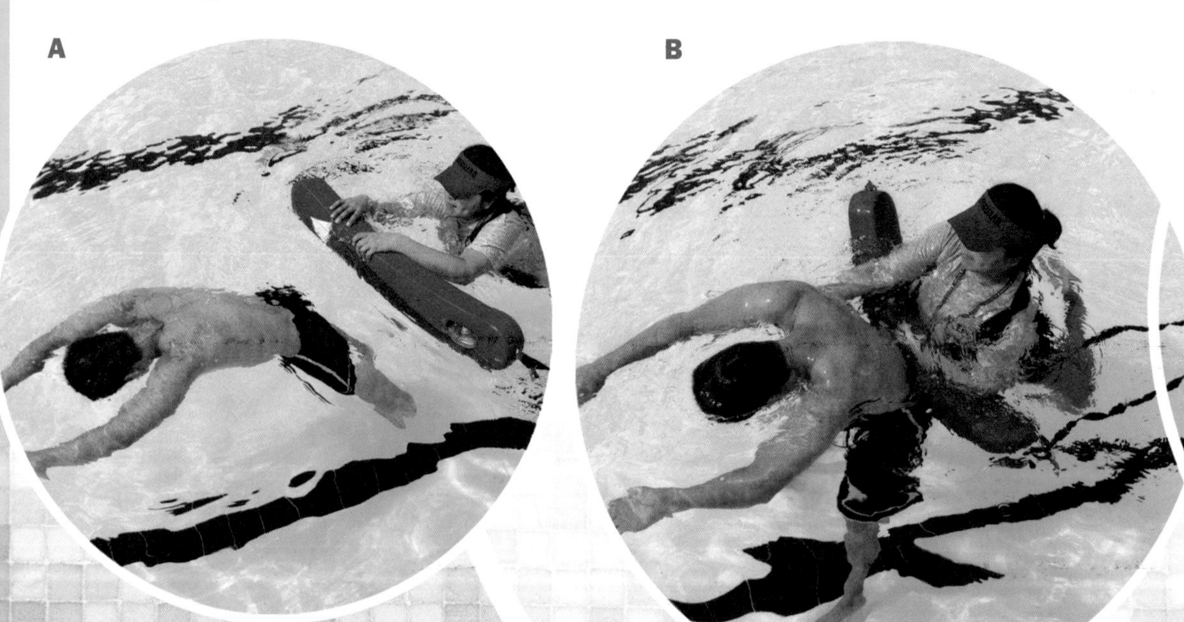

the handle of the buoy with your right hand and stabilize the victim.

5. Pull your left hand out from under the victim's back, tilt the victim's head back with your left hand, and check for breathing. If the victim is not breathing, use your resuscitation mask to perform in-water rescue breathing.
6. Tow the victim to safety.

Unresponsive victim from rear (tube)

After activating the EAP, enter the water and quickly approach the victim with your rescue pack and rescue tube. In this rescue, approach from behind a victim who is facedown in the water. (If there are signs of spinal injury, follow the procedures described later in this chapter.) If there are no signs of spinal injury, follow these steps using a rescue tube (**figure 8.14**):

1. With your right hand, bring the tube into position, crossing it in front of your body so the tail of the tube is on your right side.
2. With your left hand on the center of the tube, submerge the tube as you reach over it with your right hand and grab the victim's right armpit. Keep your fingers in the victim's armpit with your thumb on the back of the victim's arm. As you pull the victim toward you, push the tube with your left hand under the victim's back (you may need to kick hard and lean back until the victim's head is tilted back).
3. Pull the victim over the tube until the tube reaches a position below the victim's shoulder blades. Move to the right of the victim and do-si-do the victim: place your right arm over the victim's upper right arm and then under the victim's back. To secure the victim to the tube, if necessary, place your right hand between the

Figure 8.15 Rescuing an unresponsive victim from the rear using a rescue buoy.

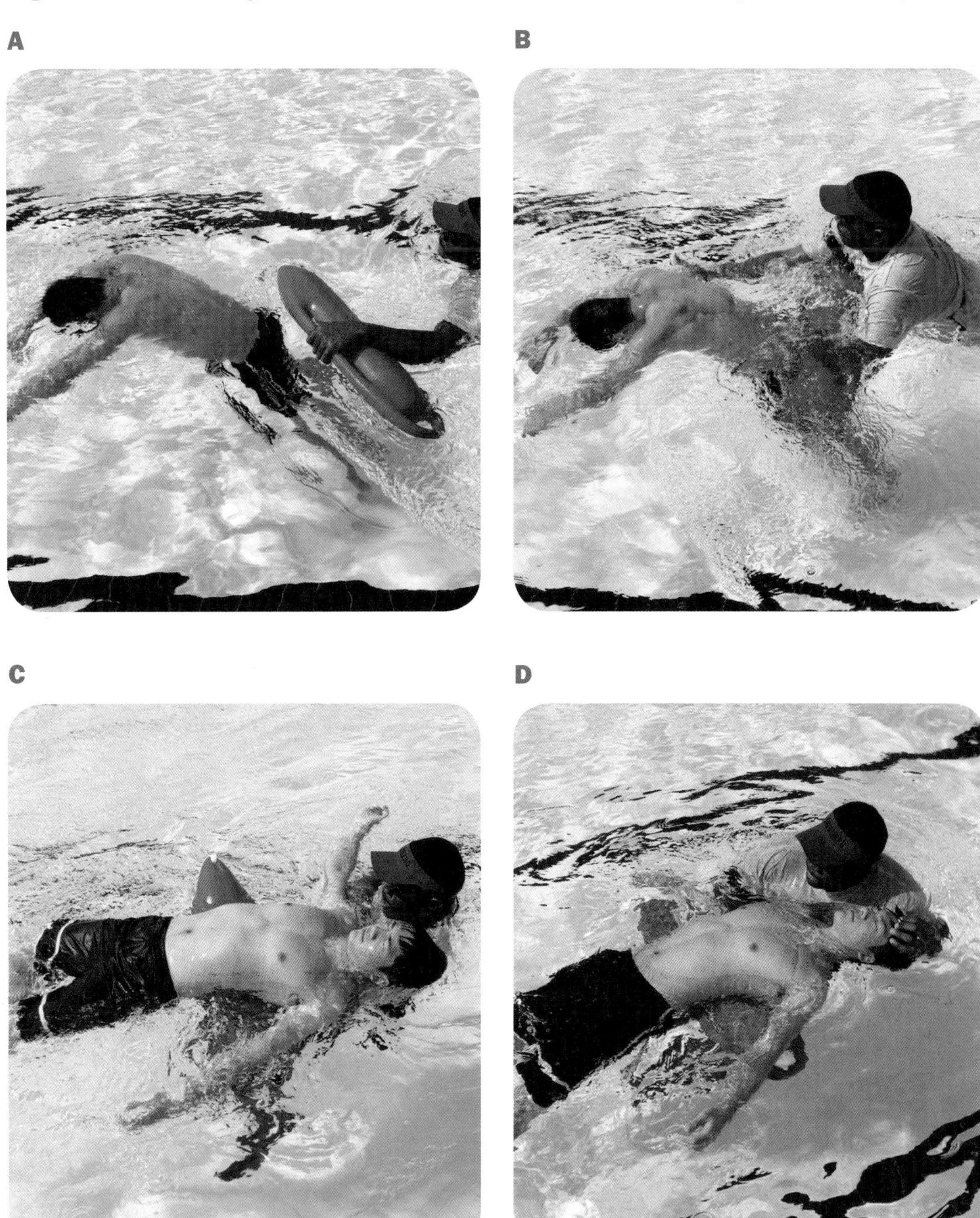

Figure 8.16 Rescuing an unresponsive victim just below the surface using a rescue tube.

A

B

C

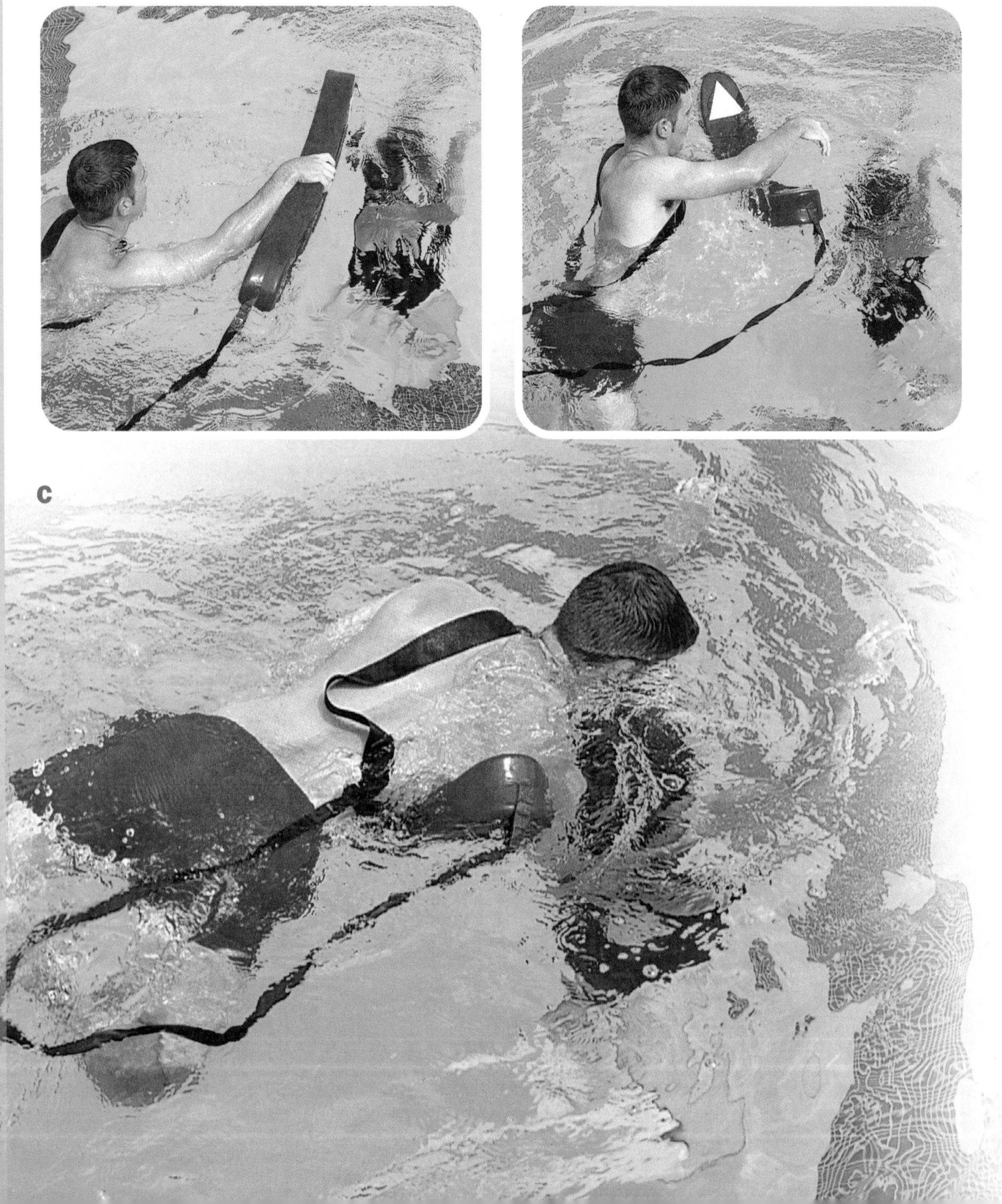

top of the tube and the victim's back. Pull your other hand from under the victim.

4. Evaluate the distance to safety. If the distance is far or for any other reason you determine it is necessary, grasp the ends of the tube and fasten them together around the victim while towing the victim to safety.
5. Move to the right side of the victim's head. Place your left hand on the victim's forehead to tilt the victim's head back to check for breathing.
6. Tow the victim to safety. If the victim is not breathing, use the resuscitation mask to perform in-water rescue breathing.

Unresponsive victim from rear (buoy)

Follow these steps to rescue an unresponsive victim from the rear with a rescue buoy, when there are no signs of spinal injury (**figure 8.15**, previous page):

1. With your right hand, bring the nose end of the buoy to a position between you and the victim. Then place your left hand over the buoy, grasping the handle with your fingers on the outside and thumb on the inside.
2. Push the buoy underneath the victim with your left hand and pull the victim over the buoy toward you with your right hand.
3. Move to the right side of the victim's head.
4. Take your right hand and move it so it is over the victim's upper right arm and under the back, gripping the buoy handle.
5. With your left hand on the victim's forehead, tilt the victim's head back and assess for breathing.
6. Tow the victim to safety. If the victim is not breathing, use the resuscitation mask to perform in-water rescue breathing.

Unresponsive victim just below the surface

You can approach from either the front or rear when rescuing an unresponsive victim just below the surface (**figure 8.16**). If you suspect the victim may have a spinal injury, follow the procedures later in this chapter. Otherwise follow these steps:

1. Place the rescue tube or buoy between you and the victim. From the front, reach over the tube or buoy and underwater to grab the victim's wrist. From the rear, reach over the tube or buoy and underwater to grab the victim's armpit.
2. Pull the victim to the surface and onto the tube or buoy.
3. Follow all other procedures for rescuing an unresponsive victim from the front or rear.

If you cannot reach the victim this way, try the procedures for a submerged victim.

Submerged victim

Speed is crucial when rescuing a submerged victim (**figure 8.17**). After activating the EAP, with your rescue pack and rescue tube or buoy, swim quickly to the approximate place where the victim was last seen. Bubbles on the surface can be a clue to where the victim is submerged. If you suspect the victim has a spinal injury, use the head-splint rescue procedure described later in this chapter. Otherwise, take a breath and make a surface dive. Use either a feetfirst or arm-over-arm surface dive (see chapter 7), and equalize the pressure in your ears as needed. If the victim is submerged so deeply that you cannot reach him or her with your rescue tube or buoy attached to your shoulder, remove the strap.

Choose the faster and more accurate arm-over-arm surface dive under these conditions:

- The water is clear.
- You know the area is safe for diving.
- You know the water is deep enough to safely dive headfirst.

Dive feetfirst when conditions are less favorable, for example:

- The water is murky.
- You are not sure of underwater obstructions.
- You do not know the depth of the water.

Approach from the rear and grasp the victim by the armpit(s). Bring the victim to the surface with a single or double armpit tow. Once on the surface, position the victim on the rescue tube or buoy as

Figure 8.17 Submerged victim.

described for the unresponsive victim from the rear. Be sure to check the airway and breathing and, if necessary, begin in-water rescue breathing while towing the victim to safety.

Multiple victims

It is possible you will encounter situations in which more than one person needs your help. To be prepared to rescue two victims, consider these principles when planning:

- Ideally, multiple lifeguards will be available to provide the best response. If only one lifeguard is available, the goal is to support both victims with the tube or buoy and tow them to safety.
- Have a rescue tube with clasps on the ends so the tube can be fastened around a victim. Or use a buoy, which has handles that can be held easily by victims. Another option is to have an inflatable rescue tube available.

These are some of the situations in which a victim might grab nearby swimmers, leading to multiple victims:

- At a beach, victims might be knocked over by a wave, lose contact with the bottom due to waves or swells, lose an inflatable support, or step off into a hole or into deeper water.
- At a pool, a victim might jump or be pushed into deep water, walk from shallow water into deep water in a pool that has no lifeline indicating the deep water slope, become tired

Figure 8.18 Multiple-victim rescue using a rescue tube.

A

B

C

while swimming across the pool width in deep water, or lose an inflatable support.

After scanning and recognizing multiple victims, assess the situation. You may see victims who are holding on to each other face-to-face or one victim holding on to another from behind or from the side. Take the following actions (**figure 8.18**):

1. Activate the EAP. Blow your whistle, use an air horn, or activate the pool alarm to indicate the beginning of a multiple-victim rescue procedure.
2. Enter the water and approach the victims from the side. Place the rescue flotation device on edge. Grab the rescue tube or buoy approximately 6 inches from the nose end with one hand (this gives you good control while submerging it).
3. Thrust the tube or buoy between the two victims.
4. Tow or push both victims to safety using a breaststroke or elementary backstroke kick.

If using a rescue tube, you can provide extra support by grasping both ends of the tube and clasping it around the top victim, providing flotation. If the other victim does not grab hold of the rescue tube, swim around and assist him or her in reaching the rescue tube, or approach that victim from the rear, extend your hands under that victim's armpits, and grab hold of the rescue tube.

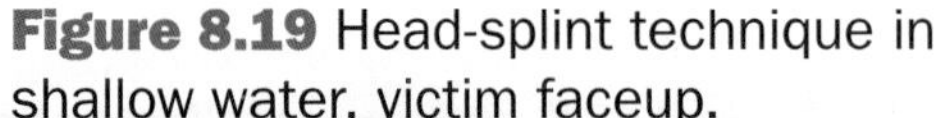

Figure 8.19 Head-splint technique in shallow water, victim faceup.

Keys to the Head-Splint Turnover

If a spinal-injury victim is facedown in the water, apply the head-splint before turning the victim to a faceup position. Remember that seconds count when the victim's face has been submerged in the water.

1. Grab the victim's upper arms near the elbows.
2. Trap the victim's head between the arms and maintain pressure.
3. Move forward, in the direction of the victim's head, to bring the victim into a horizontal position on the surface.
4. Roll the victim over by turning him or her toward you.
5. Lower yourself to neck depth so you do not lift the victim above the water.
6. Place your forearm under the victim's shoulder for support (right forearm under right shoulder or left forearm under left shoulder). You will be facing the victim's feet.
7. Check that the victim's arms are over your shoulder, next to your ear, and that you are not lifting the victim out of the water. Keep the victim's ears in the water until the victim can be safely removed.

If using a rescue buoy, have both victims grab hold of it, assisting them in holding the buoy if necessary.

Victims with suspected spinal injuries

YMCA of the USA recommends using the head-splint technique for victims with spinal injuries. Research conducted by Gerald DeMers (1983) showed that this technique, when executed as described below, is the most effective technique a lifeguard can use to stabilize the victim's head and neck during a rescue.

Head-splint technique

The purpose of the head-splint technique is to stabilize the head and neck, known as in-line stabilization. It can be used to stabilize a victim lying facedown in the water before turning the victim over and also when a victim is faceup in the water. In-line stabilization is accomplished through the head-splint technique by squeezing the victim's arms to trap the head between them (**figure 8.19**, previous page). Avoid lifting the victim out of the water while performing in-line stabilization; a good key to remember is to keep the victim's ears in the water until the victim can be safely removed. The head-splint technique can be used in both shallow- and deep-water rescues. Keep in mind that if the victim's face is submerged, you must move quickly while performing the head-splint technique.

Figure 8.20 Using the head-splint technique to stabilize the victim's head and neck.

A

B

Spinal-injury victim in shallow water

Victim faceup

Activate the EAP and then approach the victim from the rear. Check to see if the victim is conscious.

If the victim is conscious, let the victim know that you are now going to provide in-line stabilization to protect his or her spine by using the head-splint technique. Explain exactly what you are going to do and then proceed with the following (**figure 8.20**):

1. Stand behind the victim's head.
2. Submerge so that the water level is at your neck.
3. Grab the victim's arms above the elbows (near the bicep).
4. Slowly and carefully move the victim's arms up to the sides of the head, a position that will allow you to trap the head between the arms.
5. Once the head is secure between the arms, stabilize the victim for backboarding (discussed later in this chapter).

Ask the victim the following questions:

- What happened?
- Do you feel pain anywhere?
- Can you move your fingers?
- Can you move your toes?
- Do you have any pain in your neck?

Victim facedown

Perform this rescue for a victim who is facedown in the water. Remember to consider spinal injuries any time a victim is found unconscious in shallow water. After you activate the EAP:

1. Quickly approach from the victim's side.
2. Grab the victim's upper arms just above the elbows.

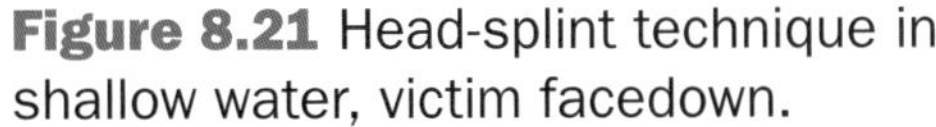

Figure 8.21 Head-splint technique in shallow water, victim facedown.

A

B

C

3. Move the arms toward the head so that the victim's upper arms cover his or her ears. This will center the victim's head between the arms.
4. Squeeze both arms against the head simultaneously and with equal pressure to hold the head in position.
5. After trapping the head between the victim's arms, move forward, in the direction that the victim's head is pointing. As you move, the victim's legs will rise. Having the legs ride higher in the water will make it easier to turn the victim.
6. Roll the victim toward you and turn your face toward the victim's feet, lowering yourself in the water to neck depth to avoid lifting the victim.
7. As you continue to turn the victim over, move your top arm (the arm that was reaching over the victim) to a position beneath the victim's shoulder. Keep your forearm in contact with the shoulder and upper arm of the victim.

Remember that speed matters when the victim's face has been submerged in the water. After you have turned the victim over, keep the victim's arms over your shoulder and close to your cheek or neck. Stabilize the victim in a horizontal position by gently supporting the victim's shoulder with your bent arm, which is under the victim. Avoid lifting the victim during in-line stabilization; remember to keep the victim's ears in the water until removal. The stabilization position is illustrated in **figure 8.21**, previous page.

Check the victim's breathing. If the victim is not breathing, quickly place the victim on a backboard

Figure 8.22 Rescuing a spinal-injury victim on the surface of deep water using the head-splint technique with a rescue tube.

A

B

C

using the techniques described later in this chapter. Use your resuscitation mask to perform in-water rescue breathing, using the modified jaw-thrust technique if necessary, and move the victim toward safety.

Spinal-injury victim in deep water

Few spinal injuries occur in deep water, but such an injury is possible. Use the head-splint technique for in-line stabilization in deep water.

Stabilizing the neck in deep water can be difficult; you need a strong kick to keep yourself in position to perform an effective rescue. It is a good idea to store a pair of fins at all lifeguard stations in deep-water areas. With fins, it is easier to maintain your position using a flutter kick (i.e., double scissors kick). Without fins, use a breaststroke, scissors, or rotary kick. The rotary or eggbeater kick is preferred because, when performed properly, it provides a more stable transport of the victim.

Victim on the surface

Activate the EAP and enter the water. Use a waveless entry if the victim is less than 10 feet away. Use the breaststroke to avoid disturbing the water while you quickly approach the victim.

When you reach the victim, perform the head-splint technique. You will need to modify the head-splint technique slightly if you use a rescue tube (**figure 8.22**). Be sure to end up at the victim's side rather than with the victim's arms next to your ears after turning the victim over. Avoid rolling the victim onto the tube because it may affect the position of the neck.

Once you have turned the victim over, check for breathing. If the victim is not breathing, quickly

A

B

C

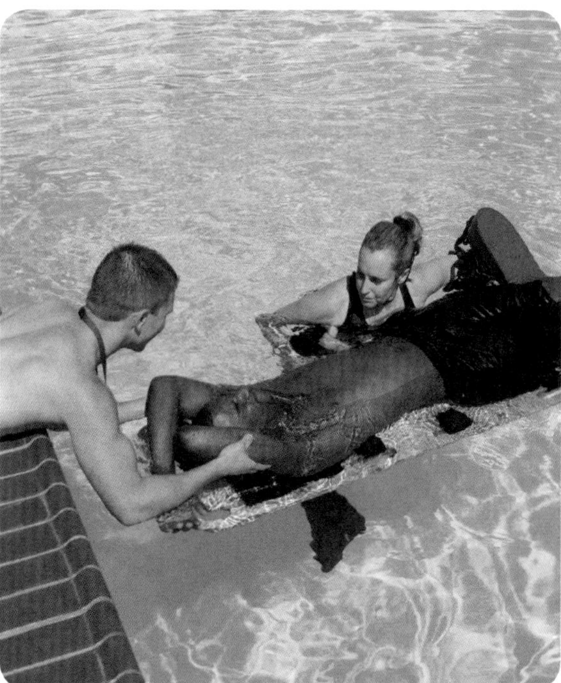

Figure 8.23 Preparing a spinal-injury victim for removal from deep water.

place the victim on a backboard using the techniques described later in this chapter. Use your resuscitation mask to perform in-water rescue breathing, using the modified jaw-thrust technique if necessary, and move the victim toward safety.

Transport the victim to shallow water if possible. If you are at a pool or diving well with no shallow section, transport the victim toward the side of the pool for removal (**figure 8.23**, previous page).

See chapter 12 for how to adapt spinal injury management in a waterpark or waterfront setting with moving water.

Submerged victim

Activate the EAP, then swim quickly to the victim's location, perform a safe surface dive, and equalize the pressure in your ears as needed. If the victim is submerged too deeply for you to reach the victim with your rescue flotation device still attached to your shoulder, then remove the strap.

Approach the victim from above or behind, depending on the victim's position. In most cases when the victim is submerged, the victim will not be flat on his or her back on the bottom. Trap the victim's head using the head-splint technique and transport the victim to the surface. Keep the victim's face angled toward the bottom to avoid getting water up the victim's nose and possibly into the stomach and lungs. As you reach the surface, turn the victim to a faceup position.

Continue to apply the head splint while transporting the victim to the nearest removal point, whether the side of the pool, shore, or shallow water. Check the victim's breathing. If the victim is not breathing, quickly place the victim on a backboard using the techniques described later in this chapter. Use your resuscitation mask to perform in-water rescue breathing, using the modified jaw-thrust technique if necessary, and move the victim toward safety.

Remember, when performing a surface dive, if you are unfamiliar with the area or you cannot see the bottom, perform a feetfirst surface dive.

Figure 8.24 Rescue stroke.

Figure 8.25 Double armpit tow.

Rescue Towing

To tow a victim to safety as quickly as possible, and when there are no signs of spinal injury, choose between these two techniques: the rescue stroke or the armpit tow.

Rescue stroke

The rescue stroke (**figure 8.24**) is used to tow a conscious victim who is breathing to the side of the pool or to shore. Hold the victim or the rescue flotation device with one arm and do a one-arm pull with the other. You can use a scissors, breaststroke, or rotary kick.

Armpit tow

If a victim is unresponsive but is breathing and has no evidence of a spinal injury, you can tow her or him to safety using a single or double armpit tow (**figure 8.25**). If you have fastened the rescue tube around the victim, tow by grasping either the tube or the victim's armpit. Grab the victim as close to the armpit as possible (right hand to right armpit or left hand to left armpit) with your thumb on the outside of the arm, and keep the tube or buoy between you and the victim. For the single-armpit tow, use any rescue stroke that allows you to keep visual contact with the victim and swim to safety quickly. For the double armpit tow, grab both of the victim's armpits and kick to safety. In any case, ensure that the victim's airway stays above the surface of the water.

Removing Victims From the Water

Once you have brought a victim to safety, remove the victim from the water as quickly as possible to start emergency first aid as necessary. The type of removal you use is influenced by conditions such as terrain, proximity to medical assistance, your own size and strength, the assistance available, and the victim's size, condition, and injuries.

The types of removal procedures discussed here are water exits and board lifts. Assess your situation to determine which is most appropriate. Whatever procedure you use, follow these guidelines:

- Call EMS if the call was not placed when the EAP was activated.
- Take charge.
- Protect yourself from blood-borne pathogens.
- Work in unison with the victim and assistants.
- Give specific directions to others who may assist in the victim's removal from the water.
- Identify a location for the victim following removal from the water (see sidebar).

If a victim is injured, special considerations are required. While the water is generally a good support for an injured extremity, it becomes challenging to provide support and stabilization while removing the victim from the water. Depending on the extent of the injury,

Positioning a Victim on the Deck or Shore

As you remove a victim from the water, attempt to place the victim in a location that is out of the sun, away from a crowd, and close to first-aid facilities. However, if the victim is not breathing or is in cardiac arrest, note that your priority is to provide resuscitation.

Lower the victim to the ground carefully to reduce the chance of additional injury. Provide cushioning whenever possible. Make sure the victim is completely removed from the water, including out of reach of waves. For example, if the victim's legs are in the water, you will not be able to perform CPR or use an AED effectively.

If resuscitation is necessary and the ground slopes, lay the victim faceup and as flat as possible so that the victim's head is level with the victim's trunk. This flat position is important because it decreases the likelihood of the victim vomiting and increases the chance of a successful resuscitation. Be aware that positioning the head lower than the trunk increases the chance of vomiting and may interfere with resuscitation. Also, positioning the head higher than the trunk can lead to problems for victims with high blood pressure. Therefore, the flat position—head level with the chest—is safest (ILS 2003a).

you may or may not require assistance or equipment in exiting the water. Make it a priority to keep the victim's airway clear and above water and observe these guidelines:

- Provide support that will eliminate movement of an injured extremity.
- Strive to remove the victim in a manner that will not cause further injury.
- Do not allow the victim to place any pressure or weight on the injured extremity.

Figure 8.26 Supporting assist.

When a victim has injuries, also consider issues such as these:

- Will additional movement of the injured part cause further damage?
- Could further injury result if I do not assist the victim in exiting the water?
- Would it be better to move to shallow water before exiting the pool?
- Where is the best place to remove a victim on the shoreline?
- How much pain is the victim currently having?
- What is the victim's level of consciousness?
- How many others are available to assist?

If the injured victim is conscious, get feedback from the victim to help you decide how to assist. Once you have towed the victim to the side of the pool or to the shoreline and he or she is floating with the assistance of a rescue tube or buoy, ask additional questions to determine the extent of the injury, such as the following:

- Do you know what happened?
- Do you have pain anywhere? How much pain do you have?
- Do you feel light-headed? Are you nauseated?
- Can you feel your arms and legs? Can you move your arms and legs?
- Are you having difficulty breathing?
- Do you feel weak?
- Are you cold?

The answers to these and other questions can help you decide how to approach removing the victim from the water. You may even decide that additional professional assistance is necessary and allow EMS to help perform the removal from the water. (Your facility's management should have already addressed such a scenario with EMS and have written documentation if EMS can and will enter the water to assist in removing a victim with injuries. See chapter 6 for more on emergency planning.)

Water exits

Effective methods for assisting victims in exiting the water include the supporting assist, the one-person drag, the one- or two-person lift, and the ladder exit. These exits are for situations when the victim shows no sign of spinal injury. If signs of spinal injury are present, remove the victim following the procedures described later in this chapter.

Supporting assist

If a victim is weak but conscious and can stand, you can walk him or her to safety using a supporting assist (**figure 8.26**). Stand next to the victim, pull the near arm across your shoulder, and secure it by grabbing the wrist with your far hand. Use your free arm to support the victim's waist. Walk the victim to a safe place and provide necessary care.

One-person drag

The one-person drag (**figure 8.27**) is probably one of the quickest and most efficient ways to carry an unconscious or exhausted person from an open body of water or zero-depth pool. After you have ruled out the possibility of spinal injury, wrap your arms around the victim from behind, positioning your arms under the victim's

Figure 8.27 One-person drag, rescuer grasping own wrists.

Figure 8.28 One-person drag, rescuer grasping victim's wrists.

Figure 8.29 Rescuer #2 picks up victim's legs to perform a two-person carry.

armpits, and grab your wrist with the other hand to lock you grip. Lift the victim and walk backward, dragging the victim's feet. Be careful when lifting the victim; use your legs and arms to avoid injuring your back.

If you are smaller than the victim, you may have difficulty reaching all the way around and grasping your wrist. If you cannot easily maintain a tight grip, you may find it more secure to grasp the victim's wrists (your right hand to the victim's right wrist and your left hand to the victim's left wrist) and cross the victim's arms slightly, holding the arms against the victim's chest as shown in (**figure 8.28**, previous page).

Two-person carry

If you are the second rescuer on the scene, you can assist the first rescuer who is performing a one-person drag by lifting the victim's legs. Stand facing the victim and place your hands under the victim's knees, then lift the legs, holding a leg in each hand at your sides. From this position, called a two-person carry (**figure 8.29**, previous page), you can move the victim to a safe place much more quickly. Again, lift using your legs and arms, not your back. Position the victim on deck or shore, assess the victim, and provide necessary care.

One- or two-person lift

This lift is used primarily in deep water and is best performed as a two-person lift (**figure 8.30**) because two rescuers are generally required to lift an adult victim. However, a one-person lift can be done safely depending on the size of the victim and the strength and skill of the rescuer.

To begin, position the victim next to the side of the pool and facing the wall or deck. Position yourself to the rear of the victim. Reach under the victim's arms and grab the side of the pool to support the victim. You can also support the victim on your knee. With a second rescuer standing on the deck,

Figure 8.30 Two-person lift.

A B C D

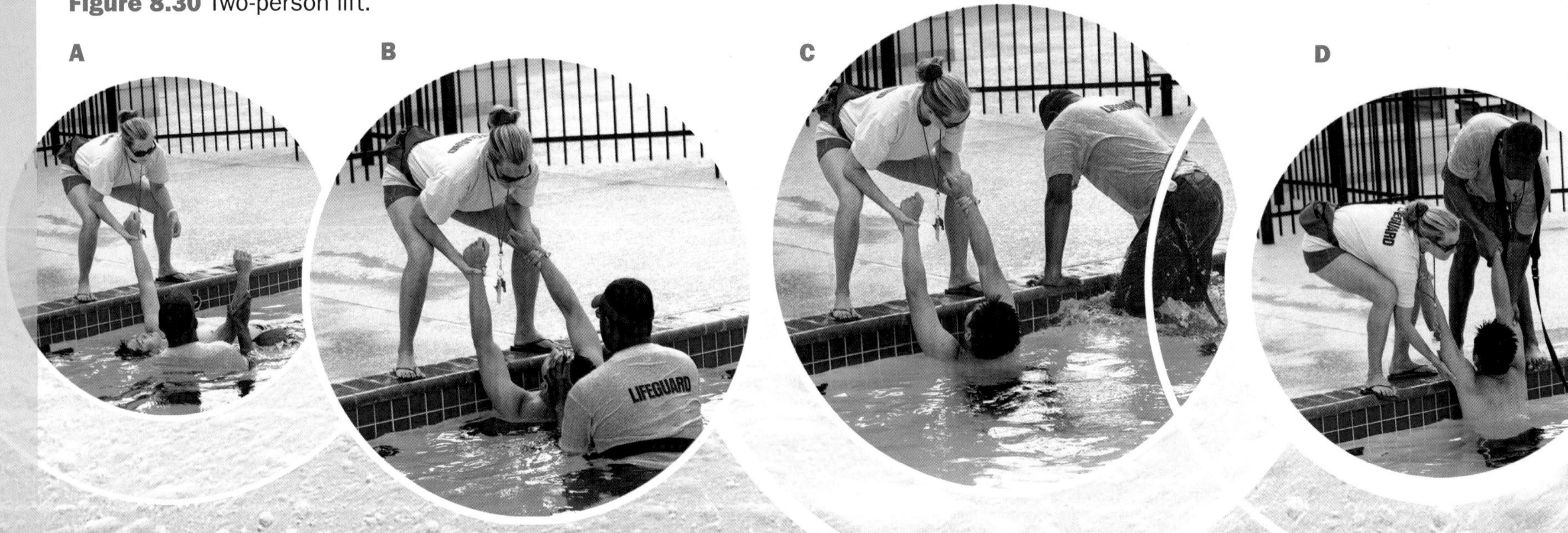

pass the victim's hands to Rescuer #2, then exit the water and join Rescuer #2 on deck. If you are alone, lift the victim's hands onto the deck, one on top of the other, and hold them in place as you get out of the water. If the deck or dock is too high above the water level for you to lift yourself out of the water while maintaining control of the victim's hands and keeping her or his head out of the water, call for additional help.

With two rescuers on the deck, each rescuer grabs hold of the victim with a wrist in one hand and an upper arm in the other. With coordinated movements, the rescuers lift the victim on to the deck. If no assistance is available and you are strong enough to lift the victim by yourself, position yourself on the deck holding the victim's wrists. Then, slightly lower the victim in the water before lifting to gain momentum and make the lift easier. Be careful not to submerge the victim's face. For a large victim, it may be necessary to have one or two assistants in the water to push the victim up while those on the deck lift.

Whether you use a one- or two-person lift, protect yourself by lifting with your legs and not your back. Keep in mind that the victim's head may be leaning forward. Take care to lift the victim straight up to protect the head from injury. As the victim clears the deck at mid-thigh or lower, step back and pull the victim clear of the water. Lower the victim slowly to the deck, placing your foot under the victim's face if necessary to prevent it from hitting the deck. Roll the victim onto his or her back to begin emergency assessment procedures. Be sure that the victim is completely out of the water and lying horizontally. If the victim's legs are in the water, you will not be able to perform CPR or use an AED successfully.

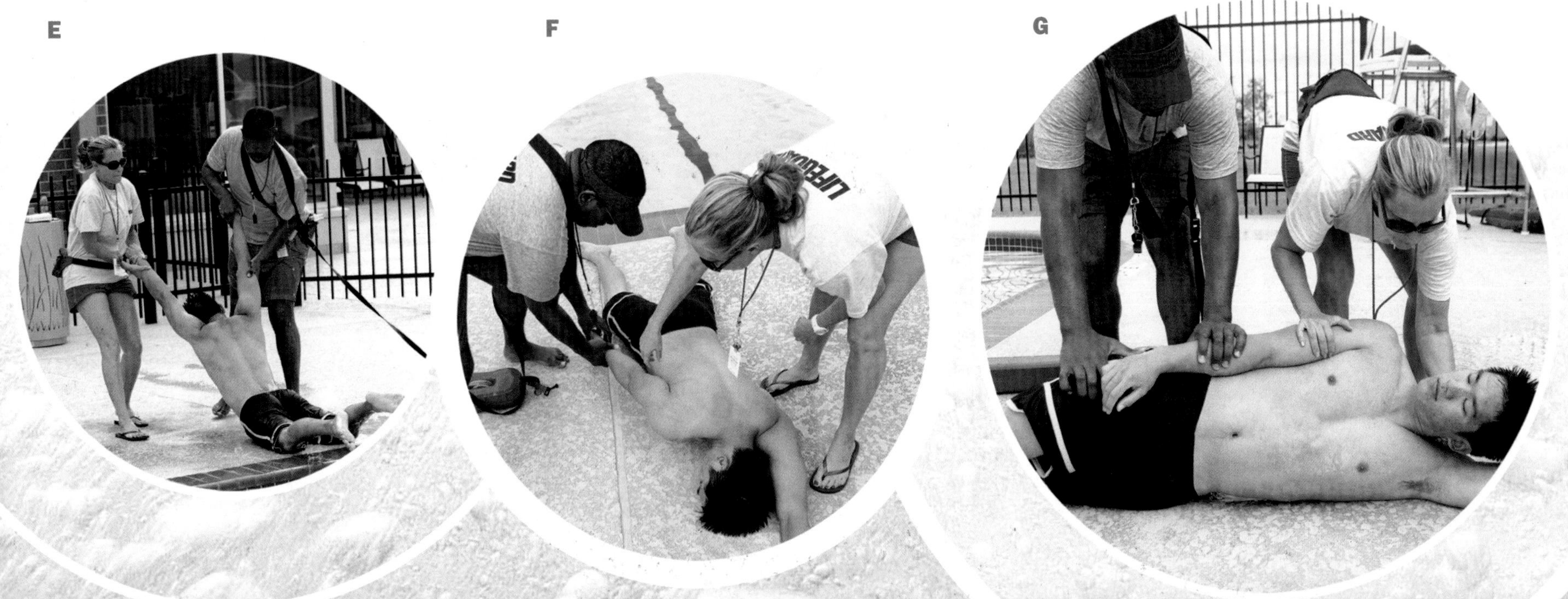

Ladder exit

The ladder exit (**figure 8.31**) is used when a victim has an upper extremity injury. Transport the victim to a ladder in shallow or deep water and then perform the following steps:

1. Instruct the victim to step on to the ladder with both feet and grab the pool gutter or the ladder railing with the hand of the uninjured arm.
2. Position yourself behind the victim, then reach around the victim with both arms and grab the lip of the gutter or the ladder.
3. Squeeze your arms against the victim to stabilize the victim on the ladder.
4. Position your chest close to or against the victim's back or hips to support the victim as you climb up the ladder with the victim.
5. Once on deck, assess the victim and provide necessary care.

Others on deck may assist by holding on to the victim. They also may help in stabilizing the victim's injured part during the climb out of the water. Remember that any movement of the extremity may cause further injury, so avoid it if at all possible.

Board lift

Using a backboard to lift a victim out of the water is a good method for removing a victim in many situations. It is especially effective when victims are difficult to remove because they are unconscious or have a lower extremity injury. A board lift also will be necessary in cases of spinal injury, described later in this chapter.

Speed board exit

Use the speed board exit with a backboard for a victim who is unconscious or has a lower extremity injury and when a spinal injury is not suspected. This exit requires two rescuers (**figure 8.32**):

1. Rescuer #1 has positioned the victim on his or her back across the rescue tube using the rescue techniques for unresponsive victim and, if necessary, is using the do-si-do method to perform rescue breathing with a resuscitation mask.

Figure 8.31 Ladder exit.

A

B

C

D

Figure 8.32 Speed board exit.

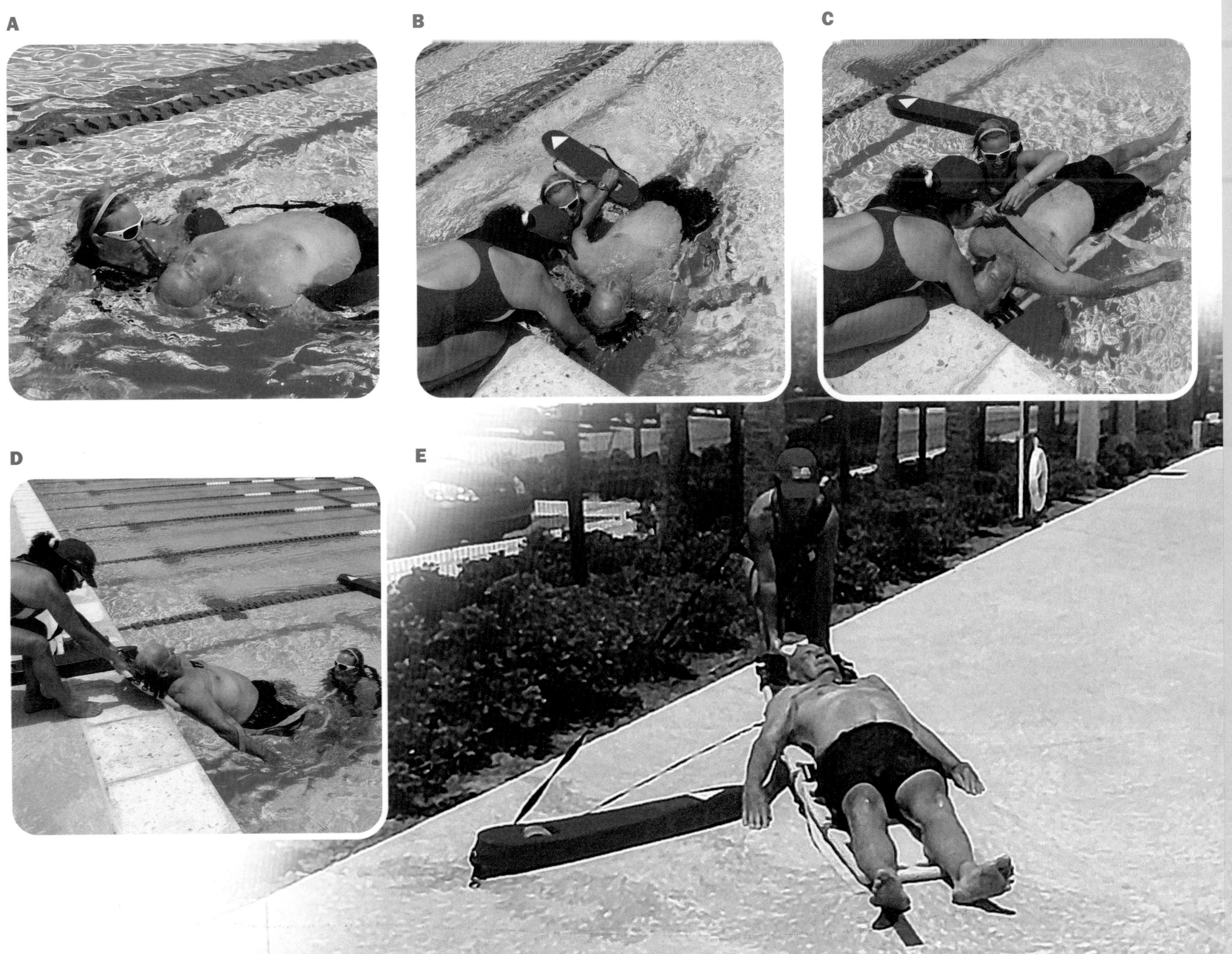

2. Rescuer #1 approaches the side of the pool or the exit point with the victim.
3. Rescuer #2 takes a backboard and meets Rescuer #1 and the victim at poolside or the exit point. The backboard has the head restraint removed and the top chest strap open. (The remaining straps may be on the board and clasped but may not be wrapped behind the board. The underside of the backboard must be clear so the board can slide easily.)
4. Rescuer #2 inserts the backboard vertically into the water with the foot of the backboard pointing toward the bottom. Note: Most boards must be pushed all the way into the water, with the top of board, which Rescuer #2 is holding, in the water and not resting on the edge.
5. Rescuer #1 releases the do-si-do position and grasps the victim's closest armpit with the fingers in the armpit and the thumb pointing up. With the other hand, Rescuer #1 slightly submerges the rescue tube and removes it from under the victim. Rescuer #1 tosses the resuscitation mask onto the deck where it will be out of the way of the exit.
6. Working together, Rescuer #2 allows the foot end of the board to rise up in the water at an angle as Rescuer #1 slides the victim onto the board. Rescuer #1 may want to grasp the board with one hand and the victim with the other hand while sliding the victim onto the board. (This technique works well with buoyant backboards.)
7. Rescuer #1 then quickly applies the chest strap: Lifting the victim's near arm, Rescuer #1 places the near end of the strap under the victim's arm and over the chest. Then, reaching across the victim (change which hand holds the victim if this is difficult), Rescuer #1 places the other end of the strap under the victim's arm and across the victim's chest and fastens the strap. Make sure the strap is tight enough to hold the victim snugly in place. Rescuer #2 stabilizes the board with both hands while Rescuer #1 applies the chest strap.
8. Prepare to remove the victim from the water. Make sure the victim's feet and legs are centered on the board. Rescuer #2 prepares to stand up on the deck. Rescuer #1 communicates the count of when to lift and remove the victim.
9. Rescuer #1 can stay at the head of the board and help lift or can move to the foot of the board and push down on it to drive the head of the board up to Rescuer #2. Rescuer #2 tilts the board back, pulls, and slides the victim out of the water, making sure the board is entirely on the deck or dock. Place the victim several feet away from the water's edge and away from standing water in case you will be using an AED.
10. Assess the victim and prepare for emergency care.

Backboarding procedures for victims with spinal injuries

Gutter and deck construction and the type of backboard you have may influence the procedures you use while backboarding. For example, the rescuer on deck may need to adjust his or her position to allow the most effective in-line stabilization procedure. Thus, you may have to slightly alter the following in order to make backboarding procedures effective at your facility. Management may develop specific procedures for your facility, using in-service training and rescue drills to establish and test those procedures.

The backboarding procedure described here is for both shallow and deep water. It requires two rescuers: Rescuer #1 is in the water, and Rescuer #2 can be positioned standing in shallow water (see **figure 8.33**), sitting on a step, or lying on the deck. If your facility is a deck-level pool, Rescuer #2 may sit on the side of the pool. The backboard is placed within arm's reach on the deck, and the head immobilizer is removed and lying near at hand.

Preparing the victim for the backboard (**figure 8.34**)

1. While Rescuer #1 maintains in-line stabilization and moves the victim to a position perpendicular to the side of the pool, Rescuer #2 moves into position and prepares to take over providing in-line stabilization.
2. When Rescuer #1 is near the side of the pool, Rescuer #2 grasps the victim's upper arms and continues in-line stabilization. Rescuer #1 releases

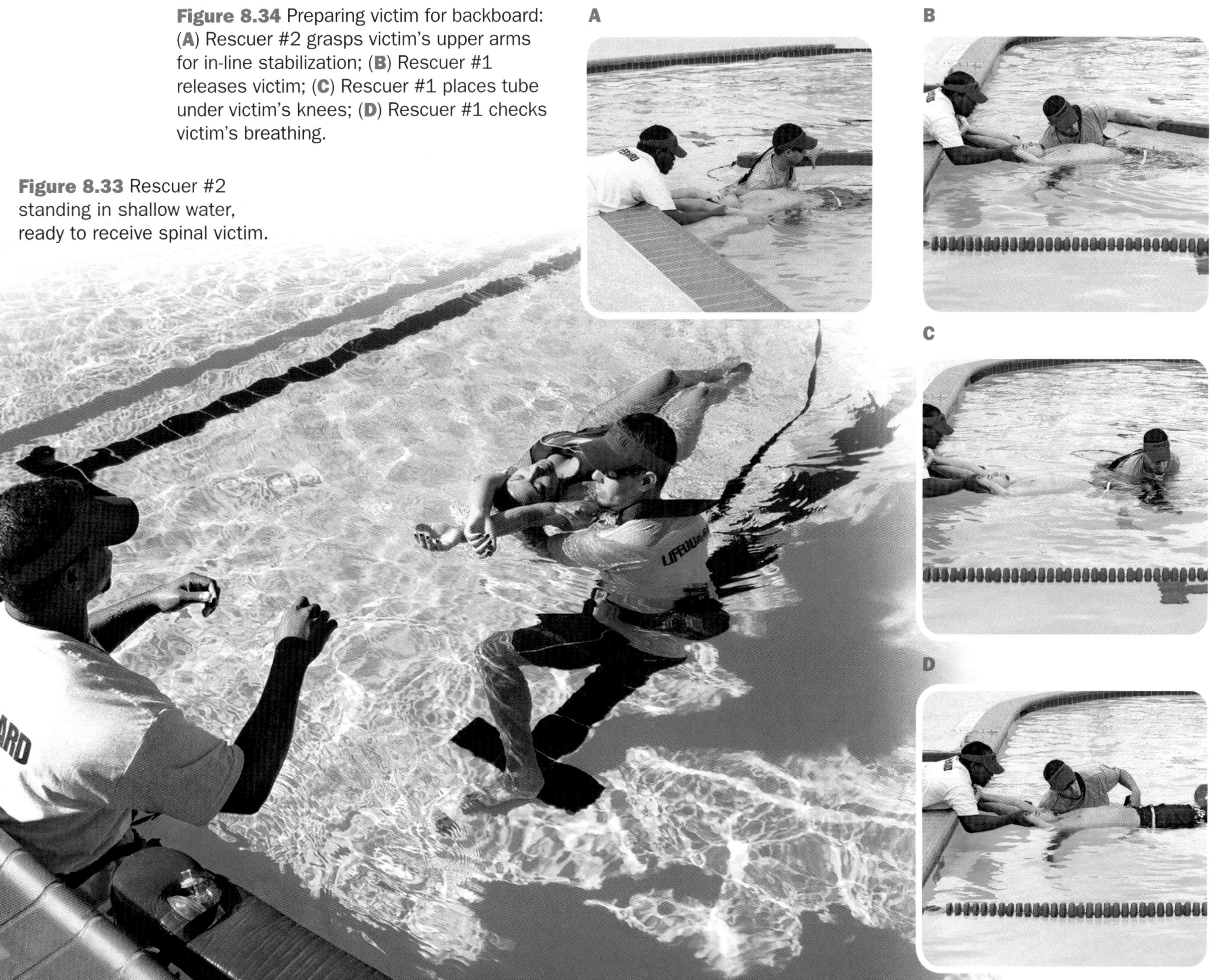

Figure 8.34 Preparing victim for backboard: (**A**) Rescuer #2 grasps victim's upper arms for in-line stabilization; (**B**) Rescuer #1 releases victim; (**C**) Rescuer #1 places tube under victim's knees; (**D**) Rescuer #1 checks victim's breathing.

Figure 8.33 Rescuer #2 standing in shallow water, ready to receive spinal victim.

the victim and Rescuer #2 maintains the victim in a horizontal position.

3. Rescuer #1 places a rescue tube under the victim's knees to maintain the victim in the horizontal position and checks the victim for breathing.

Strapping the victim to the backboard (**figure 8.35**)

1. Rescuer #1 turns the backboard on edge and aligns the head-restraint pad with the victim's head. Rescuer #1 then submerges the board, centers it under the victim, and allows the board to float up under the victim.
2. Once the board is in place, Rescuer #1 attaches the chest strap, making certain the strap is above the chest (high in the armpits) and is tight and snug. If Rescuer #1 cannot reach over the victim without touching him or her, Rescuer #1 moves around to secure the straps.
3. Rescuer #1 positions a forearm on the victim's sternum so he or she can cup the victim's chin—with fingers on one side and thumb on the other side—and places the other arm beneath the backboard to hold the victim on the board.
4. Rescuer #2 lowers the victim's arms to the person's sides.
5. As Rescuer #1 continues to hold the victim's chin, Rescuer #2 positions a head-immobilizer pad on each side of the victim's head (placing a thumb in the ear-hole of the pad if necessary) and applies the head strap.
6. Rescuer #1 continues securing the victim to the backboard as follows: Attach the waist strap so that it secures the victim's arms and waist. Move the rescue tube from under the

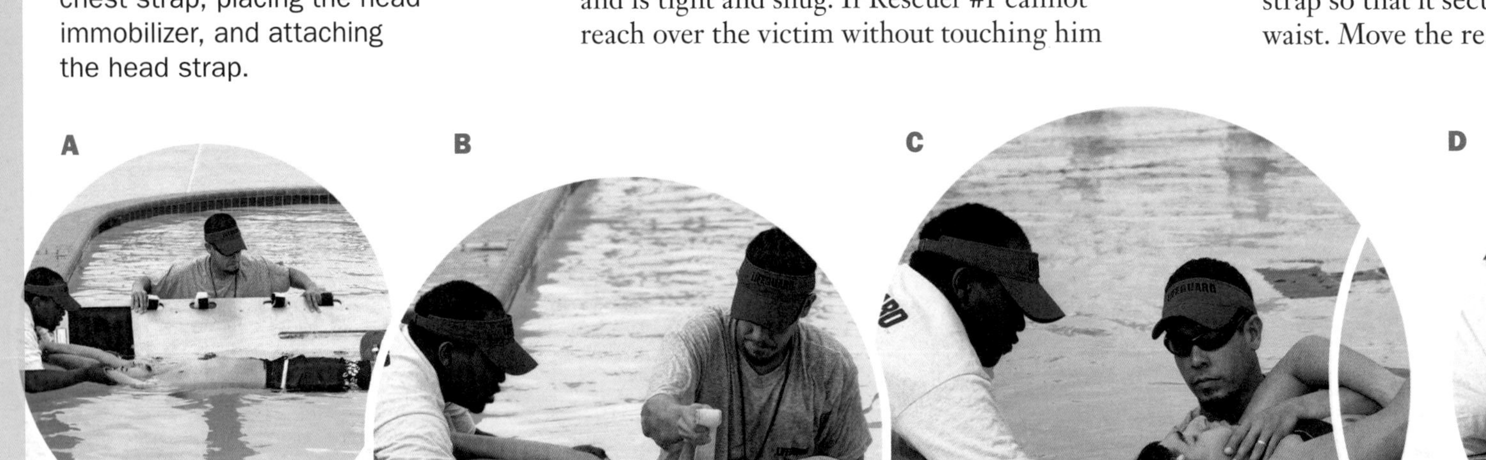

Figure 8.35 Positioning the backboard, attaching the chest strap, placing the head immobilizer, and attaching the head strap.

Figure 8.35 (cont.) Attaching waist strap, moving the tube under the backboard, and attaching the leg strap.

victim's knees to a position under the foot end of the backboard and attach the leg strap. All straps are snug and clear of the underside of the board. Place a second rescue tube under the foot end of the backboard if necessary. The victim is now ready to be lifted out of the water.

Lifting the victim from the water (figure 8.36)

1. Rescuer #1 stabilizes the backboard while Rescuer #2 gets into position to begin the lift from the water.
2. Rescuers #1 and #2 lift the head end of the backboard onto the deck (coordinating efforts for this lifting process). Rescuer #1 can assist either from the water or move to the deck while removing the victim from the water.
3. Rescuers #1 and #2 slide the backboard and victim onto the deck. See the information earlier in this chapter about positioning the victim on deck.

Backboarding victims in extremely shallow water (figure 8.37)

Zero-depth pools, wave pools, spray pools, and waterfront facilities are just some examples of extremely shallow water, defined as water less than 2 feet deep. Follow these procedures for spinal injury management when a victim is located facedown in extremely shallow water:

1. Approach the victim from the side. Grasp the victim's upper arms near the elbows and move the victim's arms carefully into position to apply the head splint.
2. While walking forward with the victim's head trapped, begin rolling the victim toward you. As you roll the victim, maneuver yourself into a position at the top of the victim's head. During the rollover, lower your arms and hands to the water surface to keep the victim's head at the surface of the water. You will end up looking toward the victim's feet.

It is preferable to roll the victim directly on to a backboard, if one is readily available. This requires a second rescuer to assist:

1. Rescuer #1 applies the head splint.
2. Rescuer #2 moves to the victim's side and places the backboard parallel to the victim.
3. Rescuer #1, who is positioned at the head of the victim, moves slightly to one side of the backboard while continuing to apply the head splint and begins to roll the victim over toward Rescuer #2.
4. Rescuer #2 submerges the backboard and guides the victim onto the board as Rescuer #1 continues to provide in-line stabilization and completes the rollover.
5. Rescuer #2 moves next to Rescuer #1 at the head of the backboard, grasps the head of the backboard, and drags the board and victim out of the water and onto the deck or shore while Rescuer #1 continues to apply the head splint.

If a backboard cannot be positioned as quickly as Rescuer #1 can get to the victim to perform the head-splint turnover, the board must be placed beneath the faceup victim by submerging and sliding it underneath the victim while Rescuer #1 maintains in-line stabilization. Remove the victim from the water as described above.

Figure 8.36 Lifting victim from the water: (**A**) Rescuers position themselves and begin removing victim from water; (**B**) Rescuers slide the backboard and victim onto the deck; (**C**) Rescuer moves the victim to a safe location; (**D**) Rescuer checks airway and breathing.

A

B

C

D

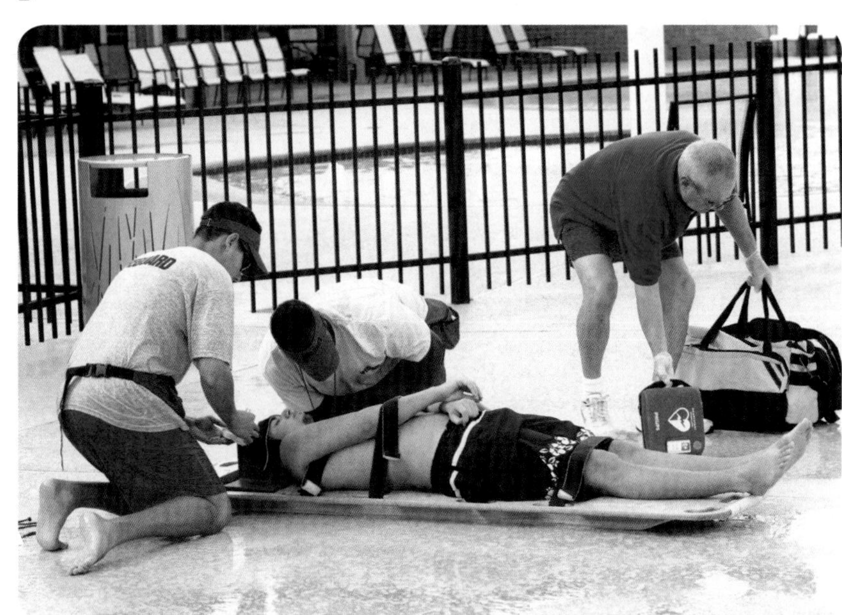

Figure 8.37 Backboarding in extremely shallow water: (**A**) Rescuer #1 approaches the victim; (**B**) Rescuer #1 traps the victim's head; Rescuer #2 brings the backboard; (**C**) Rescuer #2 submerges the backboard as Rescuer #1 rolls the victim onto the board; (**D**) Rescuer #2 drags the board and victim from the water; (**E**) Rescuer #1 maintains head splint during removal; (**F**) Rescuers monitor the victim.

Removing a spinal-injury victim who is not breathing

After Rescuer #2 takes over applying the head splint from Rescuer #1 and has stabilized the victim at the edge of the pool, Rescuer #1 checks for breathing. If the victim is not breathing, focus on removing the victim from the water as quickly as possible while maintaining the head splint. Use a backboard for support but expedite the removal as follows:

- Rescuer #1 quickly places the board under the victim.
- Rescuer #2 maintains the head splint.
- Rescuer #1 places the edge of the board on the deck and either pushes the victim and board out of the water or hops out of the water and drags the victim and the board out of the water.

In a waterfront setting or challenging aquatic setting, if you are concerned with keeping the victim secured to the board, quickly apply the chest strap before exiting the water. Otherwise, do not take the time to apply the strap; focus on removing the victim quickly while maintaining the head splint.

Once the victim is positioned on deck or shore (discussed earlier in this chapter), carefully move the victim's arms away from the head and begin rescue breathing using the modified jaw-thrust technique (see next section). Check for a pulse. If the victim has no pulse, begin CPR. Be sure to use your personal protective equipment, including resuscitation mask and disposable gloves, when performing rescue breathing and CPR.

The Backboard

Many different types of backboards are available, such as the one pictured here. Any model is acceptable as long as it meets the following requirements:

- It is made of wood or lightweight resins. (Note: If a backboard is contaminated, resin boards are easier to clean than wooden boards.)
- It has slats or risers underneath the board or handles, which help prevent rescuers from pinching their fingers when setting the board on the deck.
- It has ample slots on each side of the board to adjust strap placement.
- It has a professional head restraint attached to the board.
- It is long and wide enough to allow rescue of victims of various sizes.
- It has a minimum of four straps connected to the board (one head strap, one chest strap, one waist strap, one leg strap).

Keep backboards on deck and ready for use at all times the facility is open. Have all straps connected to the board in a manner that duplicates how the straps will be connected once the victim is placed on the board.

Resuscitation of spinal-injury victims

Modified jaw-thrust technique for rescue breathing

If you suspect the victim may have a spinal injury, do not tilt the victim's head back to perform rescue breathing because it could cause further damage to the spinal column. Instead, use the modified jaw-thrust technique, making sure to wear disposable gloves. To perform the modified jaw thrust, place your thumbs on the victim's cheekbones as illustrated in **figure 8.38**. The right thumb is on the right cheek and the left thumb is on the left cheek. Position the index and middle fingers of both hands on the jawbone so you can lift the victim's jaw forward (you can feel the corners of the jawbone near the victim's ears). This action moves the tongue away from the back of the throat without tilting the head back. Putting light pressure on the cheekbones will help to keep the victim's head in a neutral position.

Once you have moved the jaw forward, check the victim for breathing. If the victim is not breathing, position the resuscitation mask over the victim's mouth and nose. Press down on the mask with your thumbs while pulling the jaw forward to open the airway (**figure 8.39**). Give two full breaths and check the victim's pulse. If there is no pulse, begin CPR. If there is a pulse but no breathing, continue rescue breathing. If you cannot get air into the victim, it may be necessary to carefully tilt the victim's head back slightly.

Depending on when the victim stopped breathing, the head immobilizer may already be applied. If the victim stops breathing after the head immobilizer is in position, work your index and middle fingers down between the head-immobilizer pad and the victim's jaw to pull the jaw forward.

Figure 8.38 Modified jaw-thrust technique.

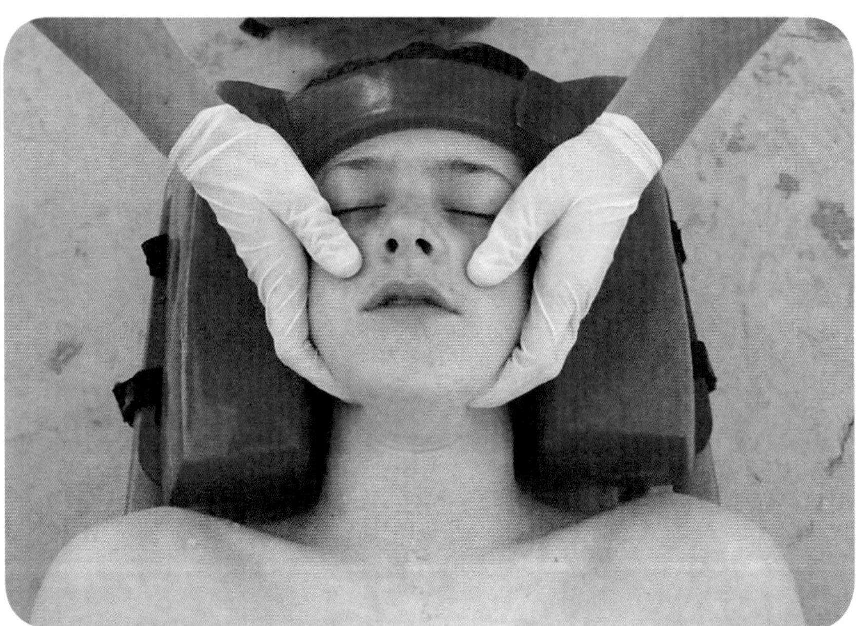

Figure 8.39 Modified jaw-thrust technique with pocket mask.

Victim vomiting

If the victim vomits during neck stabilization, rotate the victim to the side and have an assistant clear the mouth of foreign matter while you maintain in-line stabilization (**figure 8.40**).

If the victim vomits while strapped to the board, use the following procedure on deck or, with minor modifications, in the water:

1. Maintain in-line stabilization. Have at least three assistants position themselves on one side of the victim, with the strongest located at the victim's shoulders.
2. Have each assistant reach across and grab the victim. Be sure the assistants grab the victim, not the board; grabbing the board will result in pinched fingers. The assistants press the arms that cross the victim against the victim to trap him or her against the board.
3. Coordinate the tilt by counting, "One, two, three: tilt."
4. On the signal, have the assistants lift up on the side of the backboard nearest them until the victim and board are on their side (turned 90 degrees).
5. Have an additional assistant (wearing disposable gloves) clear the victim's mouth of vomit, using a clean cloth to wipe it out or a manual suction device.
6. On a signal and in unison, have the assistants lower the victim back to a flat position. Continue to monitor the victim's breathing.

Figure 8.40 Rescuers turn the victim on a backboard to clear vomit from the victim's mouth.

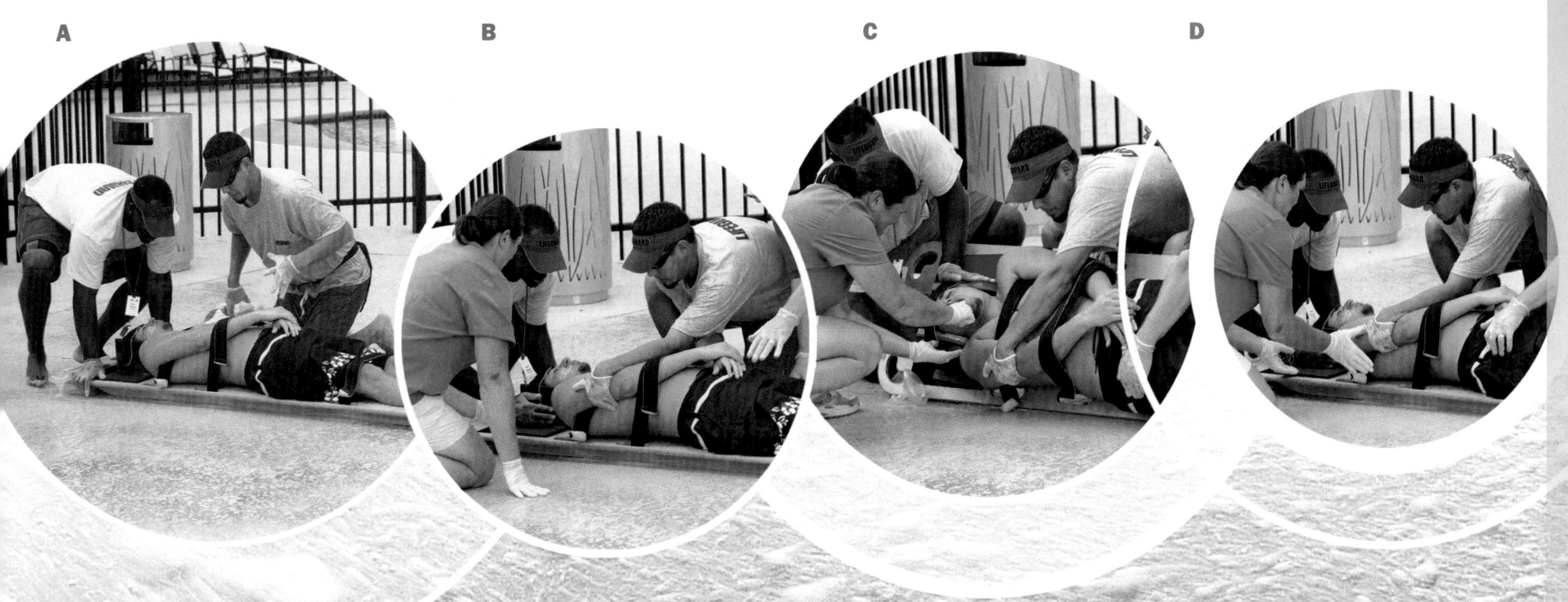

Off-Duty Rescues

Many YMCA lifeguards ask, "How can I rescue someone when I am off duty and without the proper equipment?" These situations may occur any time a lifeguard is near water. You may feel a moral obligation to help in these situations, even when equipment or backup is not available. It is important to help if you can, and you should be careful and aware of the risks. There is significant danger in rescuing others, especially without appropriate equipment or backup from other professionals.

Whenever possible, it is important that everyone, even lifeguards, swim only in guarded areas. However, this is not always possible, especially when people are scuba diving, boating, surfing, waterskiing, or pursuing other aquatic activities.

The simplest solution to not having equipment is to take a rescue tube or buoy and personal protective equipment (PPE) with you whenever you plan leisure activities around water. If space is limited in your vehicle or watercraft, consider taking an inflatable rescue tube. Currently, two inexpensive models are available: one that can be inflated orally and one that uses a carbon dioxide cartridge for quick inflation.

If you attempt to rescue a distressed swimmer when you are off duty and do not have your professional equipment, try to use a reaching, throwing, or wading assist (see chapter 7) to reach the victim while protecting yourself from being grabbed. Another possible rescue is a swimming extension rescue using a towel, canoe paddle, ring buoy, swim noodle, or other similar item. You may be able to guide a distressed swimmer to safety if you swim nearby but not close enough for contact and coach the person to swim to safety (USLA 2003).

Grabbed by a distressed swimmer (off duty)

If you are in the water, a distressed swimmer may grab you from the front or rear in an attempt to stay above water and get air. If this happens, stay calm and react quickly—your response will directly affect your safety. Remember, you are no help to the victim if the victim puts your life in danger. Escalate your response forcefully and quickly if initial efforts are unsuccessful.

Submerge defense (off duty)

The easiest option is the submersion defense. If a distressed swimmer grabs you, take a breath and tuck your chin into either shoulder. Go limp and allow your body to naturally submerge. The victim wants to climb on you to get air. If you submerge, you are no longer helpful to a distressed swimmer trying to stay on the surface. Submerge using a feetfirst surface dive (**figure 8.41**). If this is unsuccessful, place your hands under the person's elbow and push the swimmer away from you. Swim 8 to 10 feet away, making sure not to surface too close to the person or you could find yourself in danger again.

Block and turn (off duty)

To block a lunging distressed swimmer, gently place one hand on the chest of the distressed swimmer with your thumb pointed slightly upward. Use your other hand to grab the swimmer's nearest arm. Turn the swimmer around and away from you. Lean back to clear the swimmer's moving arm away from your body and face.

Unresponsive victim (off duty)

If you attempt to rescue an unresponsive victim on the surface, remember that nearby boaters, waterskiers, and scuba divers may have some type of flotation device. If so, use the flotation device to assist both you and the victim.

If you attempt to rescue an unresponsive victim who is not wearing a personal flotation device (PFD), use these steps (USLA 2003):

1. Call for assistance. Get someone to call emergency medical services (EMS).
2. Look for a piece of equipment to use in performing the rescue.
3. Swim behind the victim, making sure to remain safely outside arm's reach.
4. Check for spinal injury. If the person does not appear to have a spinal injury, use a single or double armpit tow to bring the victim to a safe place. Assess the victim's airway and breathing and begin rescue breathing if necessary.
5. If the victim is clothed, grab the victim's collar and tow the victim using a sidestroke. You can also use the single or double armpit tow to bring the victim to shore. This tow helps keep the victim's head and shoulders supported above the water.

If you feel you are in danger at any time, swim away or use the submerge defense and reassess the situation.

If you suspect a spinal injury, keep the victim in the water and stabilize using the head-splint technique until EMS arrives.

Figure 8.41 Submerge defense.

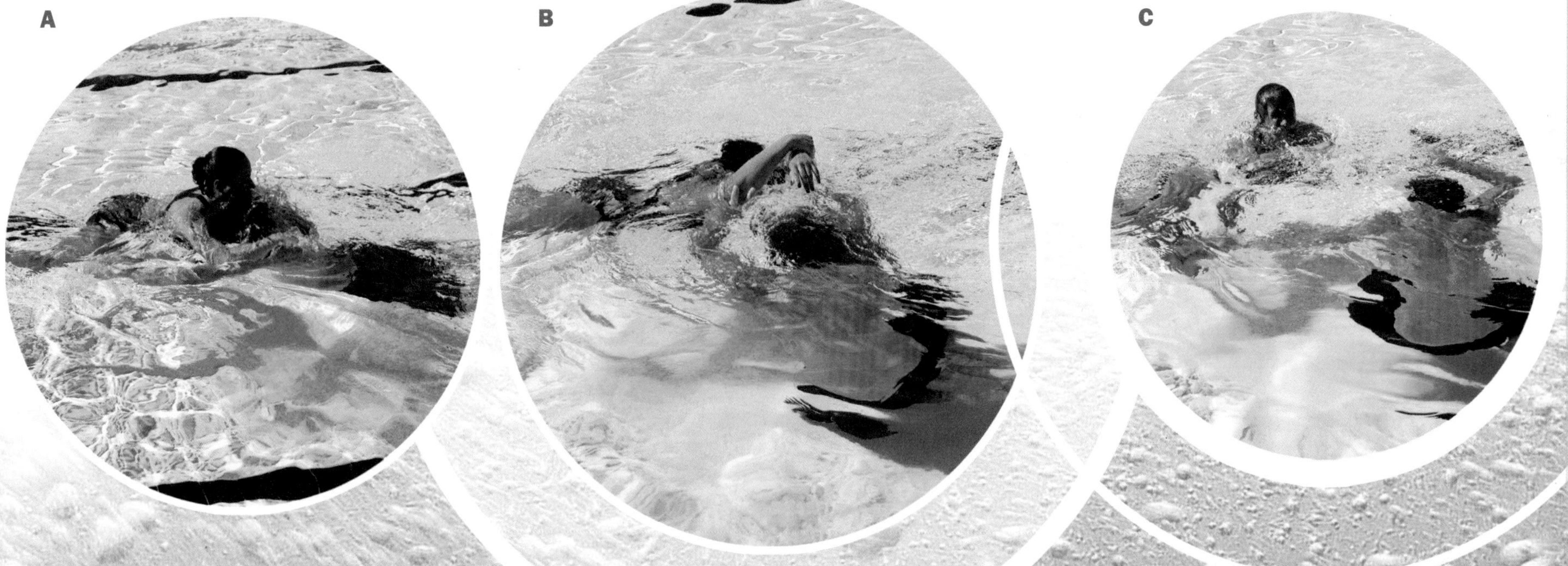

Review

Review Topics

As a lifeguard, sometimes you will have to go into the water to rescue someone. In this chapter, you learned how to safely enter the water and perform a rescue. Here are some key points to remember from this chapter:

1) The importance of a rescue tube or buoy to an in-water rescue
2) Different kinds of water entries and when to use each one
3) How to identify possible spinal injuries
4) Factors to consider when you choose an approach stroke
5) How to enter the water and approach someone who might have a spinal injury
6) Different ways to rescue a distressed swimmer who is conscious, injured and conscious, unresponsive, or unresponsive and submerged
7) How to rescue multiple victims
8) The steps involved in the head-splint technique
9) How to perform rescue breathing in the water
10) Techniques for towing a victim and exiting the water
11) How to use a backboard with different types of victims
12) When and how to use the modified jaw-thrust technique
13) The steps to take if a victim vomits
14) How to respond if a distressed swimmer grabs you when you are off duty and without your equipment

Review Questions

1. What critical step should you perform before you begin any rescue attempt?
2. Why is a rescue tube (or buoy) a necessary part of an in-water rescue?
3. What are the priorities that lifeguards should stay focused on when rescuing a victim?
4. What factors should you consider when choosing an approach stroke?
5. What factors should you consider before entering the water to reach a person who may have a spinal injury?
6. What should you check when you reach an unconscious victim in the water?
7. Why is it important to perform rescue breathing in the water?
8. Why is it important to always keep your rescue equipment between you and the victim?
9. You are swimming off duty and a distressed swimmer grabs you. What are the two techniques you can use to keep yourself safe and help the swimmer?

EMERGENCY CARE

CHAPTER 9

Emergency Care

Page 176

CHAPTER 9

Emergency Care

In addition to preventing accidents, lifeguards are trained to provide aid when accidents do occur. Because aquatic activities are accessible to people of all ages and health conditions, you must be familiar with the symptoms of and treatments for the common health risks people face in aquatic environments. You must also know how to protect yourself from exposure to health risks while on duty.

In this chapter, you will learn the following:

- First-aid kits and devices
- Protection against infection
- Common conditions that require first aid

CHAPTER 9

Importance of First Aid

In lifeguard training, we spend a lot of time on accident prevention and procedures for responding to the most severe accidents and incidents. However, most of the accidents that occur around swimming areas are minor, due in no small part to the diligence and professionalism of the lifeguards on duty and systems that the facility's management has put in place.

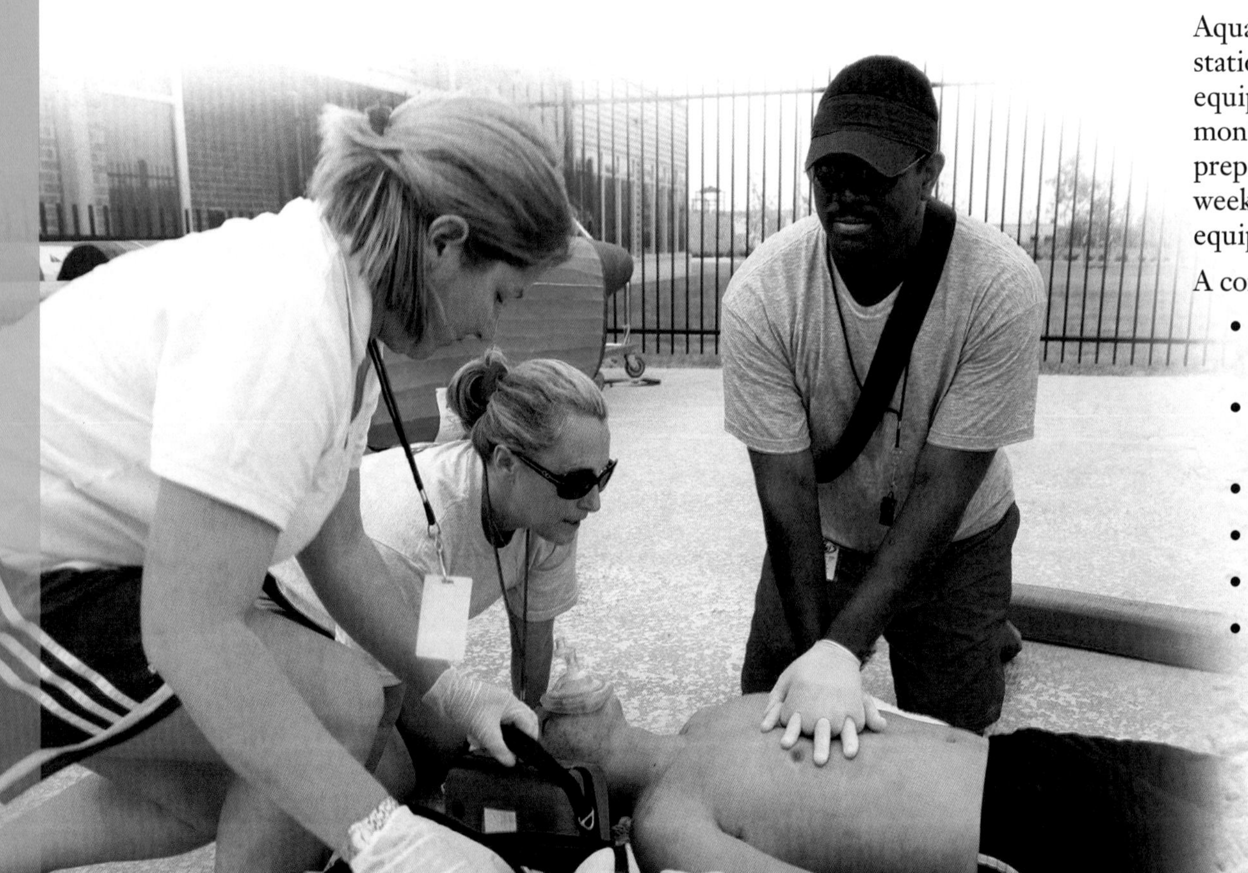

When they do happen, common types of accidents include the following:

- Slips and falls
- Cuts and abrasions
- Bites and stings
- Burns (primarily sunburn)
- Broken bones
- Problems caused by existing medical conditions, such as diabetes or epilepsy

Being an effective lifeguard means having the knowledge and skills to administer first aid to people with many different types of injuries and conditions.

First-Aid Station

Aquatic facilities require a fully equipped first-aid station that includes a first-aid kit and emergency equipment for the care of aquatic injuries. Close monitoring of the station is important for emergency preparedness. Inventory the equipment and supplies weekly and immediately replace used or missing equipment or supplies.

A complete first-aid kit includes the following:

- Bag-valve masks in infant, child, and adult sizes with oxygen port and plastic tubing
- Manual suction device with adult- and child-sized catheters
- Resuscitation masks
- Disposable gloves
- Blankets, sheets, towels, pillows
- Scissors, forceps, tweezers, safety pins, needles

- Adhesive bandages of different sizes (Band-Aids), gauze pads, roller bandages, cotton swabs, adhesive tape of various widths, and elastic wraps
- Antibacterial hand wash
- Eye-wash solution
- Antiseptic wipes
- Disposable drinking cups
- Flashlight or penlight
- Glucose, sugar, or candy
- Cold packs
- First-aid guide
- Incident/accident report forms, paper, pencils
- Emergency telephone numbers

In addition to the first-aid kit, emergency equipment located at the first-aid station, on or near the pool deck, or at the waterfront area includes the following:

- Backboard equipped with head immobilizer and four straps (for head, chest, waist, and legs)
- Oxygen unit and tubing (or the emergency action plan designates a person responsible for quickly delivering this equipment to the scene)
- Properly charged AED (or the emergency action plan designates a person responsible for quickly delivering this equipment to the scene)
- Biohazard waste bag and cleanup kit, including a pocket mask, face shield, two pairs of disposable gloves, a gown, and booties

First-Aid Devices

To become a YMCA-certified lifeguard, you must complete a professional-level CPR and AED course, a first-aid course, and an oxygen administration course. In addition, you will learn manual suction in this YMCA Lifeguard course. Together, these courses will train you in the proper use of the following first-aid devices.

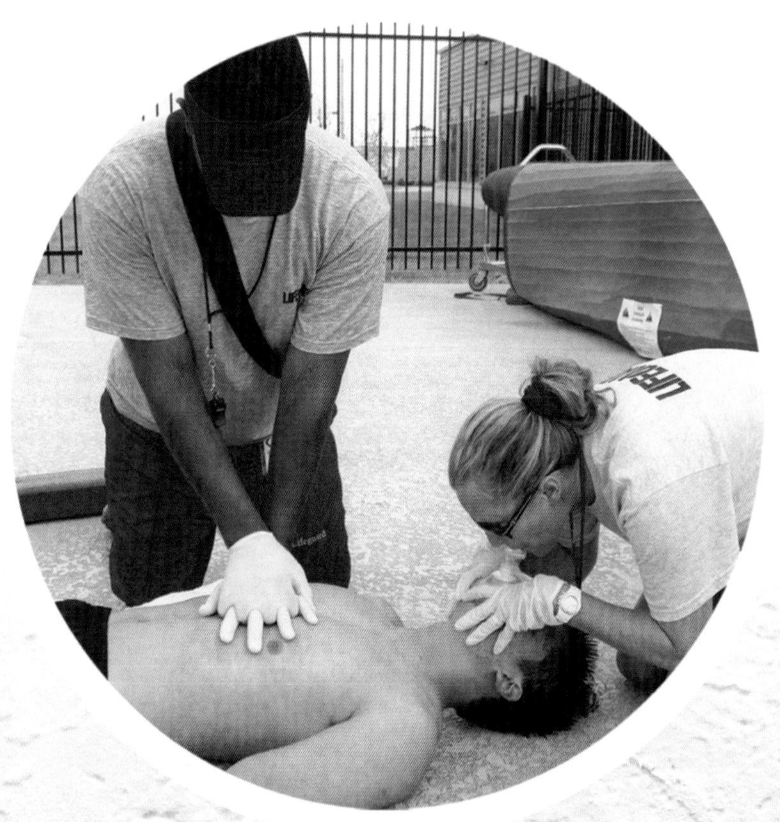

> **Will You Be Ready?**
>
> Keep your CPR skills sharp with regular practice. Quick and efficient use of CPR is critical in an emergency. In-service trainings can include CPR practice, and you can mentally rehearse the steps on your own. For effective practice, a lifelike CPR manikin offers a realistic way to simulate rescues. Manikins feature natural head tilt, simulated chest rise, and accurate anatomy for reference in hand placement.

Automated external defibrillator (AED)

The single most important survival factor for sudden cardiac arrest is early defibrillation, which is accomplished by delivering an electrical shock to the heart using an automated external defibrillator (AED) (**figure 9.1**). Sudden cardiac arrest (SCA) occurs when the heart unexpectedly stops functioning, which causes the victim to stop breathing and lose consciousness. SCA is most often caused by the malfunction of the electrical impulses that regulate the heart's rhythm so the heart cannot pump blood effectively. In sudden cardiac arrest, the person may have no warning before he or she collapses. If the person is in the water, it may be more difficult to tell that he or she has become immobile.

The primary indications for use of an AED are that the victim experienced sudden incapacity, is unresponsive, not breathing, and without a pulse. Once turned on and attached to the victim's bare chest, the AED analyzes the heart rhythm. If the AED recognizes an abnormal rhythm (most commonly ventricular fibrillation), it will either deliver a shock automatically or advise you to deliver the shock. This electrical shock can help return the heart to normal beating. The earlier the shock is received, the higher the chance the victim will survive. If no shock is advised by the AED, but the victim still does not have a pulse, continue performing CPR until emergency medical personnel arrive.

AEDs come in many different models, with different displays and controls. Some are entirely automatic, and others prompt the rescuer to administer the process. Consult the manufacturer's instructions, practice regularly, and be familiar with the models at your facility. Because AEDs are electrical devices, they must be properly charged and ready for use at all times.

Figure 9.1 Using an AED.

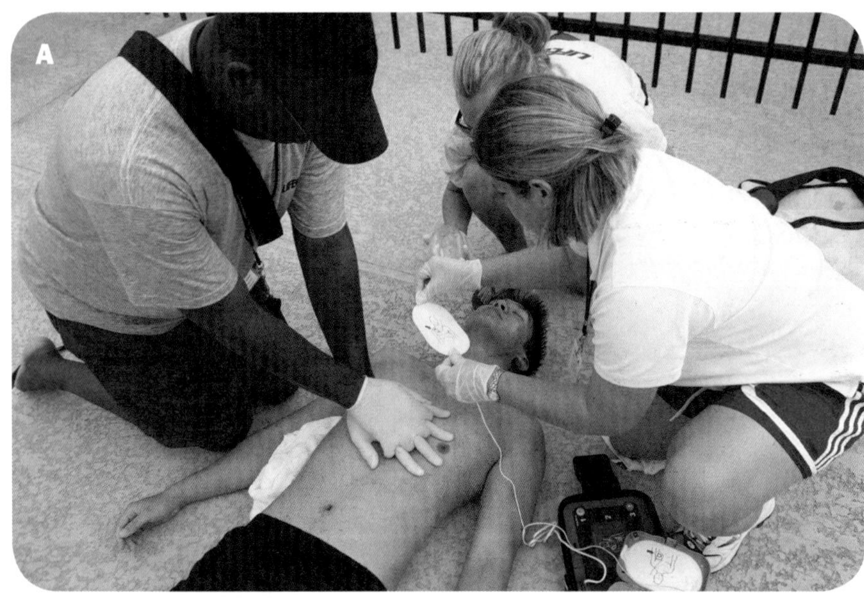

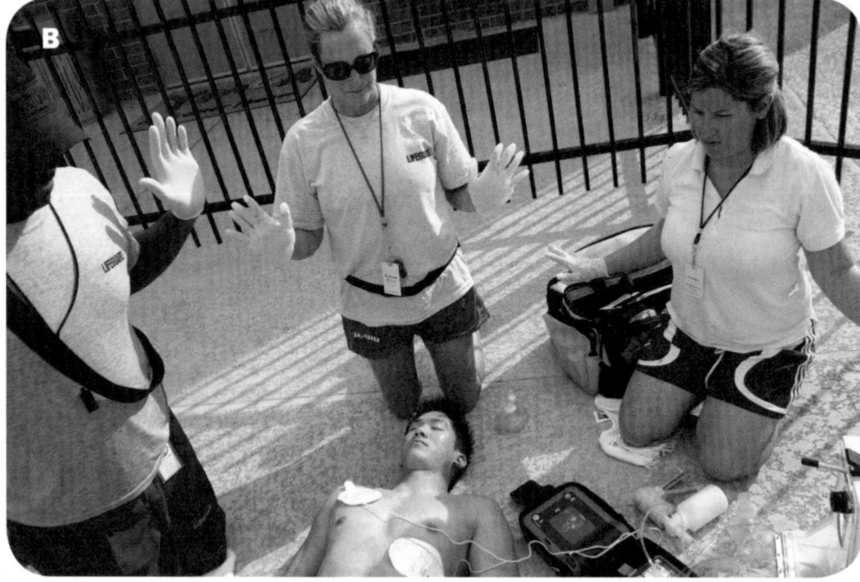

Bag-valve mask (BVM)

The bag-valve mask (BVM) is a handheld device consisting of a bag, a valve, and a mask. The bag is self-inflating: after you squeeze it, it will automatically reinflate. The valve is a one-way mechanism that prevents the victim's exhaled air from entering the bag. The mask is similar to that used in mouth-to-mask rescue breathing. The BVM provides 21 percent oxygen when used alone and can supply 90 to 100 percent oxygen when attached to an emergency oxygen unit.

Emergency oxygen

Emergency oxygen, also called supplemental oxygen or simply O2, is provided by an oxygen tank and a regulator connected to a mask (**figure 9.2**). There are two types of regulators, which provide different rates of air flow, or pressure. A fixed-flow regulator provides a constant flow of oxygen at a fixed rate, usually of not less than 6 or 12 liters per minute (lpm). Variable-flow regulators provide up to 15 liters of oxygen per minute and have a dial or similar device for adjusting the flow. Because it has a higher flow rate, you can use a variable-flow regulator with a bag-valve mask or a resuscitation mask. However, because the fixed-flow regulator delivers less oxygen per minute, it will not fully inflate a bag-valve mask; use a resuscitation mask with an oxygen port when working with a fixed-flow regulator.

Figure 9.2
Administering oxygen.

Why Administer Oxygen?

Oxygen is intended for an individual who has a sudden medical emergency. Low oxygen levels (hypoxia), which are typical in drowning events, can lead to respiratory arrest (breathing stops), irreversible brain damage, and eventually cardiac arrest (heart stops). Although scientific evidence for the use of emergency oxygen is lacking, health-care providers, lifeguards, and other professional rescuers are nonetheless directed to give oxygen during early resuscitation efforts. The International Life Saving Federation states that the benefit of immediately providing oxygen to drowning victims is clear and "advocates that oxygen should be used in all drowning victims" (2003b). Given the potential benefit to the victim, it is appropriate for properly trained lifeguards to provide emergency oxygen when it is available, as it may improve a victim's chances of recovery.

Remember that even in an emergency the clock keeps ticking. You must work quickly and efficiently to have the best chance of a positive outcome. With children, for example, it is key to provide oxygen as soon as possible for a good recovery.

Oxygen tanks are under high pressure and require careful handling. Follow the manufacturer's instructions and practice emergency oxygen procedures regularly. When used properly, an emergency oxygen unit can be easy to use and can provide 90 percent to 100 percent oxygen to a victim.

Manual suction device

Victims who have vomited, been underwater, or who are bleeding from the nose or mouth are in danger of an obstructed airway. As a rescuer, you cannot maintain an open airway or initiate rescue breathing until the person's airway is clear of solid objects. While liquid may be present, it normally does not prevent effective rescue breathing.

Manual suction devices are simple devices used to remove foreign material from a person's airway by creating a vacuum that withdraws debris. Also called hand suction devices, they do not require electricity or batteries, so if they are properly serviced and maintained, manual suction devices are always ready to work.

Apply suction by inserting the tip of the device into the victim's mouth and squeezing the handle. Whatever type of suction device you use, be familiar with its operation and do not suction too deeply. In case of large objects that the suctioning device cannot clear, follow the protocols of your CPR training.

Resuscitation mask

Rescue breathing saves lives. To protect your own life, use this critical tool. A resuscitation mask is designed to facilitate the flow of air into a victim while protecting the rescuer from infection. Resuscitation masks should fit well, have a one-way valve, be made of transparent material, and have a port for attaching to an emergency oxygen unit. Mouth-to-mask ventilation can deliver an adequate volume of air (16 percent oxygen) to a victim while protecting you from the transmission of disease.

Medical Alert Tags

Medical alert bracelets and tags, whether simple or flashy, serve a very important purpose. They provide you and the emergency response team with medical information about the injured person. Quick, accurate assessment is important to providing quality emergency care.

Most medical alert tags list details about the wearer's condition, allergies, and regular medications. A medical alert bracelet might inform you, for example, that the person has epilepsy or diabetes, which might provide some clues as to the reason for a loss of consciousness. Some tags provide a phone number to call for current medical information about the person. Look for these pieces of jewelry around the wrists, ankles, or necks of swimmers at your facility.

If you notice that a patron has a medical alert tag, take some time to talk about it; most wearers are happy to discuss their special needs with you. They can help you prepare to assist them in an emergency.

Protecting Yourself From Infection

You can contract illnesses through direct contact with an injured, ill, or drowning individual's body fluids, such as blood. These illnesses are caused by blood-borne pathogens, microorganisms that live in human body fluids. Three of the most serious blood-borne pathogens are the hepatitis B virus (HBV), the hepatitis C virus (HCV), and the human immunodeficiency virus (HIV), all of which can be life threatening. That is why it is important that you understand these illnesses and how to protect yourself from exposure.

Hepatitis

Hepatitis is an infection or inflammation of the liver that is usually caused by a virus. The virus and resulting infection can take many forms. Type A, formerly called infectious hepatitis, is usually spread by contact with an infected person's stool. Often, hepatitis A is passed through fecal contamination of food, such as when infected food preparers do not wash their hands after using the toilet. Most people who contract hepatitis A recover within a few weeks without medical treatment.

Hepatitis B

Type B (HBV), formerly called serum hepatitis, is spread by contact with blood or other body fluids of an infected person. Once contracted, the virus may be present for years, so any time you come in contact

Universal Precautionary Procedures

1. **Use a barrier.** The use of gloves, masks, face shields, mouthpieces, gowns, and other barriers protects you from contact with the blood and body fluids of a victim. Assume that all victims are infected.
2. **Wash your hands.** Good hygiene also reduces your risk. Wash your hands with soap and warm water after you come in contact with another person's blood or body fluids—even if you were wearing gloves.
3. **Clean up.** Clean surfaces that have been exposed to blood or body fluids with a mixture of household bleach and water. Combine 1 part bleach with 10 equal parts of water. (Note: Once made, this solution has a shelf life of 24 hours.) There are also commercial disinfecting products for cleaning up spills. Wear protective gear during the cleanup procedure.
4. **Keep sharp objects and waste separate.** It is unlikely that you will use any sharp objects, such as needles, with victims, but sharp debris can pierce the skin and cause bleeding. Dispose separately of any sharp object that has been exposed to blood or body fluids. Facilities have labeled red containers and biohazard bags designed specifically for such hazardous material (**figure 9.3**, next page); place contaminated material in these waste containers.
5. **Avoid contamination.** Do not allow swimmers to share towels or otherwise come in contact with materials contaminated with blood or body fluids.
6. **Launder or dispose of soiled linens separately.** Linens contaminated with blood or body fluids should be handled separately and double-bagged in plastic. Laundry personnel should handle the parcel as infected material and wash the linens in detergent with hot water.
7. **Cover wounds.** When someone receives a cut, scratch, or other open wound at your facility, require that it be covered. This procedure not only helps protect that person from infection, it also decreases the chance of other patrons coming in contact with that person's blood.
8. **Provide CPR using a barrier.** There is a very low risk of contracting the AIDS virus through contact with saliva. However, the use of a bag-valve mask or resuscitation mask reduces your exposure to AIDS and other diseases by decreasing mouth-to-mouth contact.
9. **Protect yourself.** If you have an open wound, avoid providing first aid to a victim with an open wound if at all possible. If you must provide first aid, wear gloves.

Adapted from CDC 1987/1996.

with another person's blood or body fluids, you risk contracting HBV. Always have your personal protective equipment with you and wear disposable gloves when caring for a victim.

According to the CDC (2009a), people with increased risk of contracting HBV include injection drug users, people whose sex partners are infected, and health care and public safety workers at risk of occupational exposure to blood or blood-contaminated body fluids. The signs and symptoms of HBV vary, and some infected persons may not have symptoms. When present, symptoms can include fever, fatigue, loss of appetite, nausea, vomiting, and jaundice (a yellow coloration of the skin and eyes).

Anyone exposed to the blood or body fluids of a suspected high-risk individual should seek immediate medical advice and consider a preventive injection of hepatitis B immune globulin.

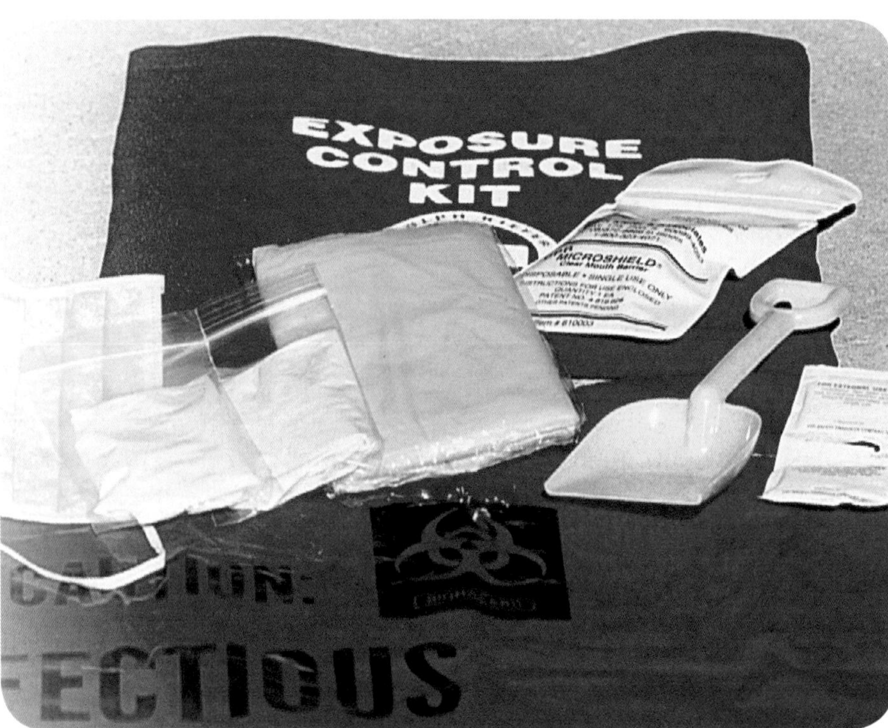

Figure 9.3 Example of a biohazard waste bag and cleanup kit.

Hepatitis C

Like hepatitis A and hepatitis B, hepatitis C (HCV) is a disease that is caused by a virus and affects the liver. HCV is passed through contact with an infected person's blood. Most people who contract HCV are those who share needles or get tattoos or piercings with improperly cleaned equipment. Also, before 1992, many people contracted HCV while receiving blood transfusions. Rarely, health workers who are accidentally exposed to the blood of an infected person contract the virus.

Most people who get the virus do not show any symptoms until the virus damages the liver, which can take up to 10 years. Others have one or more symptoms such as jaundice, swollen stomach or ankles, bruising easily, tiredness, upset stomach, diarrhea, light-colored stools, and dark-yellow urine.

HCV is not usually recognized until it progresses to chronic hepatitis C, and then is treated with drugs that slow the damage to the liver. If chronic hepatitis C causes liver failure, a liver transplant may be necessary. There is no vaccine for HCV. To protect yourself from HCV at work, always wear gloves if you have to touch someone else's blood (NIH 2009).

HIV/AIDS

Acquired immunodeficiency syndrome (AIDS) is a condition in which the elements of blood that control the immune system are damaged, leaving the body susceptible to opportunistic infections. AIDS is the term for the final stages of infection caused by the human immunodeficiency virus (HIV). You can have HIV (be HIV-positive) without having the symptoms of AIDS.

Like hepatitis B, HIV is contracted through contact with blood and body fluids. Casual contact, coughing, and sneezing do not transmit the disease, nor can it be transmitted through the water in a swimming pool (CDC 2010b). HIV can be contracted through sexual contact with a person known to have or have high risk for HIV infection, injection drug use, mother-to-child (perinatal) transmission, blood transfusions, and other unknown causes (CDC 2009b).

Fortunately, the virus is not particularly hardy outside the body. As soon as the fluid has dried or been exposed to heat, the virus dies. You can keep your aquatic area safer by decontaminating all surfaces, equipment, and other contaminated objects as soon as possible. Clean with detergent and rinse with water. Sanitize with a solution of 12 ounces (or 1.5 cups) of household beach per gallon of water (one part bleach per 10 parts water). (Note: Household bleach has a maximum strength of 5.25 percent. Chlorine used to disinfect pool water has a strength of 10 to 12 percent.) Household bleach has a limited shelf life of 60 to 90 days, so keep the supply fresh and replace it as needed. (Note: A water-and-bleach solution has a shelf life of only 24 hours.)

HIV/AIDS has a variable incubation period (the time from infection to the appearance of symptoms), ranging from several months to more than seven years. There is currently no known vaccine or cure for HIV/AIDS, so it is vital to protect yourself from contracting the virus. Learn the universal precautionary procedures (see the sidebar) and follow them every time you have the potential to come in contact with the blood or body fluids of another person.

Protecting yourself from disease transmission

To protect yourself from disease transmission through contact with contaminated blood or body fluids, follow the universal precautionary procedures developed by the Centers for Disease Control and Prevention (see previous sidebar). Also follow any procedures your facility has established for cleanup and disposal of medical waste.

When you are involved in a rescue or cleanup that might put you in contact with an individual's body fluids, wear at least one pair of disposable gloves and learn how to take them off using the following procedures (**figure 9.4**):

1. Grasp the palm of one glove, being careful to touch only the glove. Cup the hand slightly if it is difficult to grasp the palm. Do not grasp the opening of the glove near your wrist as you might contaminate your skin if there is blood on the other glove.
2. Pull the glove down toward the fingers, turning it inside out. Continue to hold onto the glove as you remove your hand.
3. Insert one or two clean fingers into the top of the other glove. Be careful not to touch the outside surface of the glove.
4. Pull the glove off, turning it inside out while pulling it over the first glove. Now the first glove is inside the second glove, and both are turned inside out.
5. Discard the gloves into a red plastic medical waste bag with the biohazard symbol on it.
6. Dispose of the medical waste bag (biohazard waste bag) in accordance with the protocols established by your department of health, local hospital, EMS, or local municipal code.
7. Wash your hands thoroughly with soap and warm water.

When performing a water rescue, begin assessment of the victim and resuscitation (if necessary) in the water, using a resuscitation mask and changing to a bag-valve mask resuscitator with oxygen when the victim is brought out of the water. When performing

Figure 9.4 Removing disposable gloves.

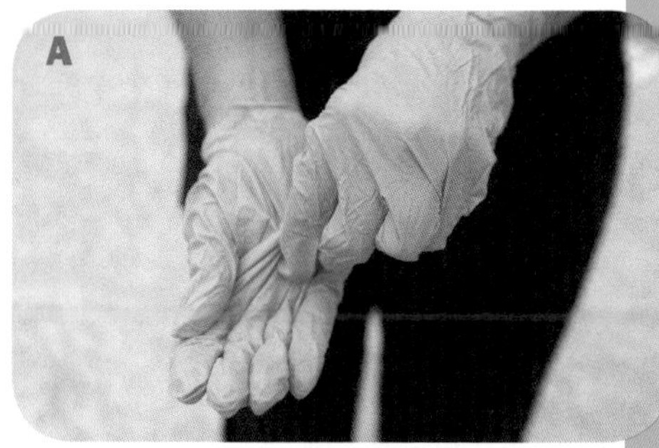

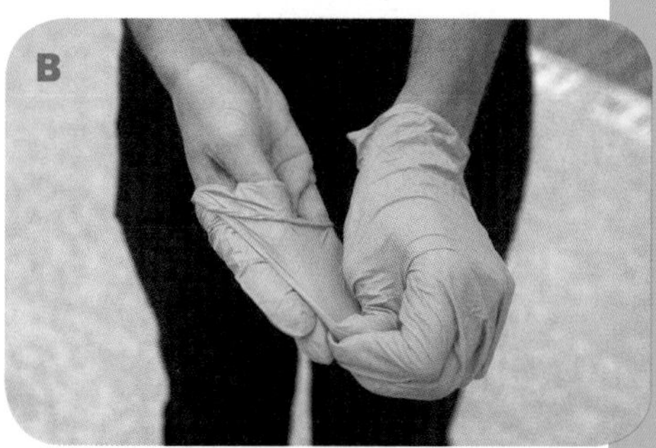

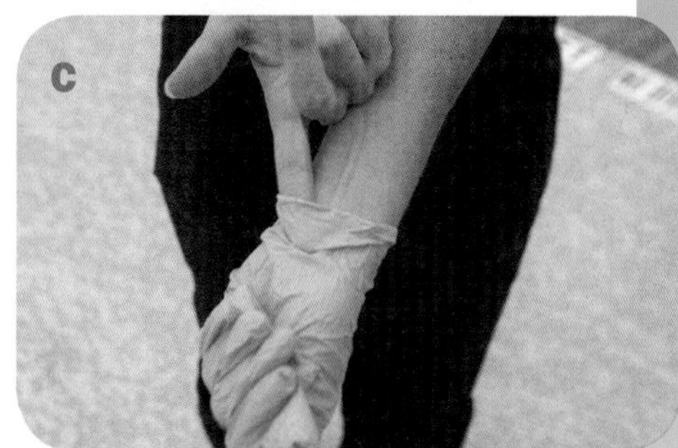

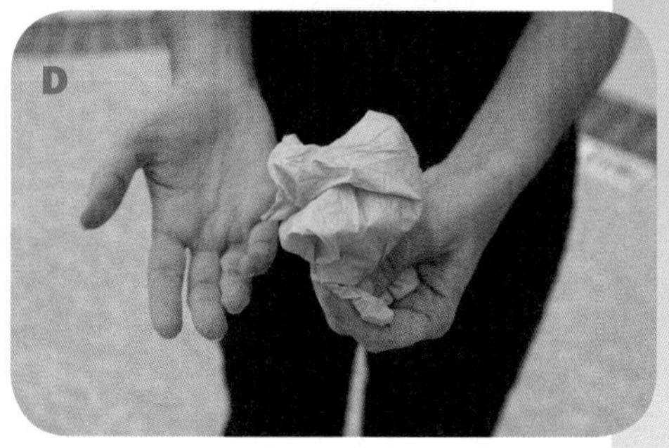

a water rescue, remember that water dilutes body fluids, but does not eliminate the risk entirely, so assume that all blood and body fluids are infected. Follow these steps:

1. During the approach, attempt to determine if blood is visible in the water.
2. If the victim is bleeding, avoid swimming in the blood-contaminated water if possible. For a conscious victim, push the rescue tube to the victim to grab. Approach from the front if blood is visible behind the victim. If blood is visible in front and the victim does not appear to be in danger of submerging, swim around behind and use a rescue from the rear. Follow the same precautions for an unresponsive victim.
3. Avoid contact with the bleeding victim as much as possible during the approach and while towing the victim. Avoid swallowing water.
4. During rescues of both unresponsive and distressed victims, keep the routes of entry into your body (eyes, ears, nose, and mouth) above water at all times.
5. During in-water resuscitation, wash away as much blood or body fluids from the victim as possible before applying the resuscitation mask (USLA 2003).
6. Be careful to avoid direct contact when assisting a victim. Chances of cross contamination are limited, but always strive to protect yourself with proper precautionary procedures. Personal protective equipment is essential for every lifeguard while on duty. Have yours with you at all times. Effective emergency response plans require that a second lifeguard equipped with barrier protection (mask and gloves) be ready to assist you in removing the victim from the water. When acting as the rescue lifeguard, apply the available precautionary barriers (as described in the universal precautionary procedures, see sidebar) before assisting with first aid or resuscitation.
7. When you provide first-aid treatment, do the following (USLA 2003):
   - Use mechanical ventilation whenever possible (e.g., an emergency oxygen unit or bag-valve mask).
   - Use disposable masks.
   - Wear gloves when handling bleeding victims.
   - If bleeding is profuse, especially from an artery, wear a mask, goggles, and a gown and gloves.
   - Wash your hands with soap and warm water after providing care.
8. When first aid and/or CPR have been completed and the EMS personnel have taken the victim to the hospital, wash your hair and entire body with soap and warn water. Rinse your mouth with an antiseptic mouthwash if you performed resuscitation with a resuscitation mask.

The pool area and pool equipment will need to be disinfected after an incident in which body fluids were released. These are the appropriate procedures for disinfection:

- The best defense against contamination of swimming pools and spas from exposure to blood-borne pathogens is sustaining appropriate free chlorine or bromine levels.
- If blood contaminates a pool deck, coping, or walkway made of cement, granite, rock, or another porous surface material, it will have to be disinfected. Mix 12 ounces (1.5 cups) of

sodium hypochlorite (liquid chlorine/bleach) with 1 gallon of water. Before applying the solution, clear the area of aquatic staff members and pool patrons. Put on gloves and, if the contamination is extensive, goggles, an apron, and shoe covers or boots. Then apply the solution to all contaminated surfaces with a garden sprayer and let it stand for 5 or 10 minutes. Rinse the surface with water from a hose directed toward a swimming pool deck drain. Repeat applying and rinsing the solution; allow the surface to dry completely before permitting anyone to walk on it or use it in any way. This same procedure can be used to sanitize diving boards, starting blocks, and wood surfaces.

- To disinfect grass, dirt, and sand surfaces contaminated by blood, mix a solution of chlorine and water using 12 ounces of sodium hypochlorite with 1 gallon of water. Wear gloves and, if the contamination is extensive, goggles, a gown, and boots or booties. Apply the chlorine solution until the area where the blood spill occurred is thoroughly saturated with the chlorine solution. Rope off the area and prohibit sunbathing or other uses of the area until the area is completely dry. If the contaminated area consists of dirt or sand, turn it over with a shovel and rake it. Saturate the sand or dirt again, and continue to prohibit use of the area until it dries and is raked a second time. As grass will be killed by the chlorine solution, waterfront and outdoor pool operators may want to remove small quantities of sod and dispose of it in medical waste bags to be incinerated. Be sure to decontaminate any shovels, rakes, brooms, or other tools used in the cleanup with the same strength chlorine solution, and rinse them thoroughly.
- Any reusable equipment used in rescue, first aid, or CPR must be properly sanitized before it is used again. This includes, but is not limited to, rescue tubes, rescue buoys, masks, fins, snorkels, backboards, straps, and head immobilizers. These items should be cleaned with a quaternary ammonium disinfectant. Be sure to follow the instructions on the label. Disposable equipment such as resuscitation masks and first-aid materials must be disposed of in medical waste bags.

Facilities provide specific policies and training for the control of blood-borne pathogens; it is important that these include the following elements:

- OSHA standard for blood-borne pathogens
- Description of blood-borne diseases and how blood-borne pathogens are transmitted
- Exposure plan (for employee training and facility precautions), including the points of the plan, the lines of responsibility, and how the plan will be implemented and documented
- Procedures that might cause exposure to blood or other potentially infectious materials at your facility
- Use and limitations of control methods at the facility to control exposure to blood or other potentially infectious materials
- Use and limitations of personal protective equipment available at your facility
- List of whom to contact concerning the following:
    - Post-exposure evaluation and follow-up
    - Signs and labels used at the facility
    - Hepatitis B vaccine program at the facility
    - Location of additional copies of the OSHA standard

Contacting Emergency Medical Services (EMS)

The universal emergency telephone number in the United States is 911. Your area or facility may have alternate numbers (as at some universities and large water parks). To promote an effective emergency response, facilities post emergency phone numbers and emergency scripts near all telephones (see the guidelines in chapter 6 for calling 911). Know whether your facility's phone system requires dialing a number to get an outside line before you can dial 911.

Calling 911 is a crucial role in an emergency. Effective emergency action plans require this role be performed by a responsible person. Many 911 systems allow the operator to immediately know the address of the caller, but this is not universal. Be prepared to provide this and other key information, including the victim's location in the facility, to the operator. Providing accurate information to the emergency team being dispatched is critical because seconds count in an aquatic emergency.

Wait for EMS personnel to attend to the victim and to provide any necessary transportation to a medical center. Never transport a victim yourself. Many reasons compel you not to take a victim in your vehicle, including potential legal consequences, lack of proper equipment and space to accommodate the victim, and inability to provide the kind of support that EMS could provide, especially if the victim's condition worsened. Always use emergency medical services rather than your vehicle for transportation. In a remote area, exceptions may be necessary depending on the type of emergency. Follow the emergency procedures set up by your facility.

Heart Attacks

Heart attack is one of the leading causes of death in men and women in the United States. In 2007, more than 400,000 people died of heart attacks in the U.S. (Xu 2010). A person who is having a heart attack could lose consciousness or die immediately. More likely, the victim will exhibit several or all of the following symptoms:

- Pains or squeezing pressure in the chest
- Pains radiating through the upper body
- Shortness of breath
- Weakness
- Profuse sweating
- Pale, sweaty skin
- Nausea and vomiting

For both men and women, pain, pressure or discomfort in the chest is a common symptom. Women, however, are more likely than men to have symptoms without chest pain, such as pain or discomfort in the neck, jaw, shoulder, or upper back; light-headedness or dizziness; and fatigue (Mayo 2009).

Contact EMS for anyone with chest discomfort (Markenson 2010). If a person experiencing chest discomfort has aspirin and wants to take it, you can help the person to do so. It is not unusual for someone to refuse to see a physician or go to the hospital; if this occurs, document your recommendation and the refusal. It is still important to contact EMS. Once on the scene, EMS personnel may be able to convince the person to accept transport to a medical facility. Anytime you are unsure of what action to take, act in favor of the patron's health and safety by requesting additional assistance.

Keep the person calm and as comfortable as possible and monitor his or her condition until EMS arrives. Assist the person in taking prescribed heart medication if she or he has such medication. Be prepared to begin CPR, use an AED, or administer oxygen, if it becomes necessary.

Severe Bleeding

Aquatic injuries can be accompanied by severe bleeding, which can be life threatening if not controlled quickly. To control severe bleeding, follow these steps:

1. Apply direct pressure to the wound using sterile gauze, or use any clean cloth if sterile gauze is not available. Use disposable gloves or any other barrier material you can find to protect yourself from disease transmission. The bleeding must be stopped quickly. Increase the amount of pressure if the bleeding does not stop.
2. After applying pressure, cover the wound with a pressure bandage, such as a roller

bandage, that covers both the dressing and the areas below and above the wound. Do not remove a dressing; removal may restart the bleeding. If a dressing becomes blood-soaked, place another dressing on top of it. Be sure to wash your hands with warm soap and warm water afterward.

3. Care for shock:
   - Keep the victim's airway open and monitor breathing.
   - Control bleeding.
   - Maintain normal body temperature by preventing chilling or overheating.
   - Have the victim lie down flat, especially when there are serious injuries to the pelvis, lower limbs, chest, abdomen, head, neck, or back.
   - If available, give emergency oxygen.

Table 9.1 lists the types of open wounds, their causes and symptoms, and first aid for each type.

Table 9.1 First Aid for Open Wounds

Type	Causes	Signs and Symptoms	First Aid
Abrasion (scrape)	Rubbing or scraping	Only skin surface is affected Little bleeding	Remove all debris Wash away from wound with soap and water
Incision (cut)	Sharp objects	Edges of wound are smooth Severe bleeding	Control bleeding Wash wound
Laceration (tearing)	Blunt object tearing skin	Veins and arteries can be affected Severe bleeding Danger of infection	Control bleeding Wash wound
Puncture (stab)	Sharp pointed object piercing skin	Wound is narrow and deep into veins and arteries Embedded objects Danger of infection	Do not remove impaled objects
Avulsion (torn off)	Machinery Explosives	Tissue torn off or left hanging Severe bleeding	Control bleeding Take avulsed part to medical facility

Internal Bleeding

Internal bleeding cannot be seen, but it is accompanied by symptoms such as these:

- Blood coming from the mouth, rectum, or vagina (nonmenstrual blood) or seen in the urine
- Visible bruises or cuts
- A rapid pulse
- Sweaty, cool skin
- Pupil dilation
- Nausea and vomiting
- Pain or tenderness, abdominal rigidity, or bruising
- Chest bruising or rib fractures

If you suspect internal bleeding, call EMS immediately and provide care for shock. Do not give the person any liquids. If vomiting occurs and the person is lying down, turn the victim on his or her side for drainage.

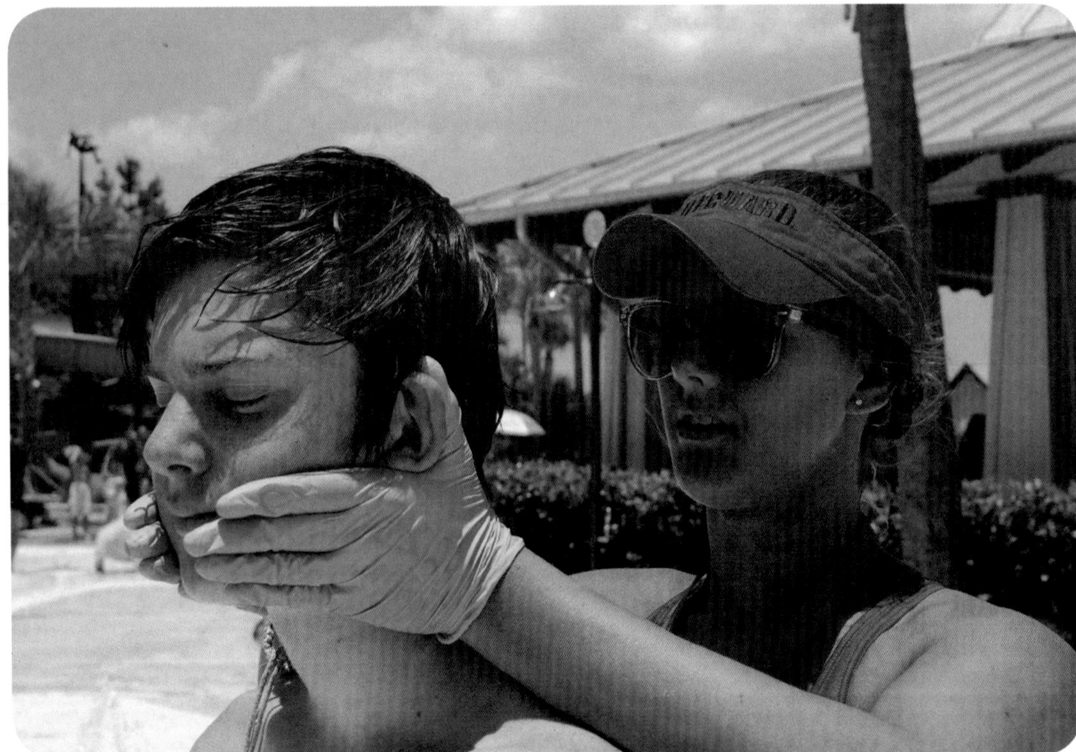

Figure 9.5 Stabilizing a victim's head and neck.

Dental Injuries

Knocked-out, or avulsed, teeth are an indication of a head injury. Carefully evaluate the victim for any injuries beyond the injured tooth, such as dizziness, head trauma, or neck soreness. Teeth that have been knocked out can often be successfully reimplanted. The keys are to properly handle and store the tooth and to have a dentist reimplant the tooth as quickly as possible (the greatest success comes when the tooth is reimplanted within 30 minutes or less).

If a patron has a dislocated or broken tooth and the lips or gums are bleeding, apply direct pressure and advise the victim to see a dentist immediately.

For a knocked-out tooth, observe these precautions:

- Handle the tooth only by the chewing surface; do not touch the root.
- Keep the tooth moist. Have the person spit into a cup and place the tooth in the saliva.
- Mild contact lens solution or commercial sports drinks can also be used. Avoid placing the tooth in water.
- Do not scrub the tooth or remove any attached tissue.
- Do not let the tooth dry.
- Do not wrap tooth in tissue or cloth or gauze.

Neck and Back Injuries

Not all spinal injuries happen in the water, and someone who has a spinal injury will not necessarily be paralyzed. A person may sprain or strain the neck or back and be sitting on the deck. A victim may even walk up to you and complain of neck pain. In these situations, follow these general guidelines:

- Stabilize the victim's head and neck. Grasp the victim's head by placing your hands on each side of the victim's face near or over the ears (**figure 9.5**). Tell the victim not to move until directed to do so.
- Ask the victim these questions:
    - Are you OK?
    - What happened?
    - Do you feel pain anywhere?
    - Can you move your fingers?
    - Can you move your toes?
    - Do you have any pain in your neck?
- Have a second lifeguard do the following:
    - Gently palpate (touch) the back of the neck slightly to the right and left of the spine. This will help identify whether there is pain in the area.
    - Call EMS—regardless of whether the victim feels pain—if there is any indication that something happened to the person that may have resulted in spinal trauma. (See chapter 8 about recognizing signs of spinal injury.)
    - Continue to support the head and neck until EMS arrives and assumes control.

Also see chapter 8 for rescue and removal techniques for spinal-injury victims.

Heat- and Cold-Related Emergencies

Temperature-related emergencies occur when the body is unable to regulate its core temperature due to excessive cold or heat. Hyperthermia (from the Greek words for *over* and *heat*) occurs when prolonged exposure to heat causes the body's core temperature to rise. Hypothermia (from the Greek words for *under* and *heat*) occurs when prolonged exposure to cold causes the core body temperature to drop below 95°F.

Hyperthermia

Heat cramps, heat exhaustion, and heatstroke are three progressively more severe forms of hyperthermia, or overheating. In each heat-related illness, environmental conditions cause the body's core temperature to increase, giving rise to a variety of symptoms. When the temperature and humidity are high, heat-related problems become more common.

Heat cramps

Heat cramps are extremely painful muscle cramps caused by the loss of electrolytes and salt in the body through sweat. These cramps are usually associated with exertion. A person suffering from this malady will normally have muscle cramps in the calves, arms, abdominal muscles, and back and may also exhibit some or all of the following symptoms:

- Sweaty skin
- Increased heart rate
- Exhaustion
- Dizziness

Heat cramps are not a life-threatening condition, but the person will want and need immediate attention. To care for someone experiencing heat cramps, take the following action:

- Get the person out of the heat.
- Provide water.
- Apply moist towels to the forehead and the cramp to aid in cooling.
- Avoid massage—it will not help and may damage muscle tissue.
- Gentle stretching of cramping leg muscles may help.

In most cases the cramp sufferer will not need to see a physician. However, if the person experiences faintness and recurring cramping, care by medical personnel is advisable.

Heat exhaustion

The most common heat-related illness, heat exhaustion, is also due to excessive loss of electrolytes and water through perspiration. Early signs and symptoms of heat exhaustion include the following:

- Heavy sweating
- Thirst

Later signs and symptoms of heat exhaustion include these:

- Pale, cool skin
- Headache
- Nausea and vomiting
- Weakness and dizziness
- Feeling faint or collapsing

Heat exhaustion requires medical attention because the condition can easily escalate to heatstroke. There are several things you can do to assist someone with heat exhaustion while awaiting medical assistance:

- Get the person out of the heat.
- Provide water or a sports drink (only if the person is conscious).
- Lay or sit the person down.
- Loosen restrictive clothing.
- Cool the body with moist, cold towels or under a cool (not cold) shower.
- Use a fan to lower the body temperature.
- Place cold compresses on the victim's neck, groin, and armpits.

There are several parts of the body where applying cold towels will speed the cooling process. **Figure 9.6** illustrates where towels should be placed to most effectively provide cooling.

Heatstroke

Heatstroke is a critical medical condition caused by overexposure to extreme heat. Nearly 60 percent of people who develop heatstroke die, even under medical supervision. However, with a rapid emergency response that provides cooling and medical treatment, the survival rate for heatstroke approaches 90 percent. Your actions can mean the difference between life and death, so it is vital that you learn to recognize the symptoms of heatstroke and move quickly to assist anyone who develops it. Contact EMS immediately.

During heatstroke, the body's temperature-regulation system essentially shuts down, and the heat generated is recycled in the body, causing other body systems to malfunction. The symptoms of heatstroke include the symptoms of heat exhaustion as well as additional signs that indicate the nervous system has become involved (Markenson 2010). For example, heavy sweating could be present, especially when exertion is the cause.

Figure 9.6 Placement of moist, cold towels for efficient cooling.

A person experiencing heatstroke may also exhibit many or all of the following symptoms:

- Altered mental status (for example, confusion, hallucination, bizarre behavior)
- Heavy sweating may be present, especially when exertion is the cause
- Skin will become red, very warm (even hot), and completely dry
- Seizure
- Unconsciousness

If you notice a number of these symptoms, do not take any chances—summon medical assistance immediately. Do not underestimate the seriousness of heat illness, especially if the person is a child or an older adult. Heatstroke can be fatal.

While you are waiting for EMS to arrive, provide the following first aid:

- Monitor the victim's airway, breathing, and circulation.
- Begin cooling with any resources available.
- Spray or pour water on the victim and fan him or her.
- Apply ice packs to the victim's groin and armpits and/or cover the victim with a wet sheet.
- Place the victim on his or her side in the recovery position to protect the airway.
- Provide continuous cooling until EMS arrives.
- Do not give the victim anything by mouth if he or she is vomiting or unconscious.

Hypothermia

Hypothermia is the opposite of hyperthermia: The body core temperature is decreased by environmental conditions. People can lose body heat in outdoor recreational pursuits, typically during the winter, but perhaps the most common cause of hypothermia is being in cold water for an extended period (immersion hypothermia). Because water cools the body 25 to 27 times faster than air does, hypothermia can occur even in warm weather. In water at 72° to 78°F, unconsciousness can occur in 3 to 12 hours. In very cool water, the arms and legs will cool rapidly. It takes 10 to 15 minutes before the vital organs and the brain begin to lose heat. **Figure 9.7** illustrates the effects of cold water on the length of time someone immersed can survive.

Watch children carefully; their smaller size makes them more susceptible to heat loss in immersion. The major arteries are closer to the skin, allowing quicker cooling of the blood.

The signs and symptoms of hypothermia vary greatly with the severity of the exposure and heat loss but include these warning signs:

- Shivering
- Pale, cold skin
- Clumsiness or lack of coordination
- Slurred speech or mumbling
- Stumbling
- Confusion or unclear thinking
- Poor decision making (for example, trying to remove warm, dry clothing)
- Progressive lack of consciousness
- Cardiac arrest may occur

If you notice any of these signs and symptoms, do not delay in giving care; hypothermia can cause complications even after someone is out of the water.

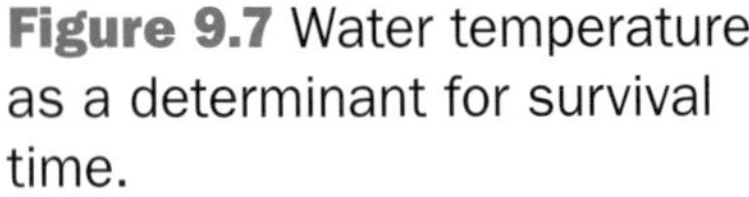

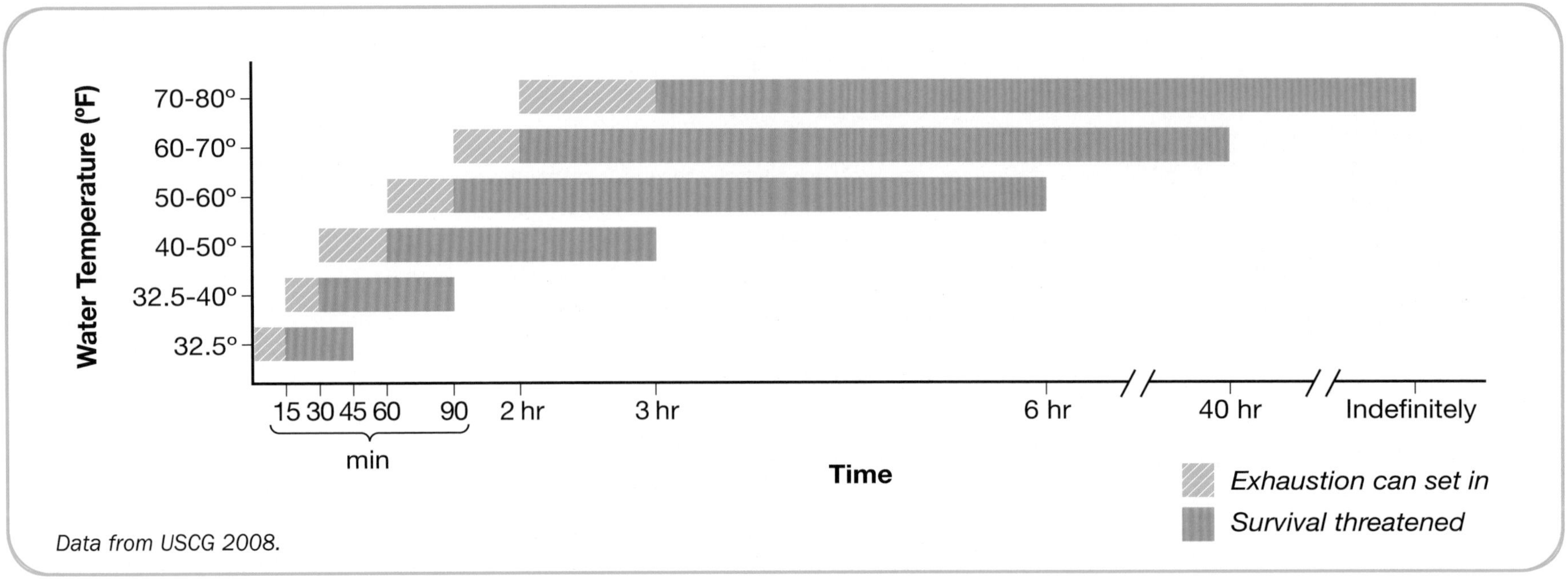

Figure 9.7 Water temperature as a determinant for survival time.

Immediately contact EMS and move the victim to a warm place out of the cold or wind. Help the person remove any wet clothing; drying the person off is important so that the air does not continue to cool the body by evaporating the water. The rest of the care you will give centers on providing warmth:

- Move the person to a warmer place.
- Remove wet clothing.
- Cover the person with something dry—blanket, coat, newspapers.
- Cover the head and neck to retain body heat.
- If no insulating material is available, hug the victim to you to share your body warmth.
- Give a conscious person warm, nonalcoholic, decaffeinated drinks. (Alcohol and caffeine dilate the blood vessels, causing a continued loss of body heat.)

Watch for quick changes in body temperature. Rewarming can cause an after-drop syndrome (described in the next section).

Cold-water drowning

Amazing stories of recovery from 30- to 45-minute exposures to cold water have appeared in media headlines since the early 1970s. The latest information available indicates that if a person is recovered from cold water, even if all signs of life are absent, CPR must be initiated immediately and continued until the victim reaches an emergency medical facility. Startling as it may seem, children who have been under the surface for up to 45 minutes have been revived, with little or no brain damage, after 4 to 5 hours of CPR and medical attention.

Such survival is possible because the body goes into a form of hibernation. The cold water causes constriction in the blood vessels of the arms and legs and a slowing or stoppage of metabolic activity in the body. Together, these changes partially eliminate the delivery of blood and oxygen to the limbs. This allows blood and oxygen to be conserved and diverted to the brain and vital organs.

As the temperature of the major body organs drops, the activity and oxygen utilization of the brain, heart, lungs, and kidneys are also reduced. With this reduction of oxygenation and the cool internal temperatures, the vital organs seem able to survive, in some cases, with the oxygen available in the organ, the surrounding tissues, and the blood.

To provide first aid, you must begin CPR as soon as the victim is removed from the water. Then call EMS to transport the person to a medical facility. Immediate transportation is vital so that the rewarming and resuscitation processes can be continued and directed by a physician.

Do not attempt to rewarm such a victim yourself. When the body is rewarmed, the cold blood from the limbs flows back to the internal core, causing the core temperature to drop. You can minimize this phenomenon, called the after-drop syndrome, by keeping the victim still.

Sudden Illness

People who have chronic diseases and conditions usually become skilled in managing their conditions over time. They carry required medications and avoid activities and substances that may cause a reaction. However, even people who are diligent about managing their condition sometimes experience complications. Those who are newly diagnosed or have not yet been diagnosed may become suddenly ill and require your care.

Extreme allergic reactions (anaphylactic shock)

Many of us are allergic to something: a food, a certain insect bite, pollen, dust, or one of any number of other elements in our environment. However, some patrons may be susceptible to severe allergic reactions that can cause the body to have a massive, possibly fatal physiological response; these reactions can result in anaphylactic shock. Should a patron have a severe reaction to an allergen, know how to handle the situation.

There are several symptoms of anaphylactic shock:

- Itchy raised lumps or hives on face and chest
- Nausea
- Adnominal pain or cramping
- Swelling of the lips, eyelids, face
- Extreme difficulty in breathing
- Wheezing may be heard
- Blueness of the skin, lips, and nail beds
- Complete airway obstruction

Regardless of how mild the reaction appears, always contact EMS. You do not know how the body will react. While awaiting EMS personnel, calm, comfort, and reassure the person. Assist the person in finding a comfortable position for breathing. Loosen any tight clothing.

If the person has medication for an allergy, help the person take it. If the victim carries a physician-prescribed epinephrine auto-injector, help the victim use it. If the victim is unable to use the auto-injector, the first-aid provider should administer it. The beneficial effect of the epinephrine will last only a short time, so the victim still requires immediate medical assistance.

Epinephrine auto-injector

Epinephrine is a drug that is used for emergency treatment of allergic reactions. Auto-injectors allow those who have life-threatening allergies to inject themselves in case of emergency. Become familiar with the procedure in case a patron needs help remembering the steps for using the auto-injector. Coach the patron to follow these steps:

- Unscrew the cap of the carrying case and remove the auto-injector from the storage tube.
- Grasp the unit with the black tip pointing down.
- With the other hand, pull off the gray safety release.
- Hold the black tip near the outer thigh. The unit should be at a 90-degree angle to the thigh.
- Swing and firmly jab the auto-injector into the outer thigh until it clicks. (The auto-injector is designed to work through clothing.)
- Firmly hold the auto-injector against the thigh for approximately 10 seconds. The window on the auto-injector will show red when the injection is complete.
- Remove the auto-injector from the thigh and massage the injected area for 10 seconds.
- Call 911 and seek immediate medical attention.
- Carefully place the used auto-injector needle-end-first into the storage tube of the carrying case and screw the cap back on. Have the auto-injector taken to the emergency room for further emergency attention.

Asthma

Asthma is a chronic condition that flares up periodically. During an asthma attack, the person has difficulty getting fresh air into the lungs. The result is a wheezing or forcing of air in and out as the person struggles for air exchange. Attacks may be brought on by strenuous activity, exposure to an allergen, or emotional stress. Symptoms of an asthma attack vary from mild to life threatening and include these:

- Constant coughing, worsening at night and early morning
- Anxiety
- Sudden onset of wheezing
- Chest tightness and pounding heart
- Shortness of breath
- Extreme difficulty breathing
- Bluish color to lips and face
- Sweating
- Altered mental status

Someone with asthma who has been active all day at an aquatic facility may be susceptible to an attack. Should a patron experience difficulty, take the following steps:

- Position the person for ease of breathing—usually sitting upright.
- Help the person take any prescribed medication. If the person is unable to administer the prescribed medication (for example, a nebulizer or a metered-dose inhaler, **figure 9.8**) without assistance, help the victim administer it.
- Alert EMS if the victim has any of the following:
    - No improvement within 15 to 20 minutes after the initial treatment with medication
    - Constant coughing
    - Difficult breathing, with the chest and neck pulled in
    - Stooped body posture
    - Struggling or gasping for breath
    - Trouble walking or talking
    - Inability to restart an activity after stopping
    - Gray or blue lips or fingernail beds
- Comfort, calm, and reassure the victim while waiting for EMS.

Figure 9.8 Using an inhaler to administer asthma medication.

Diabetes

Diabetes is a chronic disease in which the body does not make (type 1 diabetes) or properly use (type 2 diabetes) insulin. Insulin is a hormone that allows cells to receive glucose, which fuels the body's cells. An imbalance of glucose, or blood sugar, and insulin can result in a medical emergency when the blood sugar becomes either very high or very low. Proper first aid can be lifesaving in this situation.

Signs of very low or very high blood sugar include these:

- Pale, cool, and sweaty skin
- Fainting
- Unconsciousness
- A strong fruity breath odor
- Drowsiness or difficulty waking up

You do not need to be an expert on diabetes to help. Many people with diabetes know what the problem is and will help themselves or ask for assistance. If the person has low blood sugar, he or she will usually react quickly and positively to consumption of something sugary. If the person has high blood sugar, consuming a little sugar will normally not cause a major problem.

If the person is responsive (awake, able to swallow), attempt to raise his or her blood sugar level as quickly as possible by providing any sweet substance that contains sugar (e.g., fruit juice or candy). If the person has oral glucose gel, provide that instead. *Do not* provide anything that contains artificial sweetener. If the victim is unresponsive or semiconscious and unable to swallow, *do not* give anything by mouth.

Closely monitor the person's airway, breathing, and circulation. If the person does not improve within 15 minutes, or if the person's status worsens, call EMS. Calm, comfort, and reassure the person while awaiting EMS.

Note: Insulin is not considered an emergency medication. *Never* administer insulin to a person with diabetes in an emergency setting.

Epileptic seizures

Epilepsy is a chronic disorder of the nervous system in which abnormal electrical activity in the brain causes a seizure, which may be accompanied by a loss of consciousness, Seizures can be triggered by various conditions or events, including hyperventilation, physical stress, nervous tension, poor regulation of body temperature (for example, soaking in a spa or hot tub), lack of sleep, low blood sugar, illness, hormonal changes, fluid and electrolyte imbalances, alcohol, and bright light. Many people with epilepsy can control their seizures through medication or behavioral prevention. Even so, a seizure may occur.

Different types of seizures range from minor to very serious. One type of seizure, the "absence" or "petit mal" seizure, is often not noticeable. The person loses awareness for only a few seconds, staring and perhaps fluttering the eyelids.

In a "psychomotor" or "partial complex" seizure, the individual may seem confused or dizzy. He or she may perform unusual motions such as twitching a hand or arm, walking aimlessly, picking at objects, or rubbing the hands together. The person also may speak in a repetitive or incoherent manner. People experiencing such a seizure are sometimes mistaken for being intoxicated.

The "tonic-clonic" or "grand mal" seizure is more recognizable and more serious. The person may have a combination of these symptoms:

- Rigid muscles
- Jerky and convulsive movements
- Loss of consciousness
- Loss of bowel and bladder control
- Period of apnea (not breathing)

Before a grand mal seizure begins, many people with epilepsy will experience a warning in the form of an aura, often described as a bright light, a burst of color, or an odor. Upon recognizing a warning signal, the person can help you provide a safe environment for the seizure.

There is nothing you can do to stop a seizure. Your role is to protect the person from injury. If someone has a seizure out of the water, take the following steps:

- If the person tells you he or she is about to have a seizure, lay the person down in an area free from surrounding hazards.
- Do not try to move the person unless this is essential to his or her safety (for example, the person is near a place from which he or she could fall).
- To avoid injury, move objects and other people away from the person.
- Protect the person's head as much as possible, placing a folded towel underneath it if possible.
- Keep others back and let them know that there is nothing they can do.
- Never attempt to put anything in the person's mouth.

If someone in the water has a seizure, you will need to get into the water and move the person away from hazards, such as the side of the pool. Stand behind the victim and grasp both sides of the head. This will help you keep the person's head above the water while the seizure runs its course. In deep water, concentrate on supporting the victim's head above water and move to shallow water as soon as possible. After the seizure, help the person out of the water; she or he will be sleepy.

After a seizure, victims tend to be confused or embarrassed. In a crowded area, a person who has had a seizure will attract much attention, and others may stare. Check the person's airway, breathing, and circulation. If the person is uninjured and wishes to do so, help him or her move to an area away from others. Speak quietly and explain what happened. Provide whatever support you can.

Whether the seizure occurs in or out of the water, anyone who has had a seizure should see medical personnel; a number of complications could develop as much as an hour after the apparent recovery. Stay with the person until medical assistance arrives.

This chapter describes a number of conditions, illnesses, and injuries that lifeguards may be responsible for responding to on the guard.
For a helpful summary table of some of the key information presented here, see the appendix.

Review

Review Topics

As a lifeguard, you must be ready to perform first aid if an accident happens. This chapter outlined some of the emergency situations and health risks that might happen while you are on the guard and how you can handle them. Here are some key points to remember from this chapter:

1) Common types of aquatic-related accidents that may require first aid
2) How each piece of first-aid equipment works and when to use it
3) The use of medical alert tags
4) The potential health risks of administering first aid and the universal precautionary procedures used to prevent infection
5) When to use and how to safely remove disposable gloves
6) What to do when bodily fluids are present during a water rescue
7) When disinfecting procedures are required and how to perform them
8) How to help patrons who experience a sudden health problem (e.g., heart attack, trauma)
9) How to prevent and respond to the three forms of hyperthermia
10) The symptoms of common chronic conditions (e.g., asthma, diabetes, epilepsy) and how to help patrons who experience sudden illness

Review Questions

1. What is an automated external defibrillator and how does it work?
2. What precautions should you take to avoid infection while performing first aid or CPR?
3. You are attempting to rescue a victim who is bleeding in the water. What precautions do you take?
4. Why is it important that only EMS transport a victim?
5. What are the symptoms of a heart attack? What should you do if a patron has these symptoms?
6. A patron loses a tooth after colliding with the pool deck. What steps do you take?
7. Explain what an epinephrine auto-injector is and when to use one.
8. When should you summon EMS to assist a patron with asthma?
9. How can you help a patron with low blood sugar?
10. What is your role if a patron has an epileptic seizure?

REPORT

CHAPTER 10

Lifeguard Responsibilities

Page 202

CHAPTER 10

Lifeguard Responsibilities

The YMCA Lifeguard program teaches you the skills to protect and assist people in an aquatic environment. This chapter will help you understand the important responsibilities you accept when becoming a lifeguard.

In this chapter, you will learn the following:

- Your responsibilities to safety and professionalism
- Filing accident and incident reports
- Crisis control responsibilities
- Your legal duty

10
CHAPTER

Promoting Safety

Your primary responsibility as a lifeguard is to promote the safety of all patrons in your assigned zone by preventing accidents and by responding to emergencies quickly and efficiently to minimize the danger to those involved. You meet this responsibility by

- being alert and well rested for each shift you work;
- having the knowledge and skills necessary for preventing accidents, scanning, making decisions, and performing rescues;
- being in good physical condition to use your lifeguard skills quickly and successfully;
- knowing your area or zone of responsibility;
- being able to enforce and explain the rules to patrons;
- knowing how to use all personal-lifeguard, rescue, and first-aid equipment; and
- keeping your rescue and first-aid skills sharp through regular practice.

When you accept the responsibility of being a lifeguard, you also accept the legal and moral consequences of your actions and decisions. This is not a responsibility to take lightly. When you agree to protect public safety as a lifeguard, you become accountable for your knowledge and your actions.

Professionalism

As a lifeguard, you are part of a highly trained team contributing to your facility's operation. The impression you make on patrons is important. If you behave as a professional, with confidence and authority, patrons will be more likely to respect you and to follow the rules you are enforcing. The way you greet patrons; how you sit, stand, and hold your equipment; and your alertness on the job all affect how patrons respond to you. Make the following duties a habit to reinforce a professional image:

Fit for Duty

As a lifeguard, it is important to be mentally and physically fit so you can be vigilant and respond to emergencies while on duty. In addition to ensuring that you never perform your duty while under the influence of alcohol or drugs of any kind (including prescription drugs that may impair your abilities or senses), you can determine whether you are fit for duty by asking yourself the following questions:

1. Am I in good physical condition?
2. Did I get 7 to 8 hours of sleep last night?
3. Did I drink plenty of water?
4. Am I in control of my emotions?
5. Am I sensitive to the feelings of others?
6. Am I rescue ready and prepared to be vigilant and focused?

If you answered no to any of the above questions or have other reservations about your ability to guard, speak to your supervisor about getting someone else to take your shift. Do not guard if you are not physically and mentally prepared to scan effectively and be rescue ready.

Be prepared

- Be well rested and hydrated (**figure 10.2**). Get plenty of sleep and drink sugar-free fluids before your shift.
- Report to work on time as scheduled. Be in uniform at your position when your shift begins.

Focus on your duty

- Be vigilant and stay focused on preventing accidents and responding quickly if they occur.
- Have the appropriate equipment with you at all times while on duty (see chapter 7).
- Stay alert to signals from other lifeguards.
- Scan the bottom, middle, and surface of your assigned zone at all times while on duty.
- Report persistent problems to the head lifeguard or manager.

Control your environment

- Check the area for hazardous conditions when you arrive.
- Enforce all facility rules consistently and fairly.
- Keep patrons from congregating in the walk areas and around lifeguard stands.
- Keep your lifeguard chair at water's edge. (This is not always possible for waterfront locations.)
- Keep the swimming area clean and ready for inspection at all times.
- Safeguard the lives of your patrons first, but also ensure their comfort and pleasure. Do not tolerate recklessness or rough play.
- Keep all personal-lifeguard, rescue, and first-aid equipment ready and in good repair.

Figure 10.1 Signs can help explain to patrons why lifeguards are not free to chat.

- Lock all doors and gates and secure the area when a lifeguard is not on duty.

Communicate with firmness and caring

- Be courteous and diplomatic. Demonstrate the Y's values of caring, honesty, respect, and responsibility.
- Be polite to patrons who ask quick, basic questions but do not socialize while on duty (if necessary, direct them to signs explaining why you cannot chat, such as **figure 10.1**, or refer them to another staff member).
- Refer detailed inquiries to the head lifeguard or manager.
- When enforcing a rule, briefly explain the reason behind the rule and the danger that breaking the rule presents. (Remember that your first responsibility remains to protect swimmers in your assigned area. Never take your eyes off your zone of responsibility; continue scanning your complete zone even when enforcing a rule.)

Figure 10.2 Be prepared by ensuring you are well hydrated.

- Be respectful and friendly with your team members while avoiding any behavior that could undermine patrons' confidence in your maturity and professionalism.

Protecting Children

Lifeguards typically spend a lot of time around children. As a professional, you must be careful not to cause or appear to cause harm to children and you must be careful to help protect children from abuse or neglect. Be aware that child abuse includes intentional and *unintentional* physical injury, neglect, sexual molestation, and emotional harm. It is important that you, as a YMCA-certified lifeguard, never personally abuse children or become involved in situations where you could be accused of abuse. To assure this, follow these common-sense suggestions:

- Never be alone with a child, unobserved by other staff.
- Do not socialize with or become involved in activities (for example, babysitting, weekend trips, texting, e-mailing, or contacting on social networking sites) outside of your job with children who are patrons.
- Do not ever use physical punishment.
- Do not verbally or emotionally abuse children.
- Do not ever deny a child basic necessities, such as food, water, or shelter.

It is important that your employer provide you with additional training in child abuse prevention and in procedures for reporting signs of child abuse. If you have questions about your responsibilities or about your organization's policies, ask your supervisor. YMCA of the USA provides many resources to Ys to promote the prevention of child abuse, most of which are available on www.ymcaexchange.org. The YMCA Program Store, www.ymcaprogramstore.com, sells a complete abuse-prevention training package. The appendix on child abuse prevention also provides critical information for lifeguards; read it carefully.

Keeping Records

Your responsibilities as a professional lifeguard include documenting safety and maintenance procedures and recording situations where you take action. In many facilities, patrons must sign waivers of liability. By signing these forms, they agree not to hold the facility legally responsible in case they are injured while participating in specific activities. Note, however, that these waivers do not eliminate liability resulting from faulty or damaged equipment or from any intentional or reckless staff behavior.

Pool-Closing Procedure

When closing the pool between activities and at the end of the day, circle the pool, looking closely at the bottom while another lifeguard, staff member, or patron witnesses you circling the pool. Then sign out on the pool log or closing form. Write, "Pool cleared, closed, and locked by (your name)," and then write down the date and time. Then have the person who witnessed you write, "Pool clearing, closing, and locking witnessed by (witness name)," and have the witness also log the date and time. This way, if something happens after the pool has been closed and locked, the log will help protect you and the facility from any implication that you overlooked an incident that happened before you closed the facility.

Also, some people might not sign waivers, and state laws vary in enforceability, so never rely on a waiver to excuse failing to take reasonable measures to protect patrons.

Your facility will keep other records, such as staff manuals, emergency plans, posted facility rules, accident and incident reports, and chemical safety logs. These records can establish the **standard of care** provided by your facility—that is, the standard that you will be held accountable to should you be accused of not performing or of underperforming your duty. In the event of a lawsuit, these records can also include information critical to your defense. As a lifeguard, you will be asked by you manager to record your safety checks and incident reports. It is important that you complete these records systematically and file them carefully.

Protecting the privacy of victims' health information

After making a rescue or providing medical aid, you may learn private medical information about the victim, such as medications, medical conditions, or physical problems. You are required by federal law to keep this learned information confidential to protect the victim's right to privacy. Reporters, investigators, or others may ask questions about the information you learned; however, do not share private information with anyone except those directly associated with the victim's care, such as EMS personnel. The federal government created the Health Insurance Portability and Accountability Act of 1996 (HIPAA) to protect medical privacy. Sharing personal information with individuals not directly related with the victim's medical care may constitute a breach of the victim's privacy for which you may be held legally responsible. More information on HIPAA is available at www.hhs.gov/ocr/privacy/index.html.

Accident and incident reports

As a lifeguard, you are part of a global effort to prevent drowning. Experts from around the world have called for increased attention to drowning as a public health problem and to the need for better data about drowning accidents to help improve survival rates. As a lifeguard, you play a critical role by ensuring that you complete reports accurately and in detail (**figure 10.3**). Also, because you are accountable for the decisions you make and the actions you take while on duty, reports are necessary for your protection. When you respond to an emergency, completing an accident or incident report may be the only way to substantiate the procedures you followed and the actions you took if they are ever questioned. Complete all reports carefully as soon after an emergency as possible so

Figure 10.3 Lifeguards play a critical role in reporting information.

you do not forget the details—accurate detail is critical.

An **accident report** is used any time first aid is required; an **incident report** is used for any other situation, usually one in which a lifeguard, staff member, or outside agency is called into action (such as discipline problems or theft).

Because some incidents require less emergency action, your facility may not have a form for reporting them. Minor incidents, such as a patron running on the deck, do not require a report. However, if you have asked a patron to leave the facility or if an outside agency has been contacted, it is wise to prepare a report describing the situation, those involved, and the actions taken. Your facility will define when to complete incident reports.

Whenever your duty requires you to provide first aid, you are responsible for following your facility's procedures for reporting the accident, including completing the facility's report form, if one is provided. Copies of this report are sent to the appropriate authorities; be sure to keep a copy for your own records. Your facility may have different accident report forms for its unique needs. Typically, these forms ask for the following information:

- Names, titles, employee numbers, and years of experience of employees involved
- Lifeguard zone locations, hours on duty, breaks, and lunch periods
- Date and type of certification and the amount of in-service training for each employee involved
- Time and location of accident
- Number of persons involved in accident
- Number of people present at the pool or beach where it occurred
- Weather and water conditions at time of accident
- General comments of importance to evaluating the situation
- Plan or sketch of the area showing any unusual conditions and assignment of personnel if deemed necessary
- Names, addresses, e-mail addresses, and phone numbers of witnesses to the accident

Major accidents involving an EMS or police response may be followed by an investigation. If authorities conduct an investigation—whether management, public safety officials, or insurance investigators— you must be prepared to answer extremely detailed questions about everything that might be relevant to the accident, including the facility, its operation, every person involved, weather conditions at the time, and other details. Listed below are examples of the types of detailed questions you can expect; many more questions are asked in an actual investigation.

About the rescuing lifeguard

- How did the lifeguard become aware of the accident?
- How soon did the lifeguard respond to the emergency situation?
- What did the lifeguard do in response to the emergency situation?
- Did the lifeguard have to enter the water to perform a rescue?
- How far did the lifeguard have to swim?
- What action did the lifeguard take to help the victim?
- What rescue equipment did the lifeguard use, and was the equipment easily accessible?
- What did the lifeguard observe about the victim's condition?
- Did the lifeguard observe signs of spinal injury? If so, what were they?
- Did the lifeguard need assistance with the rescue, and was the emergency action plan followed?
- Did anything interfere with the rescue?
- Did the lifeguard do everything possible to help revive the victim?

About EMS

- Were police or EMS called? At what time?
- How soon did they respond?
- What action did they take?
- Was rescue breathing continued? By whom?
- When did the EMS personnel or doctor take over?
- When did the EMS personnel or doctor make a declaration of the victim's condition?
- Was the victim removed from the beach or pool area? At what time?

About weather and water conditions at the time

- Was it clear or overcast?

- Were the lifeguards in the shade or in the sun?
- Was there glare on the water?
- In a pool setting, could the lifeguard see the bottom of the pool? The drain?
- In a waterfront setting, was there a current? Was there much boat traffic?

Be aware that authorities are not trying to assign blame as they investigate the accident; they are simply gathering information about what happened as required by insurance companies and others. Be as objective as possible when answering.

Facility and injury chart

One way your facility may strive to prevent and improve responses to injury situations is to determine which types of injuries are occurring and where they occur. An injury chart can be an effective tool for gathering that information. The chart is a diagram of the supervised area, complete with all equipment, diving boards, ladders, lifelines, depth markings, lifeguard stations, fences, recreation areas, and auxiliary facilities. Each time an injury occurs, it is noted on the chart with certain codes.

Your facility may have a code system for listing all the types of injuries sustained. A letter, number, or symbol may be assigned to each injury. **Figure 10.4** illustrates an injury chart in which a number indicates the facility location where the injury occurred and a letter notes what part of the victim's body was affected.

From this chart, facility managers and staff can learn about the common accidents and injuries happening at the facility and where these are likely to occur. They can then implement measures to prevent future accidents; for example, they can establish new rules, repair equipment, install additional safety equipment, reposition lifeguards, add additional staff, or limit access to an area.

Figure 10.4 Facility injury chart.

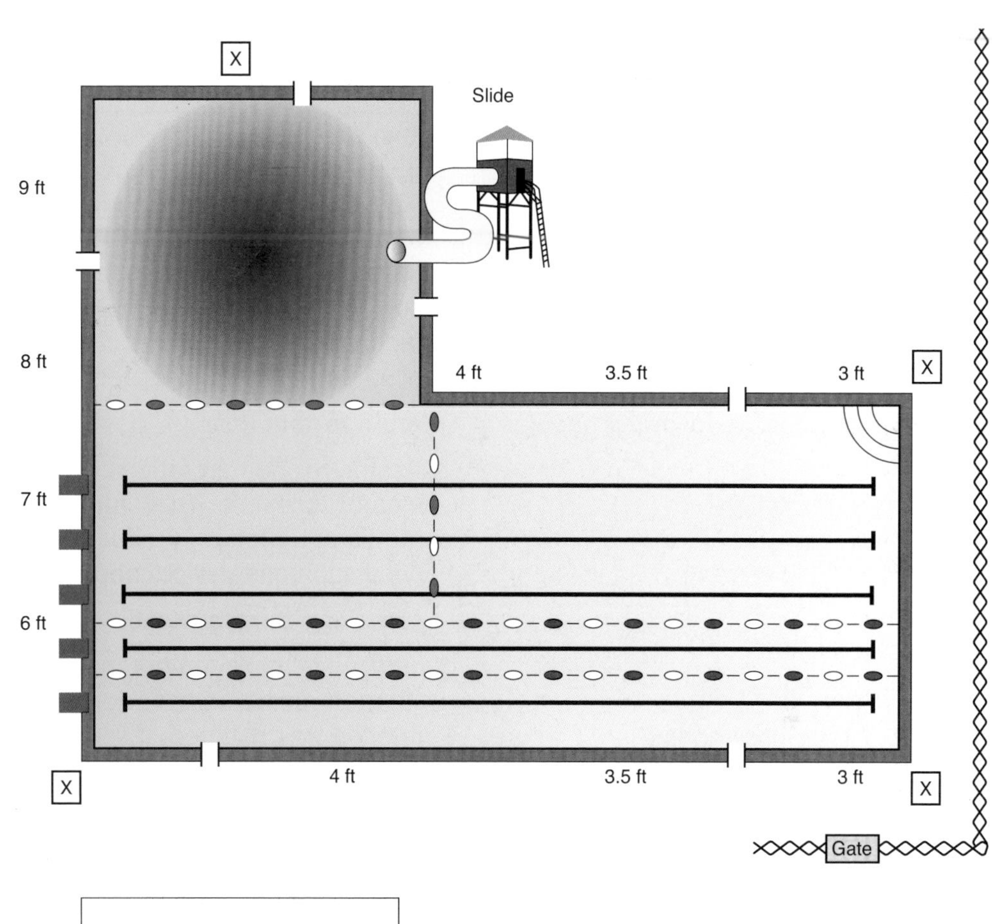

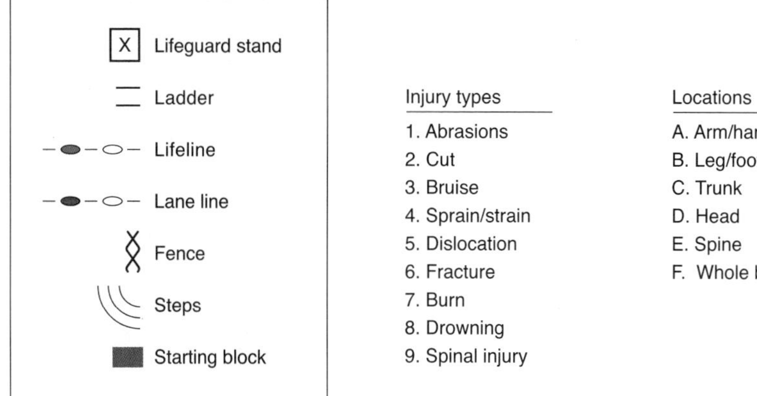

Checklist for Crisis Management

In handling any emergency situation, be sure you know the elements of crisis management shown in this checklist. Your facility may wish to post this checklist in the lifeguard staff areas and at the front desk.

Be Prepared

Know your facility's emergency procedures and review them regularly, including how to fill out reports. Make available the phone numbers for the following people or agencies:

- Supervisor/manager
- Police/sheriff
- Fire
- EMS/ambulance
- Poison control center
- Chemical accident hotline
- Health department

Maintain Order

Confusion and fear can make a bad situation worse. Stay calm and act with authority. Follow procedures as you have practiced them.

Notify the Chain of Command

Once the situation is under control, report the incident to your supervisor or another designated manager as soon as possible. Consult the emergency action plan (EAP) for the chain of command, or who calls whom after an incident.

Protect Your Facility

Make no statements to news media representatives or the general public about the incident; only the media spokesperson is allowed to discuss it publicly. File the appropriate report as soon as possible, using your facility's standard form. Include separate documentation of witnesses' statements.

Return to Your Post

Resume regular operations as soon as safely possible. This can help calm patrons and staff and reduce negative speculation and rumors about the event.

Learn From the Experience

Your facility management may work with staff members to review how the situation was handled. If you are asked to participate, openly discuss the event to evaluate your response and the actions taken. This lets you offer ideas for improving safety and express your emotions about what happened.

Seek Help When Coping With Trauma

If you experience a traumatic incident, you may need time to recover. Share your feelings with trusted friends and family members and seek professional help if symptoms of depression or anxiety appear or persist after the event. Let your supervisor know you would like to speak to someone or if you seek professional help.

Controlling Crisis

Having emergency procedures in place is the first step to managing a crisis. Another important step is to be prepared to handle people's reactions to a crisis and to think about how you will stay calm and in control during stressful situations.

Crisis communications plan

Communicating with patrons during a crisis

As part of your facility's emergency plan and training, you will learn how to respond to questions and concerns from patrons affected by an emergency. See chapter 6 for some basic guidelines for communicating with patrons during an emergency to help keep people calm and the situation under control. Be aware that if and how you communicate with patrons after an emergency is also part of your facility's crisis communications plan. Do not provide information or make statements about any situation under investigation, even to patrons you may know well, unless you are authorized to do so. Thank them for their patience as the situation is managed.

Communicating with the media about a crisis

Be prepared for media involvement in any emergency involving a large facility or when an accident or incident has been reported to EMS or the police. Follow your facility's crisis communications plan, which designates a spokesperson who manages all contact with the media and who is the only person to make public statements. It is important that all other staff members refrain from answering questions or making comments to anyone, including answering seemingly innocent questions about events at the facility or about the situation itself. If you are approached, alert your supervisor and follow your crisis communications plan.

Although most reporters wish you and your facility no ill will, news stories are not always accurate and misstatements can reflect poorly on you and your facility. Facility policy and legal responsibilities outline what information is released and by whom.

Post-traumatic stress

Any time you are involved in a rescue, you are subject to stress as a result of your duty to react to the emergency and the danger you face in doing so. Well-trained professionals generally can respond to emergencies without being overwhelmed by stress because they are able to focus on what they were trained to do. Practicing emergency procedures is critical so you will know what to do under stress and can remain calm.

You may feel emotionally drained after the emergency is over, especially if it involved severe injury or death. This is normal. Discuss your feelings, fears, and reactions within 24 to 72 hours of an emergency to help relieve personal anxieties and stress and to help prevent later emotional problems. Bottling up your emotions can have negative personal consequences, so find a way to share them. See the signs of stress listed on this page to help determine if you are suffering from stress.

The following actions also may help reduce stress reactions following a rescue (ICISF 2001):

- Get physical activity within the first 24–48 hours and alternate it with periods of relaxation. This will help you reduce physical stress reactions.
- Structure your time and keep busy. Keep as normal a schedule as possible.
- Recognize that your reactions are normal.
- Spend time with people.
- Be supportive of your coworkers. Share what you are feeling and encourage them to do the same.
- Get plenty of rest and eat a healthy, well-balanced diet even if you do not feel like eating.
- Do not fight it when you have thoughts, dreams, and flashbacks about the incident. These are normal and will decrease with time.

If you feel that the stress is overwhelming and you want or need help in dealing with it, seek professional services or support groups. You might

Common Signs of Stress

Recognizing that you are experiencing the effects of trauma is an important step to recovery. Seek professional help if you find yourself struggling with these symptoms:

- Confusion
- Nightmares
- Uncertainty
- Poor attention
- Poor decision making
- Poor memory
- Guilt
- Inability to rest
- Change in social activity
- Change in speech patterns
- Change in appetite
- Grief
- Panic
- Denial
- Anxiety
- Agitation
- Irritability
- Depression
- Withdrawal

be able to make use of the critical-stress teams many communities have to help firefighters, police officers, and other rescue workers address their psychological trauma.

An accident involving a death or serious injury may take considerable time to resolve. If you acted according to your training and your facility's policies and emergency procedures, then you performed your legal duty. Cooperate with the authorities and seek help in managing your reaction to the trauma you experienced.

Assuming Legal Responsibility

In addition to developing the physical skills and knowledge required to be a good lifeguard, you also must assume responsibility for your actions. As a professional lifeguard, you accept the duty to provide a safe environment for patrons of your facility to enjoy aquatic activities by

- providing adequate supervision for your areas of responsibility;
- communicating appropriate directions to patrons about the rules of the facility;
- anticipating potential hazards and taking reasonable action to reduce risks;
- providing necessary emergency first aid;
- proficiently performing the skills described in this manual and your facility's policy or lifeguard manual whenever necessary.

Aquatic liability

It is possible that the actions you take (or do not take) could result in legal action against you and your facility. Consequently, you must understand the legal responsibilities of being a lifeguard. Liability may arise when injury results from a lifeguard performing an incorrect action or failing to perform an action that should have been performed. Because specific laws regarding aquatic liability vary from state to state, this section outlines only general terms and principles. Check with your supervisor to learn about laws governing aquatic facilities in your area.

Common legal terms

Take the time to familiarize yourself with the legal terms listed in **table 10.1**, which apply to lifeguarding. These terms are important to help you understand the legal responsibilities of a professional lifeguard.

The legal process

After any accident, it is possible that the injured person (or a representative of the injured person) will file a lawsuit against the aquatic facility and the on-duty lifeguards. The legal process then usually follows the same general path, which is shown in **figure 10.5**.

In U.S. society, a lawsuit can be brought against almost anyone for almost any reason. Consequently, the filing of a complaint to initiate a lawsuit does not necessarily mean that the lifeguard or facility will be found liable for any wrongdoing. Rather, at this stage it merely means that someone has alleged that he or she has suffered damages as a result of the actions or inactions of the lifeguard or facility. However, regardless of the ultimate outcome of the lawsuit, the facility, its staff, and the community it serves will be significantly affected by the time, energy, and expense of responding to a lawsuit. To prevent this, aquatic facilities and staff focus their efforts on providing the safest possible environment for swimmers.

Even for the most prepared lifeguard, the threat of liability exists. Most facilities have liability insurance to protect themselves and their employees, and many personal general-liability insurance policies include such liability coverage. Your employer can explain what coverage is available to you and when it applies. Take time to learn about the insurance available to you before you accept any lifeguarding position.

Negligence

In the law of negligence, the **plaintiff** (person alleging damages) must prove all of these four elements of a negligence claim against the **defendant** (person accused of wrongdoing):

- The **defendant** owed a duty to the plaintiff.
- The defendant **breached** that duty.
- The plaintiff suffered some **injury or loss**.
- The injury or loss was **caused** by the defendant's breach (proximate cause).

While on duty, a professional lifeguard assumes a legal duty to provide the services he or she was trained to provide to each patron of the facility. That does not mean that you guarantee the safety of patrons. Rather, it means that you must provide the **standard of care**, which is the care that a "reasonable and prudent" professional lifeguard would use in the same or similar situation. Failure to meet this standard of care is a breach of that legal duty. If that breach is a **proximate cause** (i.e., a cause resulting in the damages) of a patron's injury or loss, then you and your facility may be found liable in a negligence lawsuit.

In summary, the skills and guidelines set out in the *On the Guard* manual represent the best practices in the aquatics industry and in many cases exceed the standard of care in the aquatics industry as a whole. As a YMCA-certified lifeguard, always strive to live up to these goals. Be professional. Use the knowledge and experience gained from the YMCA Lifeguard program at all times when you are on duty.

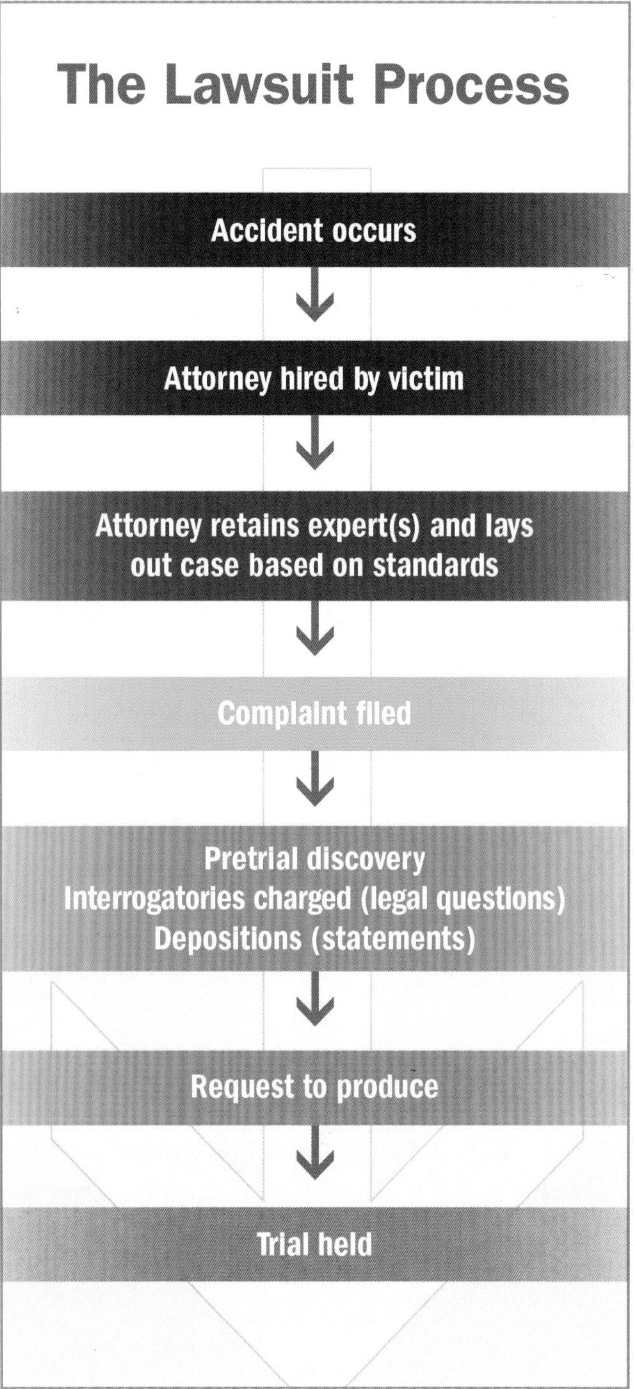

Figure 10.5 Path of the lawsuit process.

Table 10.1 Common Legal Terms

Term	Definition	Legal Implications (Relevance to lifeguards)
lawsuit	Legal procedure by which an individual pursues legal remedy.	A lawsuit will take valuable time from your life, cause you to expend considerable emotional energy, and can be stressful for many years until the suit is resolved. A lawsuit following a drowning may take several years to resolve.
plaintiff	The plaintiff is the individual, or group of individuals, who brings the lawsuit.	The plaintiff is either the injured party or a representative of the injured party.
defendant	The defendant is the individual, or group of individuals, called upon to answer for the wrong asserted in the lawsuit.	If a lawsuit is brought against your facility, you may be named as an individual defendant.
liability	Legal responsibility. Liability is a synonym for duty, responsibility, and obligation.	As a lifeguard, you accept legal liability for your actions or inactions.
negligence	Actions that fall below the standards established by law for protection of others against unreasonable risks. Negligence is an unintentional breach of a legal duty, causing damage that was reasonably foreseeable and without which breach the damage would not have occurred.	A plaintiff must prove all elements of negligence (duty, breach, proximate cause, and damages) in order to prevail in a lawsuit.
duty	Duty is a legal obligation to act in accordance with a prescribed standard of care in order to protect others from unreasonable risks.	You have a legal obligation (duty) to protect the patrons in your swim area from unreasonable risk.

Table 10.1 Common Legal Terms (continued)

Term	Definition	Legal Implications (Relevance to lifeguards)
standard of care	Considered by law to be the level of ordinary care, practice, and conduct within the profession; it is the action likely to be taken by a reasonable and prudent professional.	The skills and guidelines set out in *On the Guard* represent the best practices in the aquatics industry, and in many cases exceed the standard of care in the aquatics industry as a whole. As a YMCA lifeguard, always strive to live up to these goals. Be professional. Use the knowledge and experience gained from your YMCA Lifeguard training at all times when you are on duty.
breach of duty	The failure to exercise that care which a reasonable and prudent person of the same experience and training would exercise under similar circumstances.	As a lifeguard, if you do not fulfill your duty (that is, if you "breach your duty"), you could be found negligent in a legal action.
proximate cause	That which in natural and continuous sequence unbroken by any new independent cause produces an event, and without which the injury or loss would not have occurred.	In order for a lifeguard to be found negligent and liable to the plaintiff, the failure to use reasonable care (i.e., breach of duty) must have proximately caused the ultimate injury.
damages	Monetary compensation awarded to one who has been injured by the action of another, such as by a breach of duty.	Damages compensate the plaintiff for the injury sustained. In a lawsuit following a drowning, damages vary considerably depending on a variety of factors but can be millions of dollars.
Good Samaritan laws	These statutes provide protection from legal liability to a trained person, acting in good faith while off duty, to provide emergency medical assistance at the scene of an accident or emergency. Good Samaritan laws differ from state to state.	If you are off duty and at another aquatic venue, Good Samaritan laws may protect you from liability in the event that you respond to an emergency if you are currently certified. Because these laws vary, know the law for your state.

Review

Review Topics

In your work as a lifeguard, you will be responsible for the safety of yourself and others. You will also be accountable for filling out reports and complying with legal obligations. This chapter outlined what you will be expected to do beyond your efforts to prevent accidents and save lives. Here are some key points to remember from this chapter:

1) The characteristics of a lifeguard who is fit for duty
2) The importance of professionalism
3) Your role in recognizing and preventing child abuse (also refer to the appendix)
4) The importance of keeping accurate logs of facility equipment
5) What HIPAA is and how it applies to your responsibilities
6) The importance of completing reports and when they are necessary
7) The use of an injury chart
8) The importance of having and following a crisis communications plan
9) The causes and signs of post-traumatic stress and how to handle it
10) The definition of legal terms, including negligence and liability, and how they apply to lifeguarding
11) What the Good Samaritan law is and how it applies to lifeguarding

Review Questions

1. What does it mean to be fit for duty? Describe a situation where a responsible lifeguard might ask another lifeguard to cover a shift.
2. Explain how professionalism and respect affect the safety of patrons in an aquatic facility.
3. Describe a situation where a well-intentioned lifeguard could become vulnerable to an accusation of child abuse. What could the lifeguard have done to eliminate this misperception?
4. Why is it important to file reports completely and immediately?
5. What is the purpose of an injury chart and how is this information used?
6. Explain the term "chain of command" and its role in a crisis.
7. What is post-traumatic stress and how might it be relevant to lifeguards?
8. Explain what "standard of care" means in your own words.
9. Define the term "negligence" and give an example of how it could apply to a lifeguard.
10. What are Good Samaritan laws and when might they affect you?

SLIDES AND TIDES

CHAPTER 11

Waterparks and Attractions

Waterparks and attractions range in size from a single water flume in a camp lake or community pool to multi-attraction indoor water recreation parks to 50-acre outdoor waterparks to waterpark resorts. They are all meant to give patrons fun, thrilling rides, and special lifeguarding precautions are necessary to ensure the attractions are also safe.

In this chapter, you will learn the following:

- General safety principles for guarding waterparks
- Common causes of accidents
- Communicating rules and safety concerns to patrons
- Precautions for specific waterpark attractions

11
CHAPTER

Water Recreation Attractions

Today, water recreation areas in the United States include not only pools and diving areas but also a wide variety of attractions (**figure 11.1**). These can be divided into two types: rides and play structures. On rides, water helps control the rider's speed, reduces friction between the rider and the ride surface, and catches the rider in a landing area at the end of a ride. The second type, play structures, includes attractions such as theme areas, floating water walks, water goals and hoops, vortex pools, spray areas, and interactive playgrounds.

Rides and play structures of all kinds at water recreation attractions require the same attention to proper lifeguard zone coverage as described in chapter 1. The number of lifeguards required for any water recreation attraction depends on several factors, including these:

- Activity and excitement levels in the area (on the deck and in the water)
- Size and shape of the pool or play area
- Equipment and play features in the pool area (such as slides and flotation devices)
- Bather load
- Skill and age of swimmers
- Glare from sunlight
- Sight lines (ability to see below and around play features)
- High-use areas
- Capacity to manage emergencies in a proper and effective manner
- Meeting or exceeding state and local codes and manufacturer guidelines
- Zone size

Figure 11.1 Interactive water recreation attractions.

In this chapter, you will find some fundamental safety guidelines for water recreation attractions, general causes of accidents on attractions, and information on how to communicate rules and safety concerns to patrons. In addition, each attraction requires specific supervision. Take time to learn the characteristics of each attraction, the rules and precautions for safely using each, and the stations for lifeguards on each.

Safety Guidelines for Guarding Waterparks

Water recreation areas offer many different types of rides and activities. While each attraction should be supervised and guarded according to its individual characteristics, this section addresses important safety guidelines that apply to waterparks in general. Effective scanning, for example, is vital for preventing incidents no matter what kinds of attractions are present. For all water recreation attractions, observe the following safety guidelines:

- Always emphasize accident prevention.
- Get orientation and in-service training specific to each attraction you guard. Enforce the safety requirements established by the manufacturers.
- Use the victim-recognition skills discussed in chapter 4 and also be especially alert if patrons
    - slip and fall;
    - collide with another rider, side wall, end wall, or bottom;
    - lose body control on an attraction;
    - fall from an attraction;
    - become airborne and hit a hard surface;
    - fail to read signs or listen to recorded messages and warnings;
    - act as if under the influence of drugs or alcohol;
    - appear to be experiencing a medical problem, such as a heart attack, seizure, or heat exhaustion;
    - fail to heed warnings such as height, weight, or age restrictions; or
    - act disoriented or unstable.
- Enforce rules consistently and help make sure that rules are posted by each attraction and at pool entrances and that rules are easy to read and understand.
- Stop any horseplay and overcrowding on attractions.
- Be aware of communication devices and signaling systems provided by your facility, such as an intercom system, public-address system, signal lights, telephones, cell phones, two-way radios, air horns, or whistles.
- Follow equipment inspection and testing protocols. The safe operation of waterparks includes complete inspection and testing of each attraction according to the manufacturer's instructions each day before use. If this is part of your preshift duties, complete the inspections and record them in the appropriate log. After inspection and before an attraction is opened for use, a staff member rides each attraction as it would normally be used by patrons. Any necessary maintenance is to be performed before the attraction is opened, or the attraction is closed until the required maintenance can be completed. All maintenance procedures are recorded in the appropriate log.

Avoiding Lifeguard Lung

Lifeguard lung is a respiratory illness associated with indoor waterparks, spas, and indoor water recreation attractions such as spray devices, waterfalls, mushroom-shaped cascades, serpentine slides, and drop slides. Its symptoms include shortness of breath, coughing, fatigue, fever, vomiting, and other flu-like symptoms. It can be treated with antibiotics.

Pseudomonas aeruginosa, the bacteria commonly associated with lifeguard lung, grows in poorly disinfected water left in the circulation systems of sprayers, water slides, and spa jets when they are turned off overnight. Under some circumstances, bacteria-laden spray and vapor fill the air around the device when it is turned on the next day, infecting anyone nearby. Because lifeguards stationed next to spray devices continuously breathe in the affected air, they are more likely to develop lifeguard lung than patrons.

Facility management can help reduce the incidence of lifeguard lung by taking these preventive steps (see chapter 14 for more on pool maintenance):

- Maintain a free residual chlorine of 2.0 parts per million (ppm) daily.
- Shock the circulation system weekly by raising the free residual chlorine at 5.0 ppm for 8 hours. Then reduce the free residual chlorine to the standard level of 2.0 ppm, using sodium thiosulfate pentahydrate.
- Maintain good negative airflow for indoor facilities.
- Position lifeguards and lifeguard chairs away from spray and vapor devices.

- Inspect first-aid, safety, and rescue equipment, including first-aid kits, personal protective equipment, resuscitation masks, bag-valve masks, manual suction devices, oxygen units, and biohazard waste bag and cleanup kit. Check the battery of the AED. Record the results of the inspection in the appropriate log.
- Test and adjust the water chemistry balance each time the filters are cleaned; test and adjust the pH and disinfectant levels at the appropriate times (see chapter 14 for more on water chemistry).
- Know and practice your facility's written emergency and accident management procedures specific to each attraction as well as emergency procedures for an unplanned shutdown of each attraction.
- Be aware of the drowning risk caused by hydraulics in attractions where water cascades into a pool. Hydraulics are caused by the waterfall effect created when water rushes into a catch pool, which produces a reverse-circular current. A hydraulic can make it extremely difficult to stand up, especially for young children or weak swimmers, and may even hold a person on the bottom.

Figure 11.2 Enforce the requirements for each attraction.

In addition to knowing and following general safety principles while on duty, as a lifeguard, you may find it helpful to understand the primary causes of accidents that occur at waterparks so you will be aware of potential hazards and can support management in creating a safe environment for patrons.

Common Causes of Accidents

Over the past 30 years, enough information has been acquired to provide a clear picture of the primary causes of accidents at water recreation attractions, which include the following:

- **Unsafe design.** Attractions may be manufactured and put into use without proper safety testing that uses appropriate design research and experimental testing. There may be insufficient consideration given to how lifeguards can actively scan an activity or area.
- **Facility operations.** After attractions have been installed on site, problems may arise if they are not operated properly. Increasing water-flow rates or not maintaining proper water depths for slides, run-outs, and catch pools may increase the risk of accidents. Maintenance may also be substandard. When facilities update or add new features such as permanent or floating structures to a water attraction, these may change the original

layout. Without proper attention to safety, added structures may create blind spots for lifeguards.

- **Poor supervision.** Lifeguard duties at recreation attractions are complex and require high-performing teams with excellent communication. Due to limited budget or other reasons at a given facility, the number or effectiveness of lifeguards may be inadequate.
- **Patron behavior.** Water recreation patrons may have medical problems, such as a heart condition, that may affect their safety on attractions. Many patrons also are first-time visitors, unfamiliar with the rules or the attractions' characteristics. In their excitement, visitors often fail to read signs or listen to recorded announcements. Some patrons also may choose to disobey rules.
- **Poor communication by management.** Signage and recorded messages are key safety features at water recreation areas. If signage is of poor quality or difficult to read, patrons may fail to see and understand the important information on the signs. The number and position of signs can also affect safety. Having too many signs or placing signs where they are hard to read may affect patrons' attention to them. Failure to provide pictorial and bilingual signs or to consistently use signal words such as *danger*, *warning*, and *caution* may cause patrons to overlook signs. Recorded statements played while patrons wait in line may also fail to communicate if the recording is hard to hear or to understand, or if the message is too long or played so frequently that patrons do not recognize it as important information.

Communicating Rules

Waterparks are exciting, sometimes even chaotic places. They offer a variety of attractions, each with specific rules for its safe operation and to minimize the risk to patrons. When guarding a water recreation attraction, you are responsible for communicating its rules and restrictions to patrons and preventing unsafe behavior to the best of your ability. Know the requirements for each attraction you guard and help patrons read and understand any warning or safety signs posted for their protection (**figure 11.2**).

Figure 11.3 Enforce rules in the dispatch area.

Waterparks may post rules and warnings on signs or play recorded safety messages for patrons as they enter an attraction or wait in line. However, most patrons are excited and eager to ride as many attractions as possible. As a result, they sometimes may not read the rules and warning signs or listen carefully to recorded messages. You may have to repeat warnings and rules verbally in a dispatch area (the starting point for a ride) (**figure 11.3**), even though patrons have been presented with signs and recorded messages along the way into or up to an attraction. Be aware that patrons who are visiting for the first time may be more likely to injure themselves than those who frequent the attractions regularly; take care to help new patrons understand the rules.

Written messages

Waterparks use signs to communicate the warnings and rules required to protect patrons' safety. For example, a sign on a ride may indicate that patrons must be a minimum height or weight or be free of certain medical conditions. Signs may indicate what types of clothing or jewelry are prohibited for safety reasons. Signs may also provide critical information to riders on how to position themselves for their protection. For example, riders may be required to lie on their stomach or to keep their legs crossed at all times. Riders may be prohibited from making certain movements, such as extending their arms out to slow or stop themselves. Because of the speed of some attractions, riders' body position and movements can be critical—not following the posted rules may lead to serious injury or death.

As a lifeguard, understand that you are in charge of enforcing the rules and warnings posted for the individual attraction you are guarding and for the waterpark in general. Your responsibility is to ensure that patrons understand proper and safe behavior on the attractions, to stop inappropriate behavior and prevent unnecessary risk to the best of your ability, and to respond to accidents should they occur.

Scanning Tips

- Watch for each patron to come to the surface after dropping from a slide. Swimmers may not realize the depth of the splash pool or catch pool.
- Scan and think about who is at the most risk. Keep an eye on those most likely to become victims: nonswimmers, very young patrons, excited patrons. Keep your eyes moving and move yourself so you can see all areas of your zone. Be sure to look under, around, and over the attraction you are guarding.
- When guarding a play structure or any floating structure or water attraction, know that you and your fellow lifeguards must have a 360-degree view with no blind spots. For some structures, this may require two or more lifeguards. It is critical that blind spots not prevent you from seeing your entire zone; this can be particularly challenging with attractions such as slides, inflatables, and trampolines placed at lakefronts. Roving and floating lifeguards may be necessary to provide 360-degree coverage.
- Carefully manage the number of people on and around each attraction. Overcrowding can limit visibility and your ability to scan effectively.
- When scanning a play structure, pay special attention to these high-risk areas:
  - Under the dump bucket
  - Slide exits
  - Water walks
  - Floats
  - Moving water such as currents or water flowing out of tubes and slides and off roofs
  - Spray pads (while the water on a spray pad is very shallow, remember that depth is relative to the patron; a very young child may be at risk of falling in a spray pad and not being able to get back up)
  - Highly populated areas (risk increases as the number of patrons increases)

Recorded messages

In addition to posting signs, your facility may play recorded messages of warnings and rules through loudspeakers located along entrance paths and stairs. If you are asked to record such a message, observe the following:

- Speak clearly and slowly.
- Use inflections, avoiding a monotone.
- Make the message brief and concise.
- Use words that everyone can understand.
- Use positive messages.

Before and while you are on duty, be aware of the recordings used at your facility and help monitor that they can be heard clearly and understood by patrons. Volume, quality of the recording and playback, and location of speakers can all affect patrons' ability to use the facility safely and appropriately.

In addition to knowing the general safety guidelines, causes of accidents, and communication procedures common to all waterparks, you are responsible for knowing how to protect patrons and safely operate any individual waterpark attraction you guard.

Guidelines for Specific Attractions

Each attraction has its own hazards. As a professional lifeguard, it is important that you know each attraction's characteristics, the likely causes of accidents, and the locations where lifeguards are best stationed. The attractions covered here include wave pools, surfing systems, deep-water pools, free-fall and speed slides, serpentine slides and rapids, water coasters, lazy or winding rivers, interactive playgrounds, and inflatable play equipment.

Guidelines for installing and managing water recreation attractions may be found in the manual *YMCA Aquatic Management*, available from the Program Store, www.ymcaprogramstore.com. The information in the *On the Guard* manual is directed at the lifeguard to help in the safe operation of this equipment.

Wave pools

Wave pools (**figure 11.4**), a popular attraction, are swimming pools that simulate a surf experience. Wave patterns can be set at different intervals and speeds. A wave pool may produce waves on a cycle of small waves—for example, 10 minutes on and then 10 minutes off—or one large wave every 5 to 10 minutes. A facility may choose different wave patterns for certain times of day based on the types of patrons present; for example, younger patrons may use the pool more during the day and older patrons in the evening.

Wave-pool accidents

Hazards in wave pools relate to the size and frequency of the waves and to the concrete pool bottom. These are some common victims of wave-pool accidents:

- Patrons in the 4- to 5-foot-depth zone who are knocked over by waves
- Patrons who panic when lifted by a wave
- Patrons who are injured when waves push them into recessed wall ladders in the deep end
- Patrons in shallow water who are knocked down by people riding the waves on inflatable rafts
- Patrons floating on inner tubes in deep water who fall off the tube, submerge, and cannot return to the surface because of the number of tubes covering the surface

Figure 11.4 Wave pool.

- Patrons hanging onto pool railings who are not strong enough to swim safely through the waves to shallow water

Patrons who suffer impact injuries from contact with the wave-pool bottom or who are struck by other patrons riding on rafts may bleed or have an increased risk of spinal injuries. Be prepared to follow the universal precautionary procedures for protection from blood-borne pathogens described in chapter 9 and to provide initial care for spinal injury as described in chapter 8.

Precautions for wave pools

Both the facility and patrons can take steps to help prevent accidents in wave pools. The facility can limit the size of the waves to reduce collisions between swimmers and waves. The following guidelines for swimmers, adapted by permission of Lifesaving Society (2007), might also help prevent accidents in wave pools.

- Swimmers do not hold onto one another in the deep zone, which helps minimize collisions.
- Parents holding children stay in the shallow zone.
- Swimmers keep a safe distance from the walls, which helps prevent collisions with the walls.
- Swimmers do not bodysurf or dive in shallow water.
- Patrons enter the wave pool from the beach area only, not from the sides.
- Swimmers use flotation devices only when allowed by the facility. If the facility provides flotation devices, swimmers use only those devices while in the pool.

Guarding wave pools

According to the Lifesaving Society (2007), when a rescue is needed, stop the waves but do not evacuate the wave pool as in a regular swimming pool. Rescues usually can be completed with just local crowd control. However, when a total evacuation of the pool is necessary, for example during bad weather, a more detailed crowd-control plan is necessary. Stop the waves and, with the help of the other lifeguards, direct the patrons to leave and then supervise their departure.

Overlapping zone coverage is key to effectively guarding wave pools. Where water depth is greater than 5 feet, lifeguard chairs belong at the sides of the pool (**figure 11.5**). Standing or roving lifeguard positions are used between chairs and in shallow water. Additional lifeguards may be in the water. Wherever your position, ensure that you are able to scan your entire zone, which may mean that you stand when waves are on or move to avoid glare or blind spots. Continue to scan and stay focused and vigilant whether the waves are on or off. Be aware that flotation devices may interfere with your ability to see your zone clearly. If your facility allows flotation devices in the pool, you can divide the pool into two sections, one for swimmers and one for patrons with flotation devices. Another possibility is to limit the number of flotation devices allowed in the pool.

Teamwork is essential when guarding wave pools. For best protection, seated lifeguards handle communication, and lifeguard rotations occur only when the waves are off.

Surfing systems

The thrill of surfing or bodyboarding on real waves is exciting. Surfing systems provide this experience within the controlled environment of a pool. Some systems are designed to deliver only one type of wave. Other systems can change the break of the wave, switching from a left-breaking wave to a right-breaking wave, often through the use of an adjustable bottom. Most surfing systems have a trampoline-type surface under the water.

Surfing system accidents

Injuries most likely to occur in a surfing attraction include the following:

- Bumps, bruises, and torn nails
- Soft tissue injuries such as strains and sprains
- Broken bones or dislocated joints caused by impact with the surf surface

Guarding surfing systems

If you are guarding a surfing system, you will be stationed at the front of the ride to scan and help coach riders. Because of the variety of waves, you may find it necessary to change positions to scan effectively. You will require facility-specific training to know the best vantage points for guarding. In facilities that allow multiple surfers per wave, knowing the best vantage points is key to ensuring safety.

Deep-water pools

Deep-water activity pools are used in a variety of attractions; they can be landing areas for shotgun slides, entry areas for diving boards and platforms, and areas for bottom-anchored inflatables. Depending on the activity, the water depth may vary from 11.5 to 18 feet.

Deep-water pool accidents

Common injuries in this type of pool are related to entries. Unplanned falls or sudden drops from high above the water can result in painful impact with the water. Following are some of the accidents common to deep-water pools:

- An injured or weak swimmer panicking upon suddenly entering deep water
- A person losing consciousness who ends up lying facedown in the water due to impact with the water, another person, or some part of the attraction

Be ready to use universal precautionary procedures with impact injuries (see chapter 9).

Guarding deep-water pools

The number and locations of lifeguards are determined by the activity. For most deep-water activities, a lifeguard station is necessary near the entry point.

Figure 11.5 Standing allows the lifeguard to scan the entire zone while waves are on.

Other lifeguards are situated where they have an unobstructed view of the sides.

For shotgun slides, a dispatcher (either a lifeguard or trained staff member) is positioned at the top of the slide. A certified lifeguard is stationed near the drop zone where patrons enter the water.

Guarding deep water (15 to 18 feet) requires having mask and fins on hand to rescue a submerged victim. In-service training is necessary to learn how to use this equipment to recover a victim from the pool bottom and to practice rescue procedures regularly.

Free-fall and speed slides

Free-fall and speed slides are similar in design. Free-fall slides are long slides with very steep drops. Some are so steep that the top of the slide is enclosed, giving the rider the sensation falling straight down. Speed slides have gentler slopes and sometimes have bumps halfway down. These slides may end in catch pools or long run-outs, which is generally where accidents occur.

Free-fall and speed slide accidents

Because of the speeds attained on these slides, riders are directed to stay in a position with their legs crossed at the ankles and their arms folded across their chest. Injuries on these attractions usually result from a combination of speed and improper body position, as in these situations:

- Soft-tissue injuries, such as strains and sprains
- Serious internal injuries from entering the catch pool or run-out with the legs apart
- Broken bones or dislocated joints from impact with
  - the slide after becoming airborne from sliding over a speed bump
  - water in the catch pool
  - the wall or steps at the end of a run-out or catch pool that is too short

Guarding free-fall and speed slides

A lifeguard or trained staff member is stationed at the top of the slide to control the dispatch of riders on the slide. A certified lifeguard is positioned at the catch pool or end of the run-out area.

Serpentine slides and rapids

Serpentine slides are long slides that wind their way down a hillside or super structure, similar to a roller coaster (**figure 11.6**). They are typically constructed of fiberglass. Riders slide on mats or one- or two-person tubes, or they body-slide feetfirst with arms and legs crossed (as when using a speed slide). Rapids-type rides simulate tubing in a creek or river. Such rides wind downhill and may have one or two catch basins at points between the top and bottom where the ride funnels riders into a cave or to the next drop level.

Serpentine slides and rapids accidents

Accidents may occur anywhere from the top to the bottom of these attractions. Here are some common accidents:

- Falling off a mat and losing body control, resulting in soft-tissue or head injuries or broken bones
- Stopping on the way down and blocking riders who are following, causing impact injuries
- Riding in one- or two-person tubes and hitting the walls of the slide with the head, arms, or feet—the rider cannot control the tube as it spins and turns on its downhill course
- Getting caught in a hydraulic at the end of the ride (see Safety Guidelines earlier in this chapter)
- An excessive number of tubes collecting in a catch basin or rapids where some tubes may be overturned, causing injury or even drowning

Precautions for serpentine slides and rapids

- Be aware of hazardous conditions in the catch pool, such as currents created from the water flow.
- Know and practice the emergency procedures for each attraction.
- Enforce height requirements established by the manufacturer. It is recommended that children be a minimum of 48 inches (4 feet) tall and at least 6 inches taller than the water depth in the catch pool before being allowed to use the ride.
- Enforce weight limits established by the manufacturer. A common weight limit for serpentine slides is 250 pounds.
- Stop the water flow and the dispatch of participants during a major rescue (such as when multiple lifeguards are

involved in the assistance and care of an injured swimmer).

- Instruct riders to always ride feetfirst with arms and legs crossed.
- Perform all assigned duties relating to safety inspections, maintenance, and record keeping.
- Do not use patrons as slide safety testers.
- Support management in the identification and analysis of locations and patterns of injuries to patrons to assist in the facility's taking corrective measures to prevent further injury.
- Be aware of the effect of weather on the equipment. For example, on hot days, heat may expand the joints of the slide. If riders are permitted to slide feetfirst on their stomachs, the toe nails on the large toes may be torn off.

Guarding serpentine slides and rapids

Riders may need assistance or rescue at any point from the top of the ride to the catch pool at the bottom. The dispatch position at the top of the ride is staffed by a trained staff member or lifeguard who should be able to communicate with two lifeguards

Figure 11.6 Serpentine slide.

on deck for proper safety. Locations for standing lifeguards include the catch pool and appropriate locations along the ride. Always have your rescue tube with you while on duty (**figure 11.7**). You might find wearing aquatic shoes helps reduce slipping.

Water coasters

A water coaster is a water slide that mimics a roller coaster by providing not only descents but ascents as well. This is done with high-speed conveyor belts or water jets used to propel the rafts. Water-coaster rafts can be accelerated uphill and may become momentarily airborne—the entire raft could lift into the air and crash back down—before landing and entering a tunnel or going over a hill. Most water coasters do not offer any safety restraints, and riders can experience varying degrees of airtime and jostling depending on how they hang on to the handles. The ride finishes by zipping into a splash pool for unloading.

Figure 11.7 Always have your rescue tube while on duty.

Water-coaster accidents

Typical water-coaster accidents include the following:

- Patrons slipping or falling while getting into or out of the raft
- Patrons injuring themselves by engaging in horseplay in the raft
- Collisions between two patrons in the coaster raft, such as hitting heads while being bumped around when the raft becomes airborne

Guarding water coasters

Lifeguard stations are located at the entrance and exit points to assist riders getting into and out of rafts.

Lazy or winding rivers

The paths of lazy or winding rivers may be oval in shape or they may wind their way through a water recreation area, sometimes encircling the entire area. The rivers generally are 3 to 4 feet deep and float patrons along on inner tubes at 2 to 3 miles per hour (**figure 11.8**).

Lazy or winding river accidents

Lazy or winding rivers generally have a low incidence of accidents. Those that do occur often include the following:

- Patrons slipping or falling while getting into or out of their tube
- Patrons injuring themselves by getting out of the river and then jumping or diving back in
- Patrons injuring themselves by falling from a tube, which may be overturned by horseplay or from other patrons blocking the progress of riders

Guarding lazy or winding rivers

Every part of the river is to be within sight of at least one on-duty lifeguard at all times. Lifeguard stations are located at the entrance and exit points to assist riders in getting into and out of tubes, and lifeguards are positioned sitting or standing along the river.

Interactive playgrounds

Interactive playgrounds (**figure 11.9**, next page) combine equipment for water fun, such as water slides, with playground elements, such as climbing nets. Often the equipment is designed to follow a theme. The equipment is in water that ranges from 0 to 18 inches deep.

Interactive playground accidents

These are the accidents most likely to occur in an interactive playground:

- Patrons slipping or falling at the entrance or exit points of slides
- Young patrons injuring themselves or being knocked down when buckets dump large amounts of water on them
- Patrons hitting their heads after falling during horseplay and when older children play roughly near young children

Figure 11.8 Lazy river.

Spinal Injury in Moving Water

When a spinal injury occurs in moving water, the water's current can complicate a rescue procedure and increase risk for the victim. You can take important steps to protect the victim from further injury. The following procedure is specific to spinal-injury management in lazy river attractions; however, the same basic steps can be used in rivers or streams.

Emergency action plan for a spinal injury in a lazy or winding river

- Lifeguard #1 identifies the spinal injury and immediately activates the stop button or signals to other lifeguards to activate the emergency stop.
- Lifeguard #1 enters the water and performs the head-splint technique (see chapter 8).
- **If the water is still moving:**
  - Lifeguard #1 maintains the head-splint technique and turns the victim so the head is pointing upstream and feet are pointing downstream.
  - Other lifeguards or patrons assist in preventing other patrons or debris from drifting into the victim.
  - If the current is slow enough, Lifeguard #1 stays in place. (Lifeguard #2 brings a backboard to Lifeguard #1, and they follow the backboarding procedures in chapter 8.)
  - If the current is too strong to stay in place, Lifeguard #1 moves slowly with the current while maintaining the head-splint technique.
  - Lifeguard #2 enters the water downstream with a backboard and prepares to assist Lifeguard #1 with backboarding procedures.
  - Other lifeguards can assist in stabilizing the victim during this process.
  - Lifeguards follow the backboarding procedures in chapter 8.

Precautions for interactive playgrounds

When guarding an interactive playground, follow these safety precautions:

- Make sure that the rules are clearly written and easily understood by all.
- Enforce all rules, especially those related to running and horseplay.
- Enforce all policies, including height and age restrictions for using the playground.
- Instruct adults to closely supervise their children.
- Alert management to any safety issues, for example:
  - Sharp surfaces on any walls or pipes
  - Poor signage or depth markings
  - Inadequate visibility or sightlines
  - Slides with dangerous angles or exits
- Keep an eye out for small children using the pool as a restroom. Safety breaks are a great way to solve this problem when used to encourage children to go to the restroom.
- As with all outdoor facilities, patrons need to be aware of the sun and temperature. If you notice that someone is very cold or getting sunburned, speak with the parent or guardian.

Figure 11.9 Interactive playground.

Guarding interactive playgrounds

Special written guarding policies are necessary for each piece of equipment. When guarding play equipment, you and your fellow lifeguards require positions and zone assignments that allow you to see 360 degrees around each play element and the ability to focus on high-use and high-risk areas. Play structures with slides and potentially hazardous play areas may require additional lifeguards.

Inflatables

Even if facilities do not have permanent aquatic equipment such as slides or wave pools, they may have temporary inflatable attractions. Commonly known as inflatables, these are large floating objects usually made of commercial-grade plastic that come in many shapes, themes, and sizes. Generally, inflatables are either inflated and then sealed (i.e., sealed inflatable), or they are attached to an air blower that keeps them inflated while in use (i.e., constant-blow inflatable). (ISRM 2009)

Sealed inflatables

Sealed inflatables (**figure 11.10**) are designed to provide a floating play structure. They come in many different themes and sizes and are popular for special events.

Precautions for sealed inflatables

As a lifeguard, do not allow patrons on sealed inflatables to do the following:

- Dismount headfirst

- Stand on the object (unless it is specifically designed for this)
- Push or throw one another on or off the inflatable
- Try to knock others from the inflatable (by swimming under or trying to lift it)
- Swing, hang, or pull on the anchor ropes
- Bring pins or other sharp objects near the inflatable

Guarding sealed inflatables

In addition to the lifeguards required to guard swimmers in all areas of the pool or waterfront, when a sealed inflatable is in use, it requires a lifeguard to be stationed on each side of the inflatable so that 360-degree coverage is maintained. Additional lifeguards may be necessary to help supervise in the water if the number of swimmers or their ages or abilities require it.

Constant-blow inflatables

Constant-blow inflatables have an air blower permanently connected and constantly running while the inflatable is in use.

Inflatable slides

Inflatable slides are attached to a 3-meter diving platform or a customized frame. The active sliding length is about 26 feet. An air blower works continuously to deliver proper air pressure. Patrons slide between two large air-filled tubes.

Precautions for inflatable slides

Follow these guidelines for the safe use of inflatable slides:

- Enforce the weight limits recommended by the manufacturer.
- Enforce the height requirements established by the manufacturer. Do not allow anyone to use the slide who is smaller than the minimum recommended height.
- Allow only one person down the slide at a time.
- Allow only the feetfirst sliding position.
- Do not let participants run or jump on the slide.

Guarding inflatable slides

A lifeguard or trained staff member is positioned at the top of the slide to make sure the rider is in the proper slide posture. This staff member also controls the flow of participants using the slide and climbing the stairs. A certified lifeguard is stationed on the

Figure 11.10 Sealed inflatable.

deck to supervise the exit point of the slide and the swimmers' clearance of the splash area.

Giant inflatables

Giant inflatables, also known as aqua runs or aqua fun runs, are structures that can extend up to 40 feet in length and are designed to be obstacle courses for swimmers to travel across. Some facility managers will use giant inflatables as stationary play structures similar to sealed inflatables instead of as obstacle courses. In this case, it is necessary to establish different operating procedures and rules and to follow the guidelines for sealed inflatables. A word of caution: Having two sets of rules can confuse swimmers and make rule enforcement more difficult.

Precautions for giant inflatables

Guarding giant inflatables is similar to guarding sealed inflatables, plus the following guidelines:

- Control the flow of participants. Dispatch only one participant onto the structure at a time.
- Tell swimmers that, at the far end, they must slide off feetfirst and then swim to the nearest side.
- Instruct swimmers that if they lose their balance, they should fall off the structure and not try to dive off it.
- If the structure is being used as a sealed inflatable (that is, for play and not as an obstacle course), then allow participants to crawl on it only, not to stand on it. Posting the type of play allowed on the inflatable is important so swimmers understand the rules and so you can enforce the rules.

- Keep the air blower in constant operation while the structure is in use. Follow your facility's procedures for complying with electrical codes and regulations.
- Clear the pool area when the inflatable is being put in or taken out.

No significant research has been conducted on the best way for swimmers to get on to a giant inflatable. Until more research is completed, use your best judgment as to how swimmers should get onto the structure. For giant inflatables located in a pool, two methods are possible:

- The starting point is positioned against the edge of the pool, and a lifeguard is stationed there. That lifeguard helps each patron step carefully onto the structure before the patron traverses the obstacle course.
- A lifeguard closely supervises the swimmers as they jump onto the structure (rather than step onto it) to reduce the danger of patrons falling back and hitting the poolside.

Guarding giant inflatables

At least two designated lifeguards are necessary—one to supervise participants getting on the inflatable and another to supervise the length of it and the dismount area and to clear the dismount area. Limiting the number of patrons and spacing out the patrons as they travel across giant inflatables will help you and your fellow lifeguards in scanning and seeing everyone in your zones.

As illustrated by the wide variety of attractions discussed in this chapter, waterparks and water recreation areas provide patrons of all ages with

many opportunities for excitement and fun. However, the opportunities for injury are also significant unless proper safety and operating procedures are carefully followed and all rules are constantly and consistently enforced by all staff. As stated earlier in this chapter, as a professional lifeguard, know the risks and safety requirements of any attraction you guard, understand and communicate waterpark rules and warnings to all patrons, and consistently enforce all rules at all times. A safe waterpark experience can help bring families closer together, give young people the opportunity to play and make new friends, and provide everyone a fun way to be physically active. You can help make this happen by protecting people's safety and responding to any accidents that may occur.

Review

Review Topics

Many people enjoy waterparks, and these facilities require lifeguards to have specific skills and training. In this chapter, you learned ways that accidents can happen at water attractions and how to help prevent these accidents. Here are some key points to remember from this chapter:

1) The common causes of accidents at water attractions and why the lifeguard needs to understand them
2) Why communication with patrons is important
3) The importance of warning signs and safety rules
4) What lifeguard lung is and how to prevent it
5) Characteristics and precautions for specific kinds of waterpark attractions
6) How to rescue a suspected spinal-injury victim in moving water, such as a lazy river attraction
7) Characteristics and precautions for inflatables and play structures

Review Questions

1. What are the five main causes of accidents at water attractions?
2. Why might you have to communicate more often with waterpark patrons than with pool patrons?
3. Give five examples of warning and safety signs you might see at a waterpark.
4. What causes lifeguard lung? Why does it affect lifeguards more often than patrons? What steps can be taken to prevent it?
5. Name and describe five waterpark attractions. Give information about where lifeguards might be placed and the safety rules associated with them.
6. Describe three key concerns when guarding an interactive play structure.

CHAPTER 12

Guarding the Waterfront

Although many YMCA-certified lifeguards work in pool settings, some guard in open-water environments, such as oceans, lakes, ponds, or rivers. To manage the demands of open water, waterfront lifeguards need to know additional procedures.

In this chapter, you will learn the following:

- Waterfront set-up and equipment
- Beach and watercraft safety
- Search and rescue procedures
- Skin and scuba diver rescue

12
CHAPTER

Setting Up the Waterfront

To this point, we have primarily discussed procedures that are most appropriate for guarding a pool. If you will be working at an open-water area, you will need specific training about the beach areas, conditions, and equipment. This chapter addresses waterfronts in a surf environment, with some considerations for lakes, rivers, and ponds.

Marking the swimming area

Management will determine what portion of the waterfront to designate as a swimming area. Several factors are considered when making this decision, from the local geography to boating patterns to water conditions to operational requirements. Once the swimming area is determined, you may be responsible for marking it clearly. Swimming areas can be marked in a variety of ways, typically using buoys, lifelines, and flags.

Buoys and safety floats

Brightly colored buoys or safety floats may be placed along the perimeter of the swimming area by anchoring them to the bottom. Buoys are common at lakes and other nonsurf environments. Because of the turbulent conditions in surf environments, buoys are rarely used; more common markers are flags or signs placed at the shore. If you are guarding a beach that uses the buoy system, check the diagram of the swimming area regularly to be sure that weather conditions have not changed the location of the buoys.

Properly maintained buoys have legible markings and no sharp edges, and they are securely anchored. Regular cleaning of buoys is important to prevent organisms, which can be dangerous to touch, from attaching to the buoys. At the end of the season, remove buoys and their anchors from the water. The long winter months can damage the buoys or anchor lines.

Lifelines

Some nonsurf beach areas use lifelines with floating buoys to designate the side boundaries of the swimming area. Lines are anchored on shore and attached to a weighted anchor in the water. Set lifelines to angle toward each other so that the width of the swimming area narrows as swimmers move away from shore. The angle of the lifeline will vary somewhat with the wind and tide action.

Although some areas also place a lifeline at the edge of the swimming area farthest from shore, this practice is not recommended because swimmers may be tempted to "swim to the rope," which could take them too far for their swimming ability or stamina.

Flags

In a surf environment, where conditions make it difficult to anchor markers, some facilities will use flags or signs on the shore to mark the boundaries of a swimming area and to indicate swimming conditions. A moveable flag system is widely used in Australia and other countries, and an international consensus on what flags represent continues to grow. Whenever flags or other signs are used, however, it is critical that patrons understand what they mean. Signs explaining what different flags represent are necessary to explain the flags and help protect safety. See the visual in this chapter for more on flags.

Lifeguard stations

In waterfront situations, two types of lifeguard stations are common: lifeguard towers and floating lifeguard platforms. Each has certain advantages. Regardless of the type, lifeguard stations require proper maintenance for safe use and must meet applicable codes. As with pool environments, it is important that all lifeguard stations be designed and positioned so that lifeguards are able to scan their zones and can see all swimmers without obstruction.

Lifeguard towers

Depending on the prevailing conditions, lifeguard towers may be simple elevated chairs or may be enclosed structures. Well-designed, enclosed lifeguard towers can offer protection from the elements, fewer distractions from beach patrons, good visibility, and a storage area for rescue equipment. They also tend to be highly visible to those on the beach who need assistance.

Enclosed stations do have a disadvantage at surf beaches because they are stationary: they are usually erected at a point well above the high-tide line, and thus at low tide they are farther from the waterline. This may be overcome, in part, by use of binoculars to focus on potential problems. Another way to address this is to erect a high, sturdy lifeguard chair that is portable so that the lifeguard can move the chair to be close to the water's edge. This chair, however, does not offer storage space or protection from the elements. In almost all instances, a stationary tower is preferable to a portable chair.

Floating lifeguard platforms

On a waterfront, it may be useful to have lifeguards patrol from a floating platform such as a paddleboard, kayak, boat, or floating dock. One advantage of a floating position is that the lifeguard is already in the water should a problem arise. Being closer to swimmers also helps the lifeguard communicate and enforce rules. Using floating platforms can provide additional safety by placing swimmers between the lifeguard in the water and the lifeguard in the chair, creating overlapping zone coverage. When inflatables and other play elements are used at the waterfront (see chapter 11), floating lifeguards are key to ensuring coverage and eliminating blind spots. This is because floating lifeguards can maneuver so that the lifeguard team has a 360-degree, unobstructed view of all sides of a play element and of all participants using the equipment.

Using small watercraft as floating lifeguard platforms can be more challenging than using paddleboards or floating docks but does have some advantages. Small watercraft such as kayaks or boats may be more maneuverable and faster than paddleboards or floating docks. These watercraft also enable the lifeguard to keep other boats away from the swimming area. Special training is required for using a watercraft in rescue operations. See the information on watercraft later in this chapter.

Waterfront Equipment

The equipment required to operate a safe open-water beach is significantly different from what is needed at a pool. Besides making sure that each lifeguard has a rescue tube or buoy, your facility will have the following equipment:

- A more sophisticated communication system, ideally two-way radios on a common frequency
- Paddleboards
- For each lifeguard: mask, fins, snorkel, skin-diving vest, and possibly a weight belt
- Boats
- Vehicles
- Other specialized rescue equipment depending on the environment

As with a pool facility, inspect all emergency equipment daily.

FLAGS

You may choose to mark the boundaries of the swimming area with flags. If so, plant two flags—each with a red horizontal stripe over a yellow horizontal stripe—on 12-foot poles to designate the swimming area. The poles can be moved to allow lifeguards the flexibility to change the designated swimming area to avoid strong currents.

A second type of flag, signaling present conditions, should appear on every beach. Such flags are usually attached to posts at the entrance to the beach area and on each lifeguard stand. The flags listed below constitute the new international flag system, which uses the following color coding:

Beach Safety Flag and Color Meaning

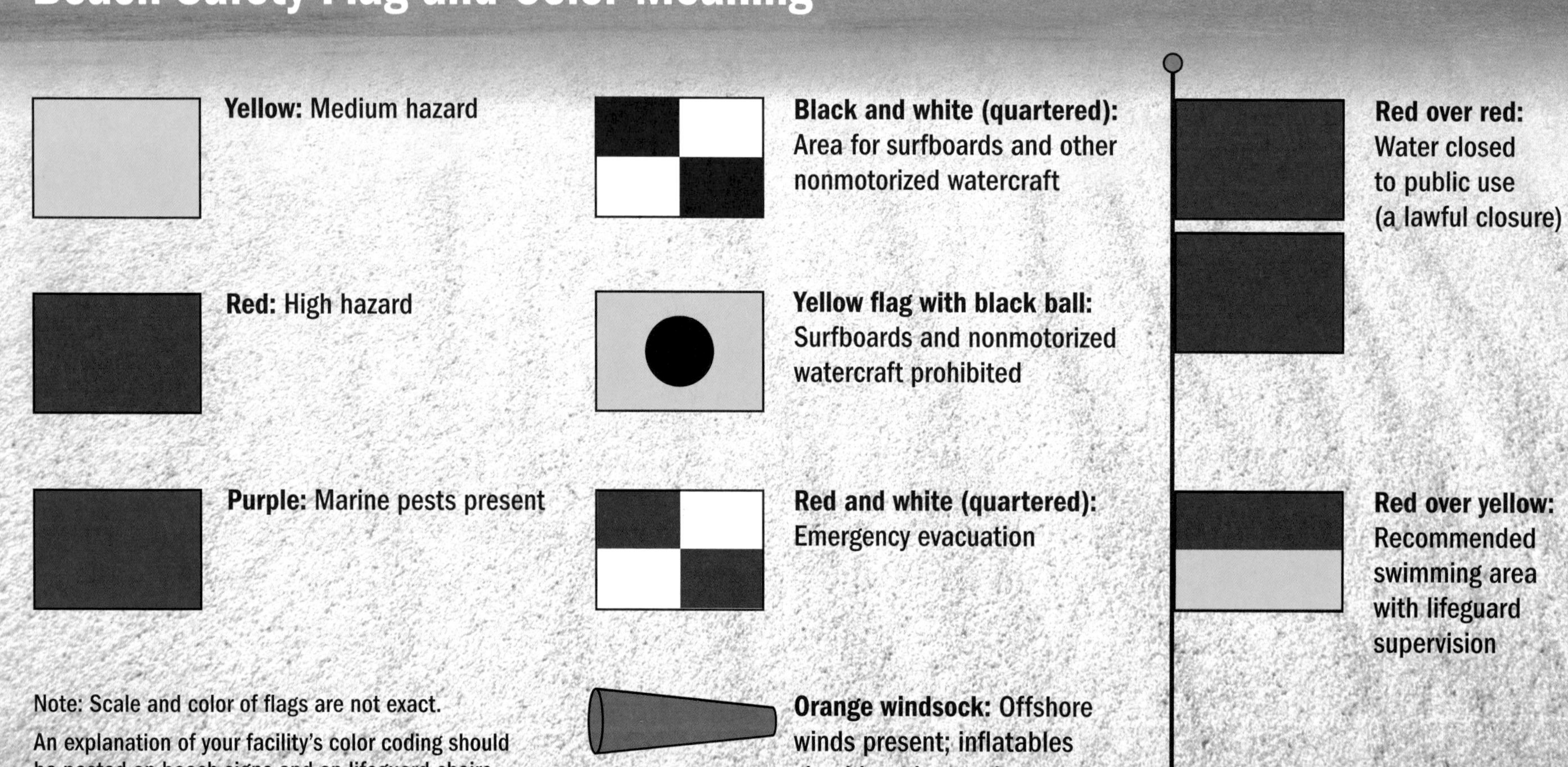

Hazards of the Open-Water Environment

Consider how the following affects guarding an open-water environment:

Natural hazards

You cannot control the presence of natural hazards; focus instead on how to keep patrons safe. Be aware of these common hazards.

River hazards

- Holes: areas of reversed current around submerged rocks that can hold in floating objects
- Strainers: fallen trees and branches that allow water to pass through but may trap swimmers and boats
- Rocks

Lake hazards

- Sudden drop-offs
- Hidden rocks
- Plant life
- Rip currents (found in some larger lakes)

Ocean hazards

- Rip currents
- Marine life

In each of these environments, consider whether the wind may affect the water's motion or the sun may reduce your ability to see by creating glare. Be aware of how these hazards may affect patrons and when it may be necessary to have more lifeguards to manage the conditions safely.

Human-made hazards

Be aware if the body of water has any human-made hazards. Rivers may have old pipelines, wires, intake pipes, and other obstructions. Consider whether a patron could get stuck in or under something. Be aware of play elements and docks; slippery surfaces on a play element might require an additional lifeguard in the water. Again, be aware when more lifeguards may be necessary to manage potential hazards. Communicate with management about potential hazards and pay attention to the conditions of any play element and your ability to manage its use safely.

Hazards created by the location of the activity

Some hazards may be a result of the location of an open-water area. For example, a waterfront located on a section of a shared public lake may introduce people or activities over which you have no control and that may affect your patrons.

Design and structure of the body of water

The design or construction of an open-water area and its attractions may require additional staff. Items such as in-water toys or other objects such as posts and docks may affect lifeguards' ability to observe patrons from certain locations or may hinder effective rescue from a particular position. Notify management of any situation where the environment obstructs your ability to scan your zone or to quickly reach patrons in need of help.

Visibility and surveillance

Guidelines for effective scanning on the waterfront do not differ from guidelines for pool environments with the exception of scanning the bottom of the water; typically, this is not possible in open water because you cannot see the bottom. Instead, you will vigilantly scan the surface of the water. While on duty, scan your entire zone of responsibility and supervise your assigned area completely, including the outer edges and area in between. The same rule of thumb for creating zones applies to open water: zones are designed to allow lifeguards to reach any victim within 10 seconds.

Multiple activities in the same location

Lifeguard positions may need to be modified and the number of lifeguards increased when multiple activities are happening in the same location.

By permission from Markel Insurance Company 2007.

Communication systems

Because lifeguard stations at a beach are more spread out and the area supervised is much larger than at a pool, it may be impossible to communicate by whistle. For communicating with beach patrons, power megaphones, air horns, and public-address systems are excellent options.

On a beach, it is best if each lifeguard has a telephone or a two-way radio to communicate with other lifeguards and emergency personnel. An advantage of two-way radios is that conversations can be monitored by all lifeguards simultaneously, so everyone is immediately notified of a problem (such as a lost child) or a need for response. Lifeguards also can carry these radios if they need to leave the lifeguard stand. Emergency phone numbers are posted with each phone. The radio systems are often linked to a local emergency frequency so that help can be summoned immediately.

Figure 12.1 Rescuer on a paddleboard.

In an emergency, quick communication of details such as a victim's location and type of injuries is critical. For that reason, many agencies have developed code systems. Check with your facility about how your local police and fire departments and EMS want you to communicate emergency needs.

When contacting emergency services, it is important that you communicate in a clear and direct manner. When sending a message on the radio, observe the following:

- Be prepared for the dispatcher to ask you what is the emergency.
- State your name and the name of the person or service you are calling.
- State your location and anything unusual about your location; include how EMS can best reach the victim as quickly as possible. The computer system used by emergency systems may identify your location automatically, but be prepared to give the closest street address and avoid using slang terms or nicknames for the location.
- Speak slowly and as clearly as possible. Try to be complete yet brief because you tie up the frequency while talking, preventing others from speaking.
- Await acknowledgment of your message.
- Sign off with your name.

Be sure to contact the dispatch center again if you need to move the victim from the original location or if other important factors change or occur that would affect how emergency responders reach the victim or what they should expect to find.

Paddleboards

Paddleboards (**figure 12.1**), also known as rescue boards or rescue surfboards, are versatile. Because of their buoyancy, they can be used as floating lifeguard platforms or for quick transportation to a victim in light to moderate surf. They also can be used to carry a victim back to shore. Their flat surfaces can be helpful for performing in-water rescue breathing.

Paddleboards are available in a variety of lengths and widths and are made of fiberglass or molded epoxy and foam. Designs may include a soft skin of rubbery material that can reduce the potential for damage to the board or injury to others. A good paddleboard is tapered underneath the front end (also called the nose or bow) to help keep the nose above the water's surface. It also has one or more skegs (a type of small keel) to keep the board from slipping sideways due to wind or choppy water.

Keep paddleboards near the water and check them daily for any necessary repairs. Keep the surfaces smooth for maneuverability and for the comfort of the rescuer and victim.

Mounting and propelling a paddleboard

You can mount a paddleboard from either side or from the rear (also called the tail or stern). From the side, reach across the middle of the board, grab the far side, and kick yourself onto the board while leaning it slightly toward you. From the rear, grab the board and press it down as you kick and slide yourself up onto the board. Be sure to center your torso and hips to prevent the paddleboard from rolling to one side when you paddle. Position yourself to be neither too far forward (the board's nose will submerge) nor too far back (the board's tail will drag). The nose (front) should ride just above the water's surface.

Depending on the water conditions, it may be faster for you to use a paddleboard to reach a victim than for you to swim. To propel the paddleboard, lie flat on your stomach and use an alternating crawl stroke or a butterfly arm movement. To make a wide turn, use a breaststroke movement with one arm while holding onto the side of the board with the other hand. To make a spin turn, in which the paddleboard turns on its axis, make a backward sweep stroke with one hand and a forward sweep stroke with the other on the surface of the water. If you kneel, keep your shins flat against the board and bend yourself at the waist to paddle.

Sonar Fish Finders

Some facilities are adding sonar fish finders to their safety and rescue equipment. They use these finders to perform checks of the bottom of the swim area during each safety break. These machines also can help locate a missing swimmer faster than a staff-intensive search-and-rescue operation can.

Effective use of a fish finder requires an emergency action plan (EAP) that incorporates the machine into lost-swimmer procedures. For example, one lifeguard can quickly begin a search by attaching the fish finder to a paddleboard and then paddling back and forth in the area where the swimmer was last seen while the search-and-recovery group gets organized. Using the technology in this manner can shift searching for a lost swimmer from a recovery situation to a rescue situation.

Paddleboard rescue techniques

Follow these steps to use a paddleboard to perform a rescue (**figure 12.2**):

1. Stop the paddleboard near the victim's head and quickly flip the board upside down, turning it toward you.
2. Crawl back onto and across the paddleboard.
3. Reach over the board and into the water to grab one of the victim's wrists. Bring the victim's entire arm across the top of the board toward you (be very careful not to hit the victim's face on the side of the paddleboard). Hold that arm on the board.
4. Reach across the board with your free hand and bring the victim's other arm over the board. Place the victim's hands one on top of the other, and then place one of your hands on top of the victim's hands.
5. Reach across the board with your free hand and grab the board's edge. Press down on the victim's hands while you roll the paddleboard over toward you. The victim is now facedown across and on top of the board with her or his arms in the water. You may need to use your knees to press against the board in order to roll the victim onto the board.

Figure 12.2 Rescuing a victim using a paddleboard.

6. If the victim is conscious and does not need rescue breathing, have the victim turn toward the front of the board once on the paddleboard. Be sure the victim's entire body is centered lengthwise down the middle of the board. Move the victim's legs so that each foot hangs over one side of the board and then climb onto the board from the rear. Lie on the board and paddle carefully so as not to turn the board over.
7. If the victim is unconscious and the water is calm, roll the victim onto his or her back and push or pull the victim so that he or she is lying across the paddleboard. Assess the victim's airway and breathing. If the victim is not breathing, use your resuscitation mask to perform rescue breathing. Paddle the victim to safety on the paddleboard. If the water is choppy, roll the victim back onto his or her stomach to paddle the board to safety as described in step 6.

Be careful when using a paddleboard in a crowded area. Its size and weight can cause serious injury in a collision with a patron. In rough surf, stay prone (on your stomach) to reduce the chances of losing your balance or being knocked off the paddleboard.

Skin-diving gear

In waterfront areas, you may have to skin dive to rescue victims who are submerged in deep or low-visibility water or to perform an underwater search and rescue. The term *skin diving* refers to diving without scuba (self-contained underwater breathing apparatus) or another source of compressed air. To do this, you will require skin-diving gear, including a mask, fins, snorkel, vest, and if necessary, a weight belt. Such gear is standard equipment and is necessary at lifeguard stations for open water, as well as for deep-water pools (pools with depths greater than 11.5 feet).

Rescue procedures that use skin diving require you to know the standard hand signals used to indicate whether a diver is OK or is in trouble and needs help. You also need to know how to fit the equipment properly and how to clear the mask and snorkel.

Masks

Masks create an air space between your eyes and the water that enables you to see clearly underwater. Several styles of masks are available, varying in the amount of peripheral vision they allow and the ease with which you can clear water out of them. Avoid masks that do not cover your nose because they do not allow you to equalize pressure in the mask.

Whatever type of mask you select, try this test to determine whether it fits properly: Without putting the strap over your head, position the mask on your face, covering your eyes and nose. Inhale through your nose, hold your breath, and let go of the mask with your hands. If the mask stays firmly in place, it will most likely fit your face comfortably and properly.

Even the best-fitting mask will sometimes become filled with water. Should this happen, do not panic. In some instances you can simply pull the mask away from your face, surface, drain the mask, and start over again. There is, however, no need to surface to clear the mask. Just follow these procedures (**figure 12.3**, next page):

1. While underwater, position yourself vertically, holding the mask in one or two hands.
2. Place the palm of your hand on the center and top of the mask and press the mask in toward your forehead. Or place both hands on the side of the mask and press the mask toward your forehead.

3. Begin to exhale through your nose. Look up and continue to exhale until all the water is out of the mask.

When you surface, protect yourself from anything that may have moved into the water above you, such as a boat. Keep your hand up and your head up and perform a 360-degree turn while ascending from a deep dive so you can view all directions above you. After surfacing, give the OK signal.

Fins

Using fins will enhance the power of your kick. Fins come in two types, closed heel (also called a full-foot shoe fin) and open heel. Shoe fins and some open-heel fins have fixed sizes, while other open-heel fins have adjustable sizes. Fins used by open-water lifeguards for swimming through rough surf have heel straps and shorter blades than those used in scuba diving. Because more strength is needed for large, rigid fins, most swimmers will want fins with moderate rigidity and medium-size blades. The ideal fins for rescue have positive (or at least neutral) buoyancy (i.e., they float), so you can quickly recover them if they come off in the water.

Put fins on in the water to prevent tripping while on land. To swim with fins, use one of three main kicks: flutter, dolphin, or scissors. Try each of the kicks to see which one gives you the greatest speed. Fins let you cover more distance in less time while expending less energy, which makes them useful when searching for submerged victims.

Snorkels

The snorkel should be attached to your mask strap with a “snorkel keeper” (see the loop on the snorkel in **figure 12.4**) to ensure proper positioning when you surface or when you clear the snorkel. As your snorkel goes underwater, water will fill it. Do not breathe in while underwater or at any time the

Figure 12.3 Clearing a mask underwater.

A

B

snorkel is filled with water. When water gets into your snorkel, you will need to clear it.

The two methods for clearing a snorkel are the blast method (**figure 12.5**) and the displacement method (**figure 12.6**). To perform the blast method, surface with your hand up and your head up. At the surface, look down and blow out forcefully to clear the snorkel, breathe in easily and blast again, and then give the OK signal. To perform the displacement method, surface with your hand up and your head up. Just before reaching the surface, gently exhale into the snorkel, making sure the top of the snorkel is positioned down. When your head breaks the surface, tilt your head forward and breathe easily using the snorkel. Give the OK signal.

Watercraft

The type of watercraft or boat appropriate for a particular beach depends on the kind of service it will provide. Boats are often used as lifeguard platforms in the water and as rescue tools. They are also used in search operations.

Two types of small motorized boats are commonly used by lifeguards in surf and nonsurf environments: personal watercraft (PWC) and the inflatable rescue boat (IRB). The PWC, often referred to by the trademarked name Jet Ski, is a small craft powered by a water jet pump rather than an external propeller. It has become the motorized rescue boat most commonly used by lifeguards. A PWC operator either sits astride or stands on the vessel and operates by means of a handlebar and a jet-drive system. These crafts are fast and maneuverable and have no propeller that might injure someone; however, the hard fiberglass hull can cause injury in a collision. PWC lack an internal deck where victims can be placed, so most deployments include a towed rescue sled to which victims can cling. PWC require advanced training to operate them safely.

The IRB is typically about 12 feet in length, with an outboard motor for propulsion. These

Figure 12.4 Snorkel attached to a mask with a "snorkel keeper."

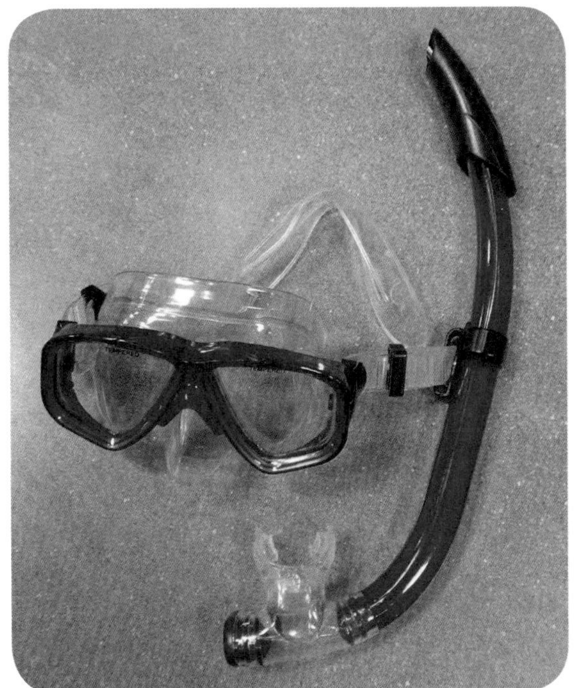

Figure 12.5 Blast method for clearing the snorkel.

Figure 12.6 Displacement method for clearing the snorkel.

boats are quite maneuverable but not as fast as PWC. Because their hulls are inflated rubberized material, they are less likely to cause injury than a PWC if the hull strikes someone, but the propeller on the outboard motor can cause injury. IRBs include an internal deck where victims can be placed. Like PWC, IRBs require advanced training for their safe operation.

Both the PWC and IRB can be used to rescue other small craft, in emergencies, although they are not ideal for towing larger boats for long distances. If the rescue boat will regularly be used to tow other small craft, a larger motorized boat (with an inboard or an outboard motor) may be more effective. Like the PWC and the IRB, use of these vessels is an advanced skill that requires training specific to the type of craft. This is especially important since they will be operated in close proximity to swimmers and other boats.

Proper equipment for motorized rescue boats includes some or all of the following:

- U.S. Coast Guard– and state-mandated safety equipment
- First-aid kit
- Motor
- Fuel receptacle
- Oars (in case of motor failure)
- Anchor and extra line (in case of motor failure)
- PFDs
- Rescue equipment
- Bailers or buckets and tools
- Fire extinguisher
- Flashlight
- Signaling device
- Mask, fins, and snorkel

Kayaks

Many waterfronts use kayaks as floating lifeguard platforms and rescue aids. Kayaks are easily maneuvered and can quickly get you to a distressed swimmer. Bringing a distressed swimmer to shore is somewhat more challenging with a kayak, since there is no easy way to get the swimmer aboard; however, kayaks help achieve the primary goal of rapidly reaching and providing flotation to a victim. Depending on the distance to shore, you may opt to swim the victim to safety or you may need to have another small craft assist with transporting the victim. To effectively use a kayak on duty, lifeguards require kayak training, should be able to go through a practice obstacle course with ease, and require in-service training for making a rescue with a kayak. If you use a kayak on duty, carry extra rescue tubes (or additional inflatable tubes) to provide flotation. As with the other watercraft, be aware of your location and that of swimmers in the water because the hard hull can cause injury in a collision.

Motor vehicles

At a pool, victims can be moved to a first-aid station with little difficulty, but on the beach victims may be some distance from emergency equipment. It is essential that the lifeguard have some sort of vehicle to transport victims to a first-aid center immediately. The vehicle may also be used for routine patrol and to transport rescuers, first-aid equipment, and public-address equipment (for crowd control) to the scene of an accident.

Valsalva Maneuver

When skin diving, one of the most important adaptations you must learn is how to handle the effects of pressure changes in water. Pressure changes rapidly as you descend (go deeper) and ascend (surface). You must keep pressure in the air spaces inside and on your body equalized with outside pressure to avoid discomfort and injury. Clear your ears early and often while descending.

The Valsalva maneuver is a way to open the eustachian tube by blocking the nostrils, closing the mouth, and gently trying to exhale. Swallowing with the mouth closed and nostrils blocked or jutting the jaw forward while yawning with the mouth closed may also work. When the pressure is not equalized often during descent, the pressure difference holds the end of the eustachian tube closed and prevents any further equalization until the diver ascends enough to relieve the pressure. It can be very painful and may cause injury if you are unable to equalize pressure. You should feel comfortable when you equalize.

A four-wheel-drive vehicle is most appropriate for waterfront terrain.

To properly equip a lifeguarding vehicle, waterfront facilities include the following:

- Rescue equipment
- First-aid equipment (which may include a backboard)
- Radio for emergency communication
- Siren and flashing lights, which are used to identify it as an emergency vehicle and to clear a path during an emergency

For routine duties, operate any lifeguard vehicle at a low speed for safety. In an emergency, however, use the siren and lights to alert beach patrons that there is an emergency and that the vehicle is moving fast.

Helicopter

The distance from many open-water beaches to an emergency medical facility can be considerable. In such instances, helicopters offer speedy transportation. Your facility will train with local helicopter services to determine landing zones and transportation procedures. Request appropriate training if helicopter transport may be necessary for your area.

In addition to having the proper equipment to guard the waterfront, as a professional lifeguard, you are responsible for knowing how to prevent accidents and how to educate patrons about their safety.

Waterfront Accident Prevention

Accidents can be caused by any number of circumstances at any swimming facility. If you will be working at a beach, become familiar with the following common causes of accidents in open water and consider how you can help swimmers avoid becoming victims. Your facility is responsible for keeping all public facilities, such as docks, diving boards, ladders, or rafts, in proper repair and safe

Waterfront Equipment List

The following summarizes the equipment necessary for open-water facilities.

- Molded-plastic rescue buoy with handles (also known as a rescue can or a torpedo buoy)
- Rescue tube
- Inflatable rescue tube
- Paddleboard
- Area-specific rescue equipment
- Megaphone, air horn, or public-address system
- Telephone or two-way radio
- Wireless or water-activated alarm system
- Binoculars
- First-aid kit for minor injuries at each lifeguard post and a more advanced kit at each first-aid station
- Universal spill kit (including a biohazard waste bag and cleanup kit for blood-borne pathogen protection)
- Emergency oxygen unit
- Manual suction device
- Automated external defibrillator (AED)
- Masks, fins, and snorkels
- Backboard (with head immobilizer and straps)
- Blankets
- Extra towels
- Boat
- Oars or paddles
- Rescue kayak
- Marker buoys for use in a submerged-victim search and rescue
- U.S. Coast Guard–approved PFDs
- Beach vehicle
- Scuba gear (based on facility requirements)
- Extra rope
- Uniforms for lifeguards
- Polarized sunglasses for all lifeguards
- Sunscreen
- Equipment to protect lifeguards from sun exposure, such as umbrellas

condition at all times. Facilities are also responsible for posting rules, regulations, and hazardous-condition warnings in prominent locations. It is important that the signs are legible and adequately secured. Daily inspection of the beach is important to identify unusual hazards; eliminate hazards as much as possible and post warnings about any potential hazards that remain.

Frequent Causes of Beach Accidents

- People in the water who cannot swim
- Currents (rip currents cause over 80 percent of surf rescues)
- Swimmers diving into shallow water
- Rough play in the water and on the shore
- Failed rescue attempts made by people who are not trained rescuers
- Hypothermia
- Drop-offs, where water suddenly changes from shallow to deep
- Changing bottom conditions
- Swimmers pulled over rocky areas or into piers and jetties
- Swimmers overestimating their swimming ability
- Intoxicated swimmers
- Use of an unapproved flotation device (for example, an air mattress or tube)
- People not wearing a PFD while boating
- Broken glass or other sharp debris
- Swimmers who venture outside the marked swim area

Beachfront safety

To help keep the beachfront safe, follow these guidelines while on duty:

- Do not permit play with rescue equipment at any time.
- Monitor the swimming area for floating debris and periodically check for debris on the bottom.
- Vigilantly guard your assigned area at all times while on duty.
- Know and practice your facility's emergency action plans (EAPs).
- If there is a dock, check it for stability and for protruding sharp objects such as splinters or nails. If springboard diving equipment is present, check it as well.

Keep rescue equipment on the swimming dock for immediate access. If there is a floating dock in your area, suggest that the following regulations be posted:

- Keep the dock clear of all unnecessary equipment.
- Walk—do not run—on the dock.
- Do not push others on or from the dock.
- Do not fish from the dock.
- Do not swim under the dock.

Encourage waterfront swimmers to follow these guidelines:

- Swim only in designated areas and only near a lifeguard.
- Always swim with a buddy.
- Stay within your ability.
- Avoid staying in the water too long; leave the water before you become cold or tired.
- Avoid long exposure to the sun.
- Never swim in an unlighted area after dark.
- Never go on a long swim without being escorted by someone in a boat or on a paddleboard.
- Never swim during an electrical storm.
- Never call for help unless you need it.
- Dive only in designated diving areas where you know the depth of the water.
- Obey all rules and regulations.

Watercraft safety

Boating is a popular recreational activity, but it can be hazardous if participants do not take some precautions and do not know what to do if they end up overboard. The following are some basics of safe boating. Encourage patrons to follow these safety precautions—and follow them yourself when your duties require you to use a boat.

Personal flotation devices

When guarding a waterfront, help ensure that people engage in safe boating practices. By

Rules for Beach Patrons

A day at the beach usually means carefree fun, but lake and ocean waters can hold serious dangers. Encourage beach patrons to follow these common-sense safety rules:

- **Swim near a lifeguard.** U.S. Lifesaving Association (USLA) statistics over a 10-year period show that the chance of death by drowning at a beach without lifeguard protection is almost five times as great as death by drowning at a beach with lifeguards. USLA has calculated the chance someone will die by drowning while attending a beach protected by USLA-affiliated lifeguards as 1 in 18 million.
- **Learn to swim.** Constant supervision along with learning to swim is the best defense against drowning. Children who are not taught when they are very young tend to avoid swim instruction as they age, probably due to embarrassment. Swimming instruction is a crucial step to protect children from injury or death.
- **Never swim alone.** Many drownings involve single swimmers. When you swim with a buddy, if one of you has a problem, the other may be able to help, including signaling for assistance from others. At least have someone on shore watching you.
- **Swim sober.** Alcohol is a major factor in drowning. Alcohol can reduce body temperature and impair swimming ability. Perhaps more important, both alcohol and drugs impair good judgment, which may cause people to take risks they would not otherwise take.
- **Leash your board.** Use surfboards and bodyboards only with a leash. Leashes are usually attached to the board and the ankle or wrist. They are available in most shops where surfboards and bodyboards are sold or rented. With a leash, you will not become separated from the flotation device or risk it striking someone else. You also may want to consider getting a breakaway leash. A few drowning deaths have been attributed to leashes becoming entangled in underwater obstructions. A breakaway leash helps you avoid this problem.
- **Do not float where you cannot swim.** Nonswimmers often use flotation devices, such as inflatable rafts, to go offshore. If they fall off the devices, they can quickly submerge. No one should use a flotation device in the water unless able to swim. Use of a leash is not enough because a nonswimmer may panic and be unable to get back to the flotation device, even with a leash. The only exception is a person wearing a U.S. Coast Guard–approved life jacket (PFD).
- **Wear a life jacket in the boat.** Some 80 percent of fatalities associated with boating accidents are from drowning. Most involve people who never expected to end up in the water, but who fell overboard or ended up in the water when the boat sank. Children are particularly susceptible to this problem, and in many states, children are required to be in life jackets whenever they are aboard boats.
- **Protect your neck—do not dive headfirst.** Every year, people sustain serious, lifelong injuries, including quadriplegia, from diving headfirst into unknown water and striking the bottom. Bodysurfing can result in serious neck injury when the swimmer's head strikes the bottom. Check for depth and obstructions before diving, and then go in feetfirst the first time. Use caution while bodysurfing, always extending a hand ahead of you. Never run and dive into a pond, lake, or the ocean. In a running dive, most people extend their arms out in front of them but hold them below their head. The arms cause the body to stay on a trajectory that could cause the hands to slip off the bottom while the head impacts with the bottom, which may lead to quadriplegia.

By permission from USLA n.d.

Safety Tip

According to the U.S. Coast Guard, the best PFD is the one you will wear! Although the law requiring PFDs on boats says only that buoyant PFDs must be present on the vessel, it makes sense to wear them whenever you are on a moving boat (note that most states do have laws requiring children to wear PFDs on boats). Inflatable PFDs, unlike buoyant PFDs, must be worn at all times to satisfy Coast Guard regulations for PFDs. Like a seatbelt, a wearable PFD can save your life only if you are wearing it.

federal law, a wearable personal flotation device (PFD), such as a life jacket or vest, is required for each person on board any recreational boat. The PFDs must be U.S. Coast Guard–approved, in good condition, and appropriately sized. The U.S. Coast Guard is the public agency that establishes minimum standards for PFDs, and devices approved by the U.S. Coast Guard have tested and proven buoyancy. Other flotation devices on the market designed to help teach swimming are not appropriate for use as lifesaving devices.

PFDs come in many sizes and styles, allowing people to choose the ones that are most comfortable and most appropriate for the situation. The traditional PFD is a buoyant PFD, which has flotation materials inside. Another common PFD, the inflatable PFD, is designed to inflate using a CO_2 cartridge, either automatically upon contact with water or by using a pull tab. While inflatable PFDs are less bulky than traditional PFDs and may be more comfortable to wear, they have important limitations and are appropriate only for people who know how to swim. To meet U.S. Coast Guard requirements, inflatable PFDs must be worn at all times while on a boat and may only be worn by people age 16 and older. It is necessary to check inflatable PFDs daily to ensure that all status indicators on the inflator are green. If the indicators are not green, the device is not serviceable and does not satisfy the legal requirement to carry PFDs. If the inflatable PFD does not inflate properly (for example, if you fall unconscious into the water and it does not automatically inflate), it will provide no buoyancy. These PFDs are not appropriate for use where impact with the water is expected, for example, when waterskiing, riding personal watercraft, or whitewater paddling.

The U.S. Coast Guard approves five types of PFDs (**figure 12.7**):

- Type I PFDs are used for offshore vessels and are meant for situations in which rescue may be slow in coming. Most commercial craft use these PFDs because they are the most buoyant, are good in rough waters, and can hold an unconscious person in an upright or slightly reclined position.
- Type II PFDs also turn unconscious people to faceup, safe positions in the water. However, they are designed for use on inland waters

Figure 12.7 U.S. Coast Guard–approved PFDs.

where the water is calm and a speedy rescue is possible.

- Type III PFDs are classified as flotation aids. They do not turn someone who is unconscious to an upright position in the water, but they are very comfortable for the wearer. Many waterskiers use this type of vest. These PFDs are best used in calm, inland waters and other places where the chances for a rapid rescue are good.
- Type IV PFDs are throwable devices, such as boat cushions, ring buoys, and other items that are designed to be held, not worn. They can be thrown to victims in case of emergency.
- Type V PFDs are designed for special use. The label on the PFD will specify its approved uses. This category of PFD includes whitewater vests, boardsailing or windsurfing vests, and work vests.

Besides keeping you afloat, a buoyant PFD will help to keep you warm in cold water, which helps prevent hypothermia (see chapter 9). A highly visible, colored PFD will make it easier for rescuers to find you as well. For more information about PFDs, visit www.uscgboating.org.

Fitting a PFD

Your PFD should fit properly, with all zippers, straps, ties, and snaps secured correctly. According to the U.S. Coast Guard, a PFD that fits properly will help keep your head above water. If it is too big, it will ride up around your face. If it is too small, it may not keep you afloat. To ensure a good fit, first check the tags to make sure you have the correct size for your height and weight. Try on the PFD and fasten it properly. Lift your arms above your head and have someone pull up on the upper parts of the armholes. You want to make sure the arm openings are not too large and that the PFD does not ride up around your face. Finally, wear the PFD into shallow water to confirm that the PFD keeps your mouth out of the water.

Heat escape lessening position

If you should fall out of a boat into the water when you are far from land, your first concern should be keeping warm until help arrives. Immersion hypothermia, the cooling of the body from suspension in cold water, is dangerous and potentially life threatening. Do not remove your clothes in cold water to help you float. Your clothes can provide some insulation against the cold water and help preserve your body heat. Your survival efforts will be aided by doing all you can to keep warm: keeping your head out of the water and protecting the front of your neck (near the carotid artery), your armpits, the front of your rib cage, and your groin. The heat escape lessening position (HELP) was developed to assist you in protecting these critical areas from heat loss.

To hold the HELP position (**figure 12.8**, next page), while wearing a PFD, do the following:

- Float in a tuck position
- Squeeze your legs together, or cross them at the ankles
- Press your arms against your sides and hold the PFD across your chest
- Keep your head above water

When several people find themselves immersed in cold water, the huddle position may help them survive (**figure 12.9**, next page). Shared body heat and greater coverage of the heat-loss areas, along with moral support, are the advantages of huddling in a group. The position, however, can be difficult to maintain.

Children are more susceptible to heat loss when immersed. Sandwiching the child between huddling adults will help conserve the child's body heat. The body heat generated by the group should cause the water in the area between them to be slightly warmer, thus prolonging the child's survival.

Personal watercraft safety

A personal watercraft (PWC) is a small craft powered by a water jet pump rather than an external propeller. They are operated by someone positioned on, rather than within, the hull. Some are for single riders; others can carry two or more people.

The U.S. Coast Guard classifies PWC as Class A inboard boats (any boat with a hull less than 16 feet in length). This means that PWC are subject to most of the same rules and requirements as other powerboats. As the operator of a PWC, you are legally in command of a powerboat, and you are bound by the boating rules of the water, as well as the laws and standards of safe boating. Know the boating laws and regulations for your state. Remember that PWC have no brakes and can be steered only when the jet is powered. If you stop the engine at high speed— in an emergency, for example—the PWC will continue forward and you will not be able to change the direction.

The Personal Watercraft Industry Association (n.d.) also notes the following:

Figure 12.8 HELP position.

Figure 12.9 Huddle position.

- Federal regulations require all PWC to be registered and to have an identification number. When your registration application is approved, you will receive your certificate of number, title, and validation sticker (if applicable in your state). Follow state and federal guidelines for displaying validation and registration numbers.
- You must have a PFD for each person on board. Choose U.S. Coast Guard–approved PFDs that fit properly and wear them. Coast Guard and state

Rules for Boating Patrons

Boating is a fun way to enjoy the water, but it presents some hazards. Here are some facts about recreational boating accidents (USCG 2009):

- The boat operator causes most boating accidents.
- Fatalities most often involve craft smaller than 21 feet in length.
- Most drowning deaths of boaters happen to people who were not wearing PFDs.
- Drowning deaths usually occur when boaters unexpectedly end up in the water when they fall overboard or the boat capsizes or collides with another object or boat.

Safe boating in large part means using common sense, but it is easy when you are having fun to forget to follow some simple rules:

- If you plan to boat, know how to swim and learn basic first aid, CPR, and boating skills.
- Before you leave shore, be sure you know how to use your craft and what emergency procedures to follow.
- Communicate when you are leaving, where you are going, and when you plan to return (this is called a float plan). Make sure someone on shore has this information and will be aware if you do not return.
- Stay alert to weather conditions. Listen to a weather report before you leave and take a portable radio or weather radio with you for periodic checks. If bad weather arises, quickly move to the nearest shore or safe harbor.
- Have everyone in the boat, including children, wear a U.S. Coast Guard–approved PFD.
- Closely supervise children in a boat.
- Do not stand up in a small craft.
- Do not boat after dark or in low-visibility conditions without navigation lights.
- Do not overload your craft. Do not exceed the load limit on the boat's capacity plate and be sure to distribute the load evenly.
- Anchor your boat only from the bow (the forward end). A small boat can be swamped if the primary anchor is attached to the stern (rear).
- For each nonswimmer, also have a swimmer in the boat at all times.
- Return all equipment to the boathouse. Tell management if any equipment needs repair.
- Do not drink alcohol in or around boats.
- Attend a course on safe boating. Free courses are offered by volunteers from the Coast Guard Auxiliary and the United States Power Squadrons. To find the courses offered in your area, visit the BOAT/U.S. Foundation website at www.boatus.com. Your local Y also may offer a safe boating course.

If you need more information regarding safe boating or PFDs, contact your local safe boating authority or one of the following:

- National Safe Boating Council, www.safeboatingcouncil.org
- U.S. Coast Guard Boating Safety Division, www.uscgboating.org
- U.S. Coast Guard Auxiliary, www.cgaux.org
- U.S. Power Squadrons, www.usps.org

rules also require you to have a fire extinguisher on board.

- Many PWC have a lanyard for your wrist that is connected to the start/stop switch. If your craft has such a switch, it will not start unless it is connected. Do not start your engine without first attaching the lanyard to your wrist. That way, if you fall off, the engine will automatically stop so your craft will not travel far from you and you can swim to it easily.
- It also is recommended that each rider wear eye protection, a wetsuit, footwear, and gloves.

According to the National Transportation Safety Board (1998), most PWC injuries result from collisions caused by rider carelessness, overconfidence, or inexperience. Riding takes practice, so allow yourself plenty of time to take formal training in PWC operation. Always use your PWC safely and responsibly, following the manufacturer's directions. (The Personal Watercraft Industry Association recommends a minimum age of 16 to operate and 18 to rent a PWC. In some states, state law mandates a minimum age for operating a PWC.)

River rafting and tubing safety

River rafting and tubing are popular forms of recreation across the country. While it is best for these activities to happen in the presence of lifeguards, that rarely occurs. Still, it is helpful for you to be aware of the dangers and some basic safety tips. Whether a lifeguard is present or not,

PWC Safety Tips

Here are some tips for safely operating a personal watercraft:

- Wear a PFD that is approved by the U.S. Coast Guard.
- Take a boating safety course. Learn the common boating rules, regulations, and safe practices.
- Refrain from jumping, or attempting to jump, the wake of another vessel within 100 feet of that vessel.
- Boating and booze do not mix. Alcohol impairs your ability to make good, quick decisions. This ability is critical when you are operating a fast and maneuverable PWC.
- Know your craft. Study the manufacturer's manual and practice handling your craft under experienced supervision and in open water well away from other boaters.
- Look out. Ride defensively. Collisions with other boats or stationary objects such as rafts or docks are the number-one cause of PWC injuries.
- Watch the weather. Check the weather forecast before starting out. Be alert for wave, wind, and cloud changes that signal the approach of bad weather.
- Be prepared for cold water. Cold water robs body heat 25 times faster than air of the same temperature. If you fall off your craft into cold water, get back on board immediately.
- Know the area. Do not assume the water is clear of obstructions. Rocks, shoals, sandbars, or submerged pilings can seriously damage your craft or injure those on board. Check marine charts and stay in marked channels.
- Carry safety equipment. Besides having the required PFDs and a fire extinguisher, also carry a whistle or other sound-signaling device and a tow rope. When operating on a large body of water, carry small flares in a watertight container.
- Do not ride at night (between sunset and sunrise). Most personal watercraft are not made with the navigation lights that the law requires for night riding.

National Transportation Safety Board 1998.

participants should take responsibility for their own safety when rafting or tubing. One of the most dangerous aspects of rivers is that the current is relentless. If you are caught against an object, while you are either above or below the surface, you can be trapped by the current. If you end up in river rapids that are not too strong, walk through them by keeping your weight low in the water, with your legs apart to form a wide base of support. Do not stand up straight. If you find yourself in strong river rapids, remain calm. Roll onto your back and float downstream feetfirst to protect yourself from head injury. Once you have escaped the rapids, swim to shore. You might need to swim diagonally with the current, rather than directly against it.

Understanding how to keep patrons safe while enjoying the waterfront will help you perform your duties effectively and protect patrons from harm; however, accidents do happen. There may come a time when you will be involved in a search and rescue, and it is important that you understand and know how to perform the appropriate procedures.

Rafting and Tubing Safety Tips

When rafting or tubing, keep the following guidelines in mind:

- Have each person wear a Coast Guard–approved PFD and, for additional safety where there are rocks, a helmet.
- Prepare before you go. Know the area you will be in—its dangers and its calm spots.
- Know and follow the local laws governing rafting and tubing. If you do not know them, contact the local conservation or park department.
- Be sure you have been trained to handle your raft or tube safely. If you have never rafted or been tubing before, consult with an experienced person before starting your own expedition. Many park districts and outdoor or wilderness stores offer training or can recommend effective training programs.
- Check your equipment before entering the water.
- Be aware of other watercraft in the area.
- Carry bailers, sponges, extra paddles, a first-aid kit, and other safety items.
- Avoid rafting or tubing after heavy rain.
- Avoid alcohol. It impairs your judgment, and you need your best judgment to remain safe.

Search-and-Rescue Operations

Because it is difficult to see in open water, if a drowning incident occurs and the victim becomes submerged, it is necessary to follow coordinated search-and-rescue procedures. Time is critical when you are searching for a submerged victim. Groups of volunteers or lifeguards can search in shallow water, and groups of lifeguards can search in deep water. When searching in deep water, you will have increased mobility and visibility with the proper equipment; mask, fins, and snorkel allow you to search a larger area more quickly than without this equipment.

The person in charge, such as the head lifeguard or lifeguard supervisor, may use the following procedures to initiate a search for a swimmer believed to be missing in open water.

1. If you suspect that a swimmer is missing, activate the emergency action plan (EAP) and alert all staff immediately. A certain number of lifeguards clear the swim area and begin a search in the water while other lifeguards perform steps 2 and 3.
2. If a person reported the missing swimmer, ask the reporting party to give a complete

description of the missing swimmer—including where the swimmer was last seen—and have the person stay in one location.

3. If no one saw the swimmer disappear, make an announcement specifying the name, description, and last location of the missing swimmer; tell patrons where to report additional information about the swimmer.
4. Instruct designated lifeguards (or, preferably, other staff members so that you have maximum availability of lifeguards for the in-water search) to check the restrooms, showers, locker rooms, snack bars, and adjacent areas. Have someone continue to make announcements because missing people sometimes reappear.
5. Depending on the staff available, have someone call the swimmer's home (or check living quarters if the person is vacationing or at camp).

Figure 12.10 Search line using sweeping foot motions.

Shallow-water search method

In shallow water with poor visibility, instruct volunteers or lifeguards to link arms or hold hands and wade in a line across the area. (Avoid using volunteers in water deeper than chest level. Have a lifeguard take the deep end of the line.) The line should progress forward slowly, with searchers making careful sweeping motions with their feet as illustrated in **figure 12.10** and trying not to disturb the bottom, which can lower visibility. When the shortest member of the search line is unable to continue due to water depth, the coordinator reforms the search line using all lifeguards capable of continuing the search through the use of surface dives. A lifeguard should coordinate each search group.

Deep-water search method

In deeper water, standardized search patterns are suggested for specific circumstances. No search can be completed in an orderly manner without planning and practice, but these standard patterns help to simplify the organization of a rescue effort. If a search is prolonged, the chances of a rescue are diminished, and the search may become a recovery rather than a rescue.

When searching, adjust the extent of each sweep of the pattern to the current level of visibility to prevent skipping any area. Also, keep in mind that the victim may not be lying on the bottom. In a line, lifeguards surface dive to the bottom and complete a predetermined number of strokes before surfacing. They use sweeping, semicircular motions with their arms just above the bottom to search. Such movements will avoid stirring up the bottom sediment. To cover low-visibility areas completely, it is important that lifeguards stay close enough together to slightly overlap one another's sweeps and to remain in visual or physical contact with one another. If they cannot see one another, they may miss something between them.

Lifeguards complete the designated number of strokes, surface straight up, and move back about 6 feet before reforming their line and diving down again. A guideline formed with one lifeguard on the surface will allow directional control because the lifeguards will be able to see the guide when they come to the surface. The lifeguard on the surface is responsible for helping the other lifeguards move back to the designated surface-dive location; this is critical to ensuring that the entire area is searched thoroughly. Remember that lifeguards may inadvertently move forward when surfacing, so it is important to back up a few strokes before the next dive (as noted above) to avoid missing areas during the surfacing and diving process.

Where visibility is better, extend a rope between rescuers to maintain spacing. In clearer water, rescuers can rely on sight rather than on touch to locate the victim, so they can remain closer to the surface and expand their field of vision and the area covered. Each facility will have a set of hand signals that all lifeguards and experienced rescue personnel use to indicate recovery or the need to surface.

Search patterns

Begin search patterns in the area in which the victim was last seen. Using one of four standard search patterns—circular, grid, parallel, and diagonal—lifeguards can search almost any area fairly efficiently. Each pattern has its own benefits.

Circular pattern

From a fixed center point, search a progressively widening circle (**figure 12.11**) using the surface dive and reforming procedures already described. The distance from the center point of each circular sweep depends on the water clarity. Expand the circle with each revolution, and make certain that a marker is placed at the starting point to assure complete coverage of the circle. The distance from the center can be readily controlled by a line that is attached to the center point and held by the lifeguards. In murky water, lifeguards may search by touch with the hand that is not holding the line. Try not to disturb the bottom while searching.

A post stuck into the river or lake bottom can serve as a center point. The anchor line of a boat also can be

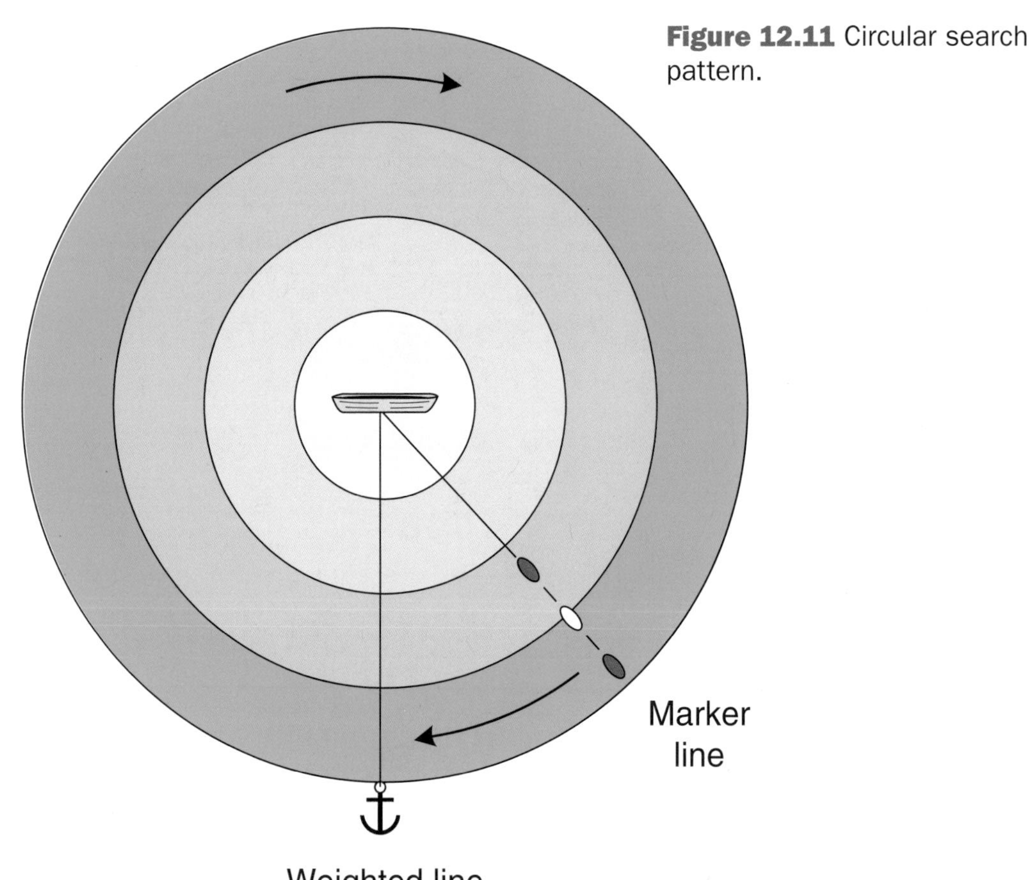

Figure 12.11 Circular search pattern.

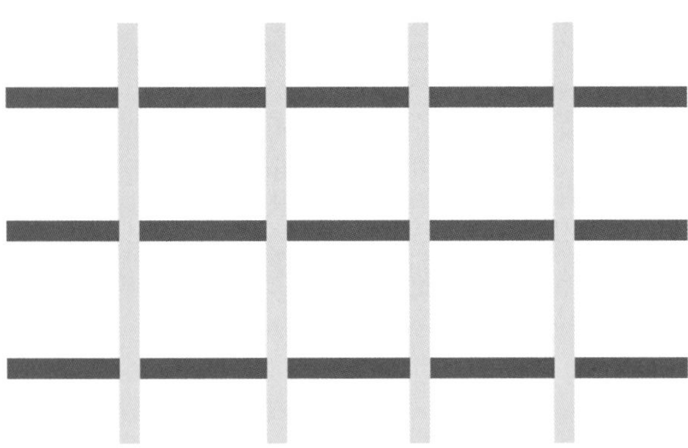

Figure 12.12
Grid search pattern.

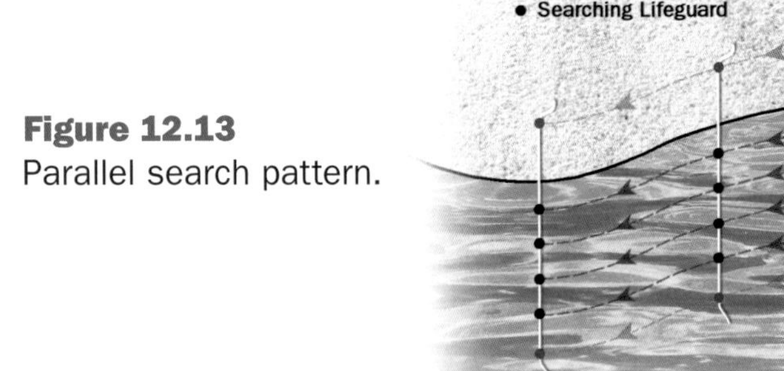

Figure 12.13
Parallel search pattern.

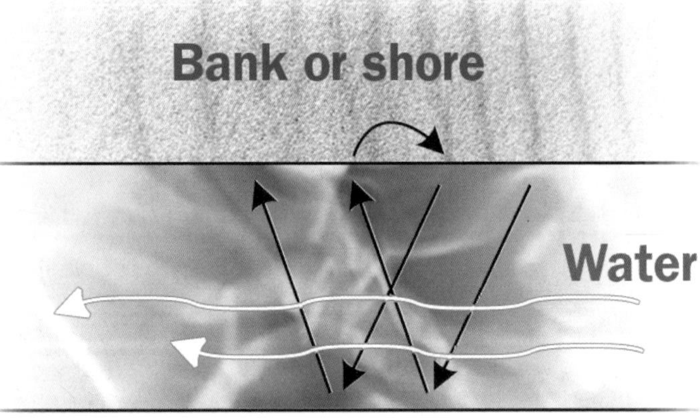

Figure 12.14
Diagonal search pattern.

used for the center, or a weight may be placed on the bottom, provided it is heavy enough to remain in a fixed position. Keep the rope taut during each sweep.

Grid pattern

Divide the area into a grid to be searched by tying ropes to fixed anchors. The pattern, illustrated in **figure 12.12**, allows the area to be covered thoroughly. Lifeguards can search one unit and then another. The size of the units should not be greater than twice the visibility distance each lifeguard has on one sweep. Two or more lifeguards can be assigned to search a unit before moving to another.

Parallel pattern

In a parallel search pattern (**figure 12.13**), a controller on shore holds a line extended to a controller in the water. The controllers walk down the shore, keeping the line taut and perpendicular to the shoreline. The lifeguards conducting the search follow the line, which allows them to search the area thoroughly.

Diagonal pattern

Swim diagonally to the shore (because the current naturally carries you on an angle, this will eliminate the need to fight the current). After crossing the current, return using a diagonal path (**figure 12.14**). Upon reaching the shore, step upstream 6 feet and start a second search. Be sure to keep your search parallel to your initial entry point. It is important to search quickly where currents are involved because the victim may drift.

Choosing a search pattern

It is important that you understand each pattern so you can select the correct one if called upon to do so in an emergency. **Table 12.1** highlights the situations for which each pattern is most valuable.

Table 12.1 Selecting a Search Pattern

Pattern	Appropriate situation for use
Circular	Flat-bottomed areas with little current (Large areas can be searched quickly)
Grid	Areas with irregular bottoms (This method is the surest search method, but it takes a great deal of time and equipment to set up and execute)
Parallel	Areas of irregular shoreline
Diagonal	Areas where currents are likely to have influenced the position of a victim

Rescuing Skin and Scuba Divers

Interest in the sports of skin and scuba diving has been growing. As a lifeguard, you may be called upon to guard a pool or swim area during skin diving or scuba classes, asked to accompany a scuba instructor to an open-water checkout site, or required to rescue a drowning diver in an open-water environment. It is important that you understand the rescue procedures for skin and scuba divers.

Segregate scuba and skin divers from other swimmers so that all groups of aquatic enthusiasts can enjoy safe, adequately supervised experiences. In open water, make sure that the diving area is marked with a flag as illustrated in **figure 12.15**. In some states such flags are required where boat traffic is possible. In a pool, remove lane lines before classes and keep the classes separate from other activities in the pool. Whether classes are in open water or in a pool, it is important to post a lifeguard next to the water who is focused specifically on the divers during the class.

If you guard scuba classes, be aware of these safety procedures that scuba class participants should follow:

- Always lay scuba tanks down horizontally.
- Be aware that placing the mask on the forehead is a distress signal. Do not do this unless help is needed.
- Before entering the water, make sure no one is swimming in the area of entry.
- When skin diving, wear a vest for buoyancy.
- When a diver is exiting the pool on the ladder, do not get behind the diver.

Many national organizations have certification standards for scuba divers. Facility management will set policy to determine which certification ("C") cards will be accepted for allowing divers to use their facility. Safe practices admit only those divers with current C cards or participants in a course led by a certified scuba instructor.

If you will be guarding a scuba area regularly, consider becoming scuba certified and taking a scuba rescue course. This will provide insights into how

Figure 12.15 Scuba dive flag.

scuba diving works and the challenges the divers face in learning and diving.

Skin and scuba diving emergency procedures in open water

Open-water scuba diving emergencies require special attention. Air embolism and decompression sickness accidents (discussed later in this section), in which gas bubbles get into tissues or blood, require immediate treatment in a recompression chamber, so time is of the essence. Where scuba diving is permitted, it is important that facility management knows and posts the location of the nearest recompression chamber and the type of emergency transportation method used to get a diver there. To obtain this information, call DAN, the Divers Alert Network. This agency runs a 24-hour hotline to answer questions regarding diving accidents at 919-684-9111, which can be called collect from anywhere in the world. In either case, always call EMS first, before calling DAN.

Special rescue procedures for open-water skin and scuba divers will vary depending on the area where you are guarding; however, the basics for determining those procedures can be developed through CARE—cognizance, assessment, rescue, and evacuation.

Cognizance

Watch divers for clues about their diving capabilities. Look for the following early warning signs in these situations.

Pool

- Problems or uncertainty setting up the equipment
- Hesitation to get into the water
- Removal of the mask, regulator mouthpiece, or both
- Hesitation to descend
- Problems with equipment, such as checking gear frequently

Open-water checkout dive

- Assembling equipment incorrectly
- Talking nervously about fear of the unknown or being extremely quiet
- Being very slow in getting into the water
- Removal of the mask, regulator mouthpiece, or both

Open-water recreational diving

- Diving alone
- Having difficulty assembling gear
- Being in an environment that is becoming hazardous (perhaps one developing large waves or strong currents)

Assessment

As you guard, continuously observe divers so you can recognize problems as they develop. Like victims of other aquatic incidents and accidents, skin and scuba diving victims may be either distressed or unresponsive victims. (See chapter 4 for more on these types of victims.)

Distressed divers

Divers who are distressed cannot make it to safety on their own. Some situations that may lead to divers becoming distressed are cramps; losing a buddy; overexertion; not wearing proper safety equipment (for example, not wearing a vest when skin diving); seasickness; improper inflation of the buoyancy compensator (BC); or wearing equipment that does not fit properly.

Distressed divers (**figure 12.16**) can become drowning victims in a short period of time. They may or may not call out for help, as they may be using all of their energy trying to keep their heads above water. Some distressed divers can assist in their own rescue by following instructions to inflate their BC or grabbing extended rescue equipment such as a rescue tube or reaching pole. Others may be unable to assist you with a rescue.

It is critical to quickly identify divers who need help—they may have as little as 60 seconds before they slip below the surface. This situation requires your immediate attention. Look for the following characteristics of a distressed diver:

- Arm waving
- Looking for a missing buddy
- Kicking to maintain an upright position
- Looking toward shore, but making no progress
- Shouting for assistance or blowing a safety whistle
- Removing the mask, regulator mouthpiece, or both
- Being caught in a rip current
- Holding the head back with the body very low or very high in the water
- Moving the arms alternately out to the sides and then overhead, raising the body into the air and sinking again, and splashing a lot
- Getting little or no support from kicking
- Being in an upright position, facing the nearest source of assistance

Many situations can contribute to a diver drowning:

- Lack of ability
- Being over-weighted
- Lack of physical fitness
- Malfunctioning gear
- A lost buddy
- A frightening occurrence, such as lowered visibility
- Injury from a marine animal
- Cramps
- Entanglement
- Cold water
- Ear problems
- Running out of air (in scuba)
- Arterial gas embolism (in scuba)
- Decompression sickness (in scuba)

Figure 12.16 Distressed diver.

A

B

The *DAN Dive and Travel Medical Guide* says the following about arterial gas embolism and decompression sickness (De Lisle Dear and Pollock 2009):

> An arterial gas embolism (AGE) can occur when scuba divers surface while holding their breath. The air trapped in the lungs expands and may rupture lung tissue, releasing air bubbles into the circulatory system. The circulatory system distributes the bubbles to body tissues, including vital organs such as the heart and brain. If trapped in these organs, bubbles can cause unconsciousness and death. Symptoms of an AGE include dizziness, visual blurring, chest pain, disorientation, and paralysis or weakness. Signs include bloody froth from the mouth and nose, paralysis or weakness, convulsions, unconsciousness (breathing may stop), and death.
>
> Decompression sickness (DCS) is caused by the formation of gas bubbles in the blood or tissues during or following ascent from an open-water scuba dive that was too long and too deep. Symptoms include unusual fatigue, skin itch, pain anywhere in the body, dizziness, numbness and tingling, and shortness of breath. Signs include a blotchy rash on the skin, paralysis or weakness, staggering, coughing spasms, and unconsciousness. Symptoms may appear within 24 hours after the victim surfaces, but in extreme cases the symptoms may appear before the victim surfaces.
>
> If you are caring for a victim who has either AGE or DCS, follow these steps:
>
> - Check the victim's airway, breathing, and circulation.
> - Contact EMS (can be simultaneous to above if you have assistance).
> - Administer high-flow oxygen (100 percent medical grade preferred).
> - Contact DAN for consultation and information on the nearest recompression chamber.
> - Collaborate with EMS and DAN to arrange emergency transport to the hospital or a chamber, considering DAN's recommendations.
>
> *By permission from DAN 2009.*

Unresponsive drowning divers

Divers may lose consciousness underwater and surface in this state, or they may struggle on the surface before lapsing into unconsciousness. They may also lose consciousness underwater and, due to neutral or negative buoyancy, not surface at all. Unresponsive divers may be found floating at the surface or submerged. They display no active movement. Situations that can cause a drowning diver to become unresponsive include:

- Running out of air
- Arterial gas embolism (in scuba)
- Decompression sickness (in scuba)
- Oxygen toxicity (in scuba)
- Heart attack or cardiac arrest
- Shallow water blackout
- Stroke
- Alcohol or drug abuse

Rescue

An advantage to rescuing a scuba diver is that you can use the diver's equipment as a flotation device to stabilize the victim at the surface and allow rescue breathing. Make sure to bring a rescue tube (or buoy) with you during all skin and scuba diving rescues.

To rescue a conscious diver who is in trouble, proceed in the following manner:

1. Recognize that the diver is in trouble.
2. Activate your facility's emergency action plan (EAP) and enter the water.
3. Perform a conscious victim rescue from the front (see chapter 8). Extend your rescue buoy or tube to the diver to provide the diver with flotation and calm the diver (**figure 12.17**).
4. Tell the diver to inflate the BC and drop the weight belt. If the diver properly follows this advice, assist the diver to safety.
5. If the diver does not grab the tube or buoy or respond to your instructions, press the diver's elbow down onto the tube (**figure 12.18**).
6. Contact EMS and DAN if necessary.
7. Contact risk management and complete the appropriate paperwork.

If the diver is unresponsive, at the water's surface, and facedown, follow these steps (**figure 12.19**, next page):

1. Recognize that the diver is in trouble.
2. Activate your facility's EAP, and have someone contact EMS and DAN.
3. For a skin diver, use the unresponsive victim rescue from the front (see chapter 8).
4. Proceed with a surface approach from the front. For a scuba diver, grasp the diver's right wrist with your right hand, keeping your thumb on top. Turn the diver faceup by pulling the arm down and then back toward the

Figure 12.17 Rescue of conscious scuba victim (from the front).

Figure 12.18 Lifeguard securing victim's arm over the tube.

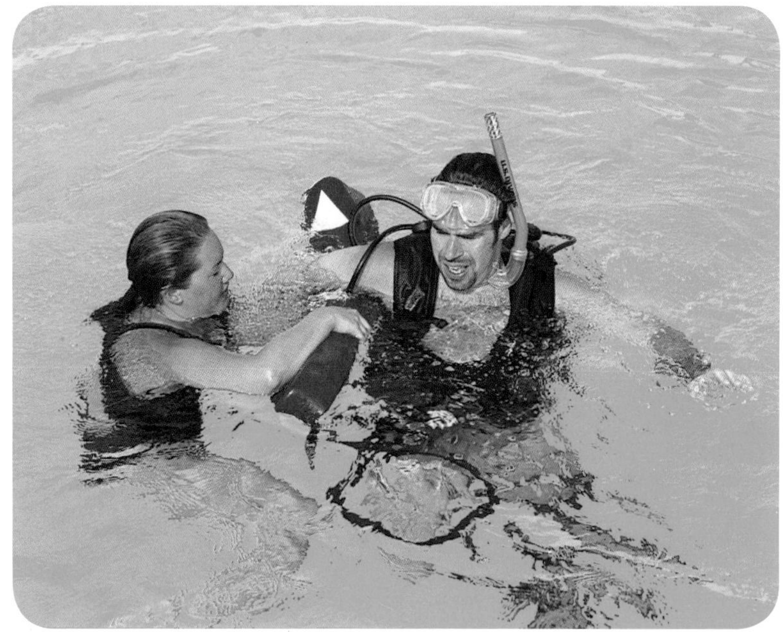

surface in a U-shaped motion. Once the diver is faceup, release the wrist.

5. Move to the diver's side and release and drop the weight belt, if you can find it quickly. Inflate the diver's BC (using the power inflator or manually) to provide buoyancy to the victim. Do not overinflate the BC; it can restrict the victim's breathing. Place the arm closest to the diver's head on the diver's forehead. Place your other arm over the diver's arm and under his or her back. Remove the diver's mask and regulator (**figure 12.20**).
6. Prepare your resuscitation mask for rescue breathing. Using the hand on the victim's forehead, open the victim's airway and check for breathing. If necessary, administer rescue breathing using a resuscitation mask.
7. Tow the diver to safety while providing rescue breathing, if necessary. When towing a diver, use the jacket or handle to tow if possible; use the tank handle only as a last resort.
8. If necessary, remove the diver's gear in this sequence:
    a. Unfasten the shoulder clips at the top of the BC.
    b. Release the cummerbund.
    c. Unclip any gauges that are fastened to the BC (not the tank).
    d. While securing the diver, press down on the tank valve and push the gear away from the diver.
    e. Remove the diver from the water.
9. Once you have moved the diver to safety, assess his or her airway and breathing again, and then administer oxygen.

Although it is unlikely to happen, you may be called upon to recover and rescue a submerged scuba diver. Thus, you should be trained and prepared for this specialized type of rescue, especially if you guard a water area in which scuba activities are conducted. In most of these rescue situations, the use of a mask, snorkel, and fins would help you perform the recovery and rescue.

Be sure to use caution and prudence in doing such a rescue. Do not dive too deep or too long and jeopardize your own safety. Also, do not use scuba equipment to rescue unless you have been properly trained and certified in its use in rescue.

Figure 12.19 Unresponsive victim rescue of a scuba diver (from the front).

A

B

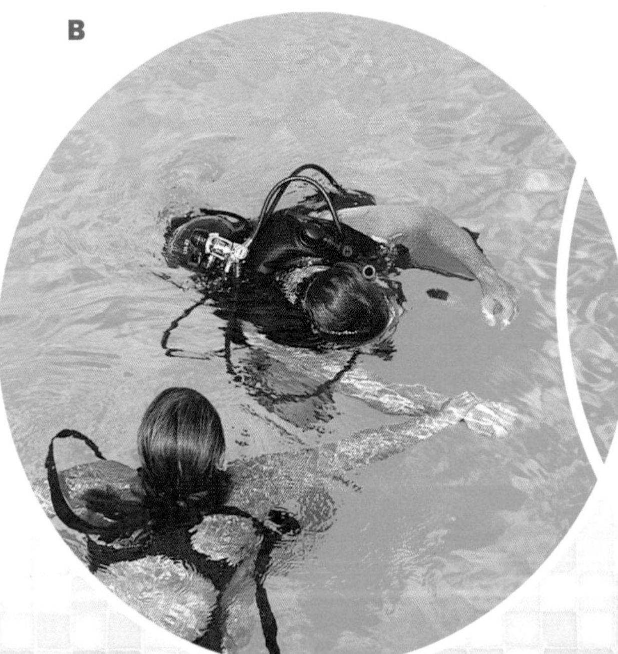

C

If the victim is underwater and unconscious, your priority is to locate and bring the diver to the surface. The sooner this is accomplished, the better the victim's chances of recovery. Once you bring the victim up to the surface, you can assess the person's airway and breathing and initiate rescue breathing if necessary.

If you are called upon to rescue a submerged scuba diver, follow these procedures:

1. Recognize that the diver is in trouble.
2. Activate your facility's emergency action plan and have someone contact EMS and DAN.
3. Put on a mask, fins, and a snorkel, if necessary.
4. Use a surface dive to reach the diver (or start from the last known location if the diver is not visible from the surface), leaving the rescue tube on the surface. Remove the rescue tube if it does not have enough line to allow you to reach the diver.
5. To bring the diver to the surface (**figure 12.21**, next page), approach the diver from behind. Drop the diver's weight belt (if it can be found quickly) and inflate the diver's BC. If the regulator is in the victim's mouth, leave it there.
6. At the surface, stabilize the diver by placing the hand closest to the diver's head on his or her forehead. Place your other arm over the diver's arm and under his or her back. Remove the diver's mask and regulator.
7. Check the victim's breathing. If necessary, provide rescue breathing using a resuscitation mask.
8. Tow the diver to safety.
9. Remove the diver's gear in the order noted previously and exit from the water, reassess him or her, and then administer appropriate first aid.

The skills necessary to successfully complete a rescue of a scuba diver are somewhat different from typical rescue skills. You will need to practice scuba rescue carefully if you are assigned to an area where scuba diving is done. Be sure to learn the procedures your facility has developed.

Evacuation

Once you have rescued a diver, get the diver out of the water as quickly as possible to start emergency first aid. The type of exit you use will depend on the location of the rescue and your proximity to medical assistance; your own size and strength; the assistance available; and the diver's size, condition, and injuries. Exits you can use include the supporting assist, the one-person drag, the one- or two-person lift, or backboarding (see chapter 8 for descriptions of these exits and backboarding).

Injured or unconscious scuba divers may be suffering from an arterial gas embolism or decompression sickness. These conditions will worsen quickly, so be sure to contact EMS immediately. Because these victims may need special facilities for treatment, call DAN to locate the nearest recompression chamber.

Keep victims flat while lifting them onto boats or into vehicles for transport to medical facilities. If vomiting occurs, roll victims onto their side and wipe their mouths clean (protecting yourself from exposure), and then maintain open airways. Administer oxygen if it is available.

Figure 12.20 Removing a diver's mask.

Figure 12.21 Rescuing a submerged diver.

A

B

Missing diver procedure in open water

If a scuba diver is missing (not simply separated from a buddy), take these steps immediately:

1. Quickly determine whether the diver could have left the diving area without notifying anyone. Identify the missing diver's buddy; ask the buddy where the missing diver is or was last seen.
2. Contact EMS. This is a medical emergency. Send for additional help (lake patrol, emergency personnel, law enforcement personnel, underwater search and rescue team, or others).
3. Determine from others where the diver was last seen.
4. Move to that area and look for bubbles.
5. Put at least two certified scuba divers enter the water immediately to search the area using a predetermined pattern. Additional lifeguards can perform a surface search to help identify the missing diver.

Be aware of currents that could alter the missing diver's location. Where currents are present, conduct the search working in a downstream direction.

Additional Training for Waterfronts

As stated in *Open Water Lifesaving—The United States Lifesaving Association Manual* (2003), lifeguarding in open water requires a high level of fitness and training. Beach lifeguards may be stationed in remote locations where advanced medical support can be delayed. They may have other responsibilities such as aiding distressed boaters, law enforcement, cliff rescue, flood rescue, and marine firefighting. In addition, as discussed in this chapter, they may need to operate emergency vehicles, rescue boats, and other technical equipment. Because of this, they require in-depth and venue-specific training. For information on advanced lifeguard training, visit the United States Lifesaving Association's (USLA) website at www.usla.org. USLA provides a training program specifically for surf lifeguards.

Review

Review Topics

Guarding a waterfront is very different from guarding a pool or waterpark. This chapter discussed how to manage some of the unique characteristics of the waterfront. Here are some key points to remember from this chapter:

1) Characteristics and advantages of lifeguard towers and floating lifeguard platforms
2) Equipment and vehicles lifeguards use in waterfront areas
3) Flags used to mark swimming areas and what they mean
4) Hazards swimmers may encounter in open water
5) When lifeguards use skin diving and what gear and precautions are needed
6) Rules for safe waterfront activities: swimming, boating, rafting, and tubing
7) Which PFDs are required for different ages and swimming abilities and for what types of aquatic activities
8) How to prevent heat loss when wearing a PFD in cold water
9) Search methods and patterns for waterfronts in both shallow and deep water
10) How to use CARE to determine rescue procedures for skin and scuba divers

Review Questions

1. Name the additional equipment required for open-water beaches.
2. List some of the key natural, human-made, and situational hazards found in an open-water environment.
3. Name eight common causes of beach accidents.
4. Describe how you would explain to patrons why they should not cry for help unless they are in distress.
5. Describe the Valsalva maneuver. When should you use it?
6. What is a PFD? When are they required by law? List the limitations of inflatable PFDs that can affect whether they satisfy that legal requirement or not.
7. Name the four underwater search patterns and describe how they are performed.
8. Name six early signs of a potentially insecure scuba diver, both in a pool and in open water.

CHAPTER 13

Managing Outdoor Hazards

Lifeguarding outdoors, whether you are guarding a pool or open water, poses challenges beyond those of the controlled environments of indoor pools and waterparks. This chapter will help you understand the outdoor environment and your responsibilities for protecting patrons from its hazards.

In this chapter, you will learn the following:

- Sources of information about weather conditions
- Dangerous weather conditions and safety precautions
- Open-water hazards and safety precautions

13
CHAPTER

Obtaining Weather Information

Knowing your local weather conditions is important to providing a safe environment for swimmers in your area. Although you cannot control the weather, you can take necessary precautions to prepare for weather changes and to protect the safety of the swimmers you are guarding.

The first step is to be aware of weather forecasts issued by the National Weather Service, which are updated regularly throughout the day. A local weather forecast may warn you that a front is expected to move through your area. Barometric changes and sudden shifts of wind direction and speed are sure signs of weather changes. As warm air meets cooler air, moisture in the form of rain or a thunderstorm usually results. The forecast is your signal to be on the lookout for storm conditions.

Sources of weather information

Weather radio

Weather radios broadcast continuous local weather information, including watches and warnings for severe weather, direct from the National Weather Service. Weather radios also broadcast non-weather-related emergency information, such as in the event of a natural disaster, an Amber alert (for an abducted child), or a terrorist attack. A special radio is required to receive weather radio broadcasts. These are available for as little as $30. Many receivers can be set so that they do not broadcast continuously but will issue an audible alert for unusual weather conditions affecting your area.

National Weather Service websites

Your local National Weather Service office provides detailed local weather information, including radar, forecasts, and warnings, at www.weather.gov. Use the site that covers your local area to track thunderstorms and other dangerous weather. From a mobile phone, go to mobile.weather.gov.

Lightning detectors

There are a number of lightning detection devices or systems available for more accurate storm tracking. These devices may help determine how far away the storm is and how fast it is moving, and they can help you determine when it is safe to reopen the pool or waterfront. Some facilities have installed lightning-detection equipment, and often this equipment has an antenna that detects the radio signals that lightning produces. The antenna feeds the signals to software installed on a computer in the facility. The software can be configured to warn of storms within a given distance or to warn if the frequency of lightning strikes exceeds a certain limit. It is important that lightning detectors be used in conjunction with other safety guidelines; that is, if you hear thunder or the sky overhead looks threatening, consider yourself within striking distance of the storm.

Battery-operated personal lightning detectors also detect the electromagnetic pulse (EMP) emitted by a lightning strike. Their small size and affordability are making them increasingly popular with people who work and play outdoors. The devices can estimate how far away the lightning was, and some can even calculate whether a storm is approaching, departing, or stationary. Note that personal lightning detectors are prone to false alerts triggered by equipment nearby that emits EMPs, such as electronic equipment, fluorescent lights, and appliances.

Dangerous Weather Conditions

Lightning and thunder

Thunderstorms and the lightning that accompanies them are serious weather conditions. The body can act as a natural conductor of electrical current from lightning when someone is in the water or touching it, which can result in death. Pools are connected to electrical equipment such as pumps and filters that can conduct charges from lightning strikes, even if the strikes are outside a building. Pools also are connected to plumbing, which can conduct charges from lightning strikes as well (U.S. Department of Commerce 1999). Even if a pool is bonded and grounded, the danger from lightning striking metal bleachers or lifeguard chairs through windows remains a real danger.

Because of this danger, the National Weather Service and the National Severe Storms Laboratory recommend that you do not take any chances when thunderstorms are nearby. Follow your facility's procedures and clear the aquatic area before a storm hits. It is important to clear both outdoor and indoor pools anytime lightning is observed or thunder is heard. Lightning can occur as far as 10 miles from the rain area in a storm, so if you are close enough to hear thunder, you are in danger of being struck by lightning. Since lightning can also occur well after the storm has passed, remain in a safe place until 30 minutes has passed since you last heard thunder.

If you are outdoors, seek shelter from lightning in a substantial building—fully enclosed buildings with wiring and plumbing provide the best protection. Sheds, picnic shelters, tents, and covered porches do not protect you from lightning. If a sturdy building is not nearby, get into a hard-topped metal vehicle and close all the windows. The locker room wet areas are to be cleared anytime the pool—indoor or outdoor—is closed for lightning.

Even when rain-bearing clouds do not produce thunder or lightning, you will want to clear the pool if the rain becomes so intense that it is hard for lifeguards to see or hear and especially if they cannot see the pool bottom. Guidelines for clearing swimmers and aquatic staff from an outdoor area depend on the type of facility, management policy, and the speed of the approaching storm. If there are no procedures for bad weather, encourage the staff and management to establish them, possibly patterned after similar facilities in your area. Once procedures are established, practice them. The safety of those in your area depends on it.

Emergency plans to clear a pool require the inclusion of safe, alternative areas for patrons. In addition to advising patrons to leave the pool, also instruct them where to go and what to do next. For example, people who leave a facility and run across the parking lot to their cars could be exposed to a lightning strike. Be prepared to help patrons find a safe location from the storm.

High winds

High winds often cause changes in water conditions that could present danger for swimmers in the water who are unaware of the change. Swimming pools are not likely to be as affected by the wind as are open-water areas such as lakes, rivers, and oceans. Wind can create or enhance the size of waves, influence currents, and reduce water visibility. In any open-water area, it is necessary for management to set standards for safe wind levels for aquatic activities.

Tornadoes and waterspouts

Whatever your aquatic environment, tornadoes and waterspouts pose grave dangers. Tornadoes occur in thunderstorms in which there is a cold downdraft. Before the cloud contacts earth or water, it is known as a funnel cloud. If it contacts land, it is

Did You Know?

Many people call the flashes of lightning they see on hot summer days "heat lightning" and believe that it carries no threat because they don't hear thunder. Some people even think that heat causes "heat lightning." The truth is that all lightning is produced by a thunderstorm, and all lightning produces thunder. What they are actually seeing is lightning from a thunderstorm that is too far away for them to hear the thunder (NOAA 2009).

upgraded to a tornado; if it contacts water, it is called a waterspout.

Tornadoes

Because tornadoes are associated with thunderstorms, they rarely arise without warning. If you are in an area that experiences tornadoes, your local civil defense should have warning systems and your weather radio (if you have one) should alert you. Typically there are three stages of tornado alert. The first is a watch, which means that conditions are right for tornadoes to develop. The second stage is a warning, which means that a funnel cloud has been sighted or indicated by radar. Finally, in most areas, a siren will sound, which means that tornado activity has been identified in the immediate area and residents should take cover immediately.

Figure 13.1 Waterspout.

Waterspouts

Waterspouts (**figure 13.1**) are tornadoes over water. They can be weak or strong, but either type is dangerous enough to warrant action.

Weak waterspouts form from one of a line of cumulus clouds when winds are very light. Showers, but not thunderstorms, are usually nearby. Weak waterspouts have winds around 40 knots (1 knot = 1.15 miles per hour) and lose strength quickly if they come ashore. Most have no particular direction and usually dissipate in about 10 minutes. Despite their short life, weak waterspouts can overturn objects or throw them around, so it is best to evacuate the water and have patrons move inland at least 100 yards. Because weak waterspouts move slowly, there is usually enough time to get everyone to safety.

Strong waterspouts are much more dangerous. They form from cumulonimbus clouds and are usually accompanied by lightning and thunder. Usually moving in the same direction as the thunderstorm, they may reach forward speeds of 50 knots or more. Strong waterspouts can spin at up to 200 knots and have been known to damage boats and structures on land and to kill people. If a strong waterspout should occur, quickly clear the water and have patrons move to a solidly constructed, permanent structure.

The National Weather Service issues a Special Marine Warning whenever a waterspout is spotted, whatever its strength. If you hear such an alert, follow your facility's procedures for getting patrons to safety.

Fog

Fog occurs when the ground or water surface is warm and the air is cool and moist. The resulting sensation of being inside a cloud can severely reduce visibility and the safety of those in your aquatic area. If the fog limits your ability to see swimmers or boaters in your area of responsibility, clear the water and close the facility until conditions improve.

Fair weather

We do not often think of good weather as dangerous, but it holds some hazards for which you should be prepared. Hot summer days usually bring people to the water. Heatstroke and heat exhaustion and sunburn are just some of the hazards presented by hot weather, treatment for which is discussed in chapter 9. Be aware that hot weather can also affect you and your ability to guard.

Sunburn is not just uncomfortable, it also can be dangerous. The primary cause of skin cancer is prolonged and repeated overexposure to sunlight. According to the American Cancer Society (2010), skin cancer is the most common cancer. In 2006, more than 2 million people were treated for preventable and curable skin cancer. In 2010, approximately 68,000 people were expected to be diagnosed with the more dangerous form of skin cancer, melanoma. To avoid sunburn and to reduce your risk of developing skin cancer, follow the guidance in the sidebar Sunburn Precautions on the next page.

Remember, as the temperature rises—even at an indoor pool—your ability to focus on a task, such as scanning, for long periods of time decreases. In high-temperature conditions, you require breaks more often (in a shaded area), a change of position while guarding, and plenty of water to stay hydrated. See chapter 4 for more on staying vigilant while on duty.

Open-Water Conditions

In contrast with pools, open-water environments have particular characteristics and risks. One of the

Tornado Safety Procedures

- Blow your whistle to clear the water and surrounding area.
- Scan the pool or beach area to make sure the water is cleared of people.
- Move patrons to a designated shelter (an approved tornado shelter or a strong structure) immediately.
- Avoid trailers, garages, and other similar structures.
- Stay away from windows and doors. The safest locations are the center or lowest parts of the building or the corner closest to the storm's approach. Interior restrooms and closets, basements, and spaces beneath stairs are good shelter choices.
- Hide under a strong table, if available, or huddle on the floor covered with towels.
- If no shelter is available, lie flat in a ditch or on a low section of ground. Where there are towers and other large objects, position yourself and others between the approaching storm and those objects. Do not seek refuge in vehicles.
- Monitor a weather station, a National Oceanic and Atmospheric Administration (NOAA) weather radio, or a civil defense frequency for progress reports on the tornado.
- Once you hear a siren warning of the tornado, remain in your safe location until you hear an all-clear signal. Such signals vary; make sure you know the one used in your community.

Sunburn Precautions

- Wear sunscreen with sufficient protection. The American Academy of Dermatology (2010) recommends using sunscreen with a sun protection factor (SPF) of at least 30. Apply sunscreen 30 minutes before sun exposure for optimal protection. Reapply it every two hours and any time after you have been swimming or sweating; no sunscreen is waterproof. Use 1 ounce of sunscreen (a palmful) to cover the arms, legs, neck, and face (pictured).
- Protect your face and eyes by wearing sunglasses and a broad-brimmed hat or a visor. Choose sunglasses that filter out 99 to 100 percent of both UVA and UVB rays. Polarized lenses that are gray, brown, green, or amber are best for reducing glare and eye fatigue.
- Cover up by wearing a uniform shirt. Wear clothing that is rated to prevent UV exposure.
- Take breaks from direct sunshine using an umbrella or a covered patio. Sun-screening UV umbrellas provide superior shelter from ultraviolet rays and are rated using SPF ratings. Some specially designed umbrellas can keep you as much as 15 degrees cooler, which in turn helps reduce the effects of heat on your vigilance and helps you fight fatigue.

To further protect yourself from the dangers of skin cancers, examine your body regularly for lesions and for changes in moles, freckles, or pigmented areas. If you notice any changes, contact your doctor or a dermatologist.

most significant differences is the constantly changing nature of open-water environments. The ocean, for example, may be calm one moment and rough and dangerous the next as a squall moves landward. In any open water, currents may shift, debris may wash in or out, and sandbars may move as conditions change. Sunken logs, debris, and silt or sand buildup on the bottom are some causes of concern for the swimmer who is preparing to run and plunge. Any object underwater can create a danger for the unsuspecting swimmer. As an open-water lifeguard, be aware of the characteristics and dangers of the environment and know how to respond to them.

Water temperature and clarity are common issues of concern in any open-water environment. In most open-water areas, water temperature varies greatly depending on the time of the swimming season. The water is generally colder both early and late in the season. As you learned in chapter 9, cold water can increase the risk of hypothermia for swimmers and lifeguards.

Monitor water clarity, particularly in an area with nearby industry. In the absence of water circulation, certain conditions could make the water excessively murky and unhealthy. Report factors such as discoloration, temperature changes, dead fish, or a putrid smell to management and local health officials. These conditions could pose health hazards in your area.

Oceans

A combination of wind and bottom conditions contributes to the size of ocean surf. The stronger the wind and the sharper the drop-off, the larger and stronger the waves. Rocks and reefs are two additional sources of hazards for ocean swimmers. Be familiar with the surf conditions in your area.

Winds

Depending on the wind conditions, waves can take many forms. The fetch is the distance of open water over which any wind blows to develop waves (**figure 13.2**). The longer the fetch, the greater the possibility of large waves. (Hence, you can expect to see larger waves in an ocean than in a lake.) Large waves can arrive at an ocean beach during periods of locally calm winds. This is because the waves (often called ocean swells) may result from storms and accompanying high winds that took place hundreds of miles from shore. Ocean waves can travel long distances.

Two other wind-related terms are important for your awareness of potential dangers. An onshore wind (one that blows toward the shore) brings debris ashore. Be alert for objects floating or suspended in the waves. An offshore wind, on the other hand, blows toward the water and can carry flotation devices and unsuspecting swimmers from shallow water into deeper water. Be aware of these possibilities and act to prevent swimmers from getting into situations they cannot handle.

Waves

Several terms are used to describe parts of waves (**figure 13.2**). The peak, or crest, is the highest point of the wave, at which it breaks. When an ocean swell arrives at the shore, it steepens and ultimately the top of the wave falls forward. The wave is said to be spilling. Foam describes whitewater; air is trapped in the water, giving the wave a foamy appearance. The shallow area where waves break is known as the surf zone.

Become familiar with the different types of waves (**figure 13.2**). Waves are composed of energy transferred to the water by the wind. While this energy moves forward through the sea, the sea surface itself moves mostly up and down. When it arrives in shallow water—at a beach, sandbar, or reef—the wave becomes progressively steeper, the top tumbles forward and the energy that has carried it so many miles is expended as waves breaking on the shore. Sea waves thus become surf.

If sea waves arrive at a beach with a gradually sloping, even bottom, they tend to break slowly. If they arrive at a beach that is very steep, or an

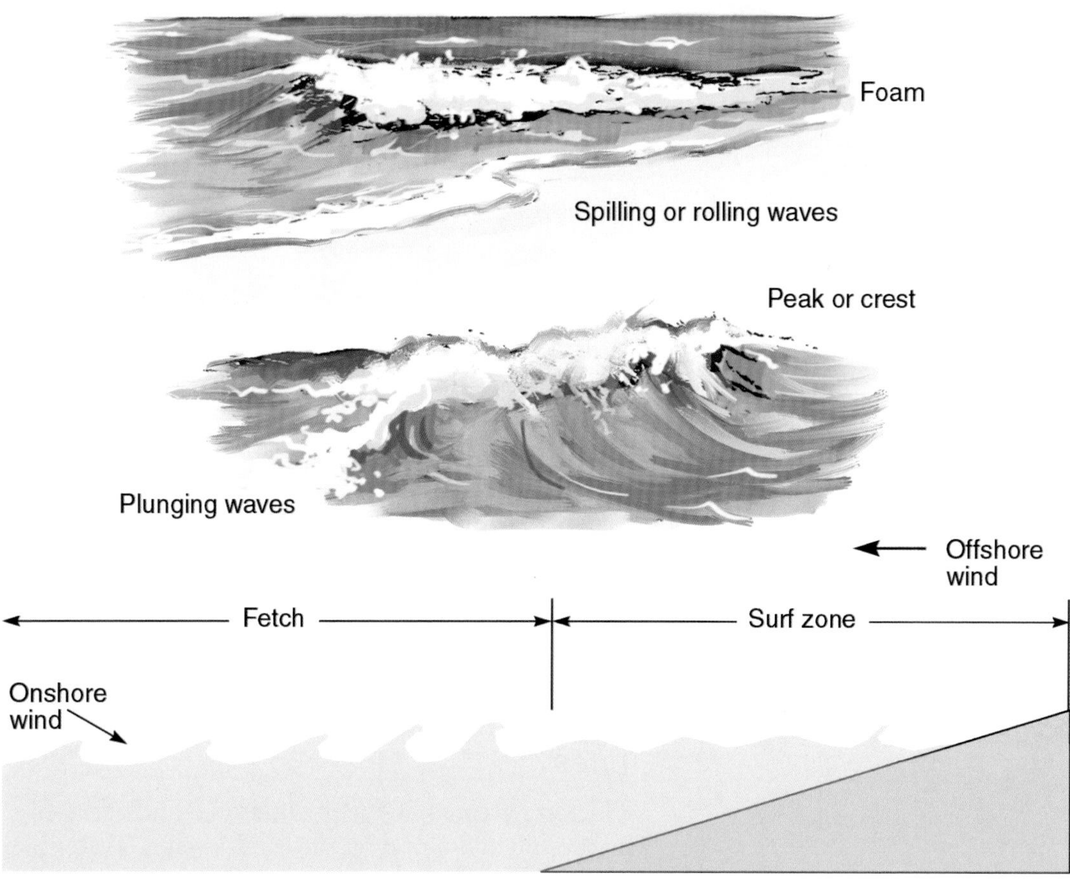

Figure 13.2 Terms relating to wind and waves.

offshore sandbar or reef, they can break suddenly and violently. These are called plunging waves or shore break. These types of waves can be particularly dangerous, especially to inexperienced bathers, who may jump up to avoid the force of an oncoming wave instead of ducking under it. When lifeguarding, you may want to warn such bathers about this danger.

Waves relate to the chief causes of spinal injury in an ocean environment: bodysurfing, bodyboarding, and diving headfirst and striking something such as an unseen shallow sandbar or some other underwater obstruction. Every swimmer should take precautionary measures to ensure a safe entry into the water. In open water, an underwater obstruction could move into the area within minutes. In camp settings, conduct a bottom check each day before the facility opens to campers. Remove known underwater obstructions or identify them with a sign or buoy. Prevent patrons from running and plunging at any open-water facility.

Sets and lulls

A series of larger-than-usual breaking waves is called a set or set waves, and the relative calm of more normal-sized waves between sets is called the lull. Any wave can be dangerous because it could knock down an unsuspecting swimmer. But lulls are dangerous too. During a lull, walkers and waders may move farther toward the ocean, and then be surprised by set waves. Lulls also may give swimmers a sense of false security. Currents can be particularly strong just after a set and can pull swimmers offshore (see the information on rip currents in this section).

Tides

Tides are created by the gravitational pull exerted by the sun and moon on the earth's water. Water is pulled away from the shore during low tide (ebb tide), becoming more shallow, and moves toward the shore during high tide (flood tide), making the water deeper. In the United States, tidal variations usually are greater on northern beaches than on southern beaches, since tides tend to vary the least near the equator.

Tidal flow is usually a gradual process, although at harbor entrances, tidal flow can be very concentrated and sweep swimmers out to sea (or into the harbor). In most circumstances, the primary danger associated with the change in tides is that swimmers may inaccurately estimate the depth of the water in which they are swimming. If there is a sudden drop-off underwater, the depth of the edge of the drop-off will vary according to the tide, affecting people of different heights at different tidal flows. This is a particular problem in a bay. A poor swimmer may panic upon trying to stand and discover that the water is too deep. A nonswimming wader may be waist deep at one moment and underwater a few moments later. As a lifeguard, be aware of these tidal variations in depth and current to protect swimmers from danger. Take time to learn about how the tides affect any area where you work or swim.

Parallel current

A parallel current usually is caused by waves that break on the shore at an angle. Also known as a longshore, lateral, or littoral current, these currents can sweep swimmers along parallel to the shore. Because the natural tendency of swimmers in a parallel current is to swim to shore, across the current, they are usually not endangered, but they can be surprised and concerned if they try to swim to a particular point on shore and are unable to do so because they have been swept alongshore. Swimmers or rescuers caught in a parallel current should not try to return straight to a fixed point on shore, even though it seems to be the shortest distance. Rather, they should go with the current and gradually angle in; this way they will arrive on shore successfully without becoming fatigued from fighting the current.

Backrush

The return flow of water from waves that have rolled ashore is called backrush. Contrary to popular belief, it does not pull objects out to sea. Backrush instead moves down the slope of the beach, under the approaching waves. The strength of backrush, which depends on the slope of the shoreline, usually lessens at a depth of 3 feet or so.

Rip currents

A rip current is a channel of water flowing away from shore (**figure 13.3**). They can occur at any beach that has breaking waves, including the Great Lakes. From the shoreline, rip currents can extend through the surf zone and past the line of breaking waves, sometimes traveling quite a distance out to sea.

Every year in the United States, rip currents are responsible for more than 100 drowning deaths. They create a hazard for all swimmers. While they are particularly dangerous for weak swimmers and nonswimmers, rip currents can sweep even strong swimmers out to sea (NOAA 2005). Because a rip current pulls seaward, it can be too tiring for swimmers to try to swim directly to shore to escape it.

Rip currents are responsible for more than 80 percent of water rescues on surf beaches (NOAA 2005). While they are the most common surf condition for which surf-beach lifeguards must be prepared, rip currents also can be used to the lifeguard's advantage to get to a victim quickly. Waves will seldom break in a rip, which may make it easier for the lifeguard to maintain eye contact with the victim upon approach.

Many factors can influence the formation of rip currents. Primarily, surf breaking on shore pushes water up the slope of the beach (uprush) and as it returns to sea, it can become concentrated. Sometimes this occurs where there is a break in a sandbar or reef just off shore or around structures such as piers, jetties, or other barriers. Some currents are present for a few hours, while others are more permanent.

A rip current usually looks different from the surrounding surf and can be spotted by a trained

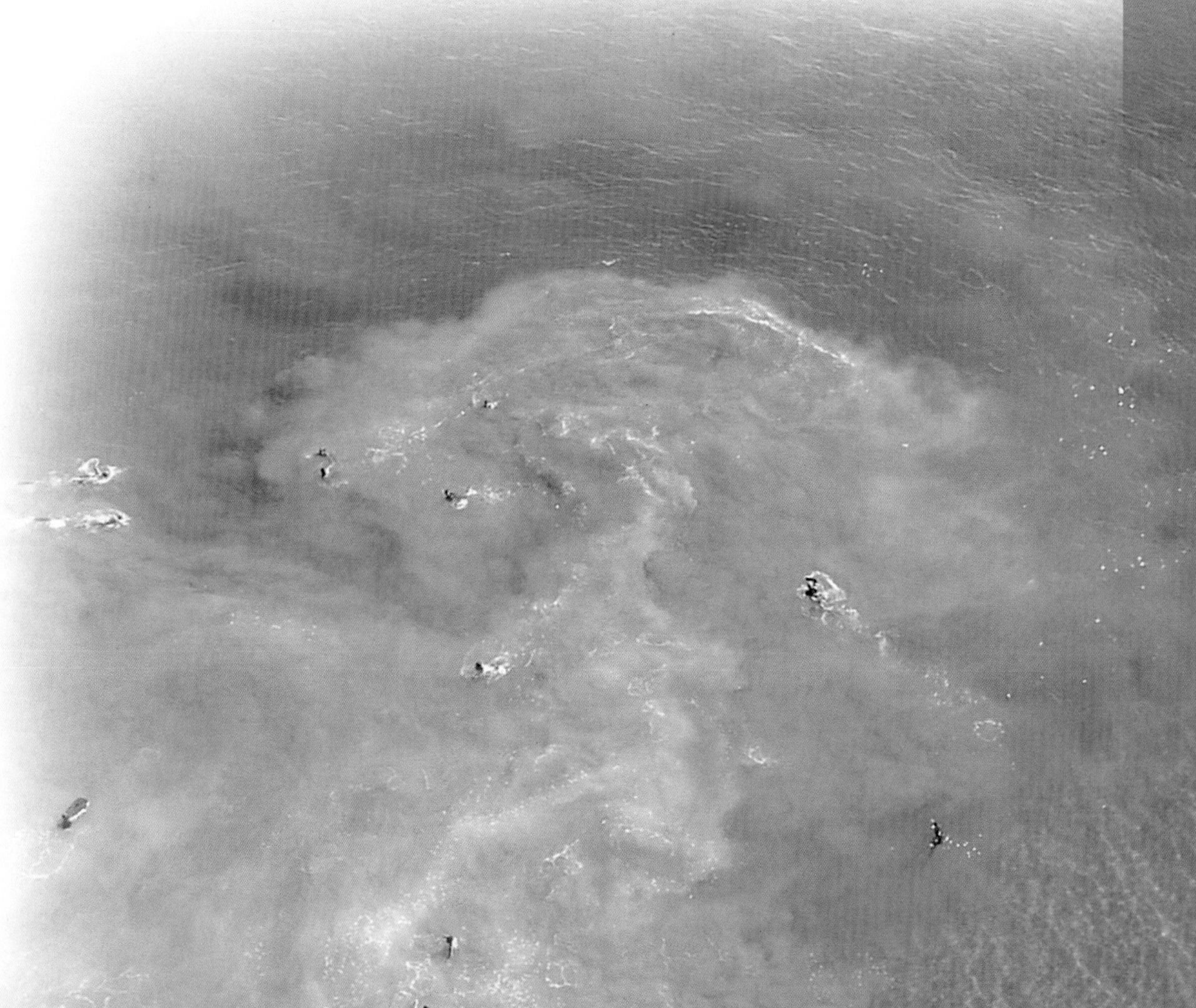

Figure 13.3 Swimmers caught in a rip current. *Photo: John Isgren.*

observer from an elevated position. Learn to spot these currents and keep swimmers away from them. Key characteristics of rip currents include the following (NOAA 2010):

- The rip may be a different color than the surrounding water, either because of dirt and sand stirred up from the bottom or because the water is deeper.
- Waves in the rip may be large and choppy, while the waves in front of the barriers that caused the rip may be smaller and calmer.
- The rip may have an offshore plume of turbid water past the barrier.
- The rip may contain floating debris moving seaward.
- Rip currents have stronger force after set waves have come ashore and a lull begins.
- People swimming in or near the rip will be drawn into the rip.
- A rip may have from one to as many as three feeder currents.

How to Avoid and Survive Rip Currents

Swimmers need to understand rip currents to stay safe when swimming at a beach. If the management for your beach has not already, suggest that they post tips for swimmers such as these (NOAA 2005):

- Always swim with others, not alone.
- Be cautious at all times, especially if you decide to swim at unguarded beaches. If in doubt, do not go out!
- Swim at a lifeguard-protected beach.
- Obey all instructions and orders from lifeguards.
- If caught in a rip current, remain calm to conserve energy and think clearly.
- Do not fight the current. Swim out of the current in a direction following the shoreline. When out of the current, swim toward shore.
- If you are unable to swim out of the rip current, float or calmly tread water. When out of the current, swim toward shore.
- If you are still unable to reach shore, tread water or float and draw attention to yourself: face the shore, wave your arms, and yell for help.
- If you see someone in trouble, get help from the beach lifeguard. If a lifeguard is not available, have someone call 911. Throw the person caught in the rip current something that floats and yell instructions on how to escape. Remember, many people die while trying to save someone else from a rip current.

IF CAUGHT IN A RIP CURRENT

- **Don't fight the current**
- **Swim out of the current, then to shore**
- **If you can't escape, float or tread water**
- **If you need help, call or wave for assistance**

SAFETY

- **Know how to swim**
- **Never swim alone**
- **If in doubt, don't go out**

More information about rip currents can be found at the following web sites:

www.ripcurrents.noaa.gov
www.usla.org

Many beach areas have permanent rip currents, which are always present in some form in the same place. These areas should be a key point in your watch and should be identified by posted warnings or warning flags, especially on rough or windy days. Bottom conditions that do not change, as well as jetties and piers, can cause permanent rips. They may be present for an extended period or may change from season to season. A flash rip current, or flash rip, is a temporary rip current generated by a sudden wave buildup, generally resulting from unusual wind or water conditions changing quickly. Flow from surf and rip currents can cause various changes in the bottom conditions and related hazards to those unfamiliar with the danger.

See the sidebar for more information about rip currents and how to protect swimmers from them.

Marine life

Most aquatic creatures are as frightened of swimmers as swimmers are of them; in fact, most are quite passive unless threatened. Still, some injuries are likely to occur. Some aquatic animals, such as jellyfish (**figure 13.4**) and the Portuguese man-of-

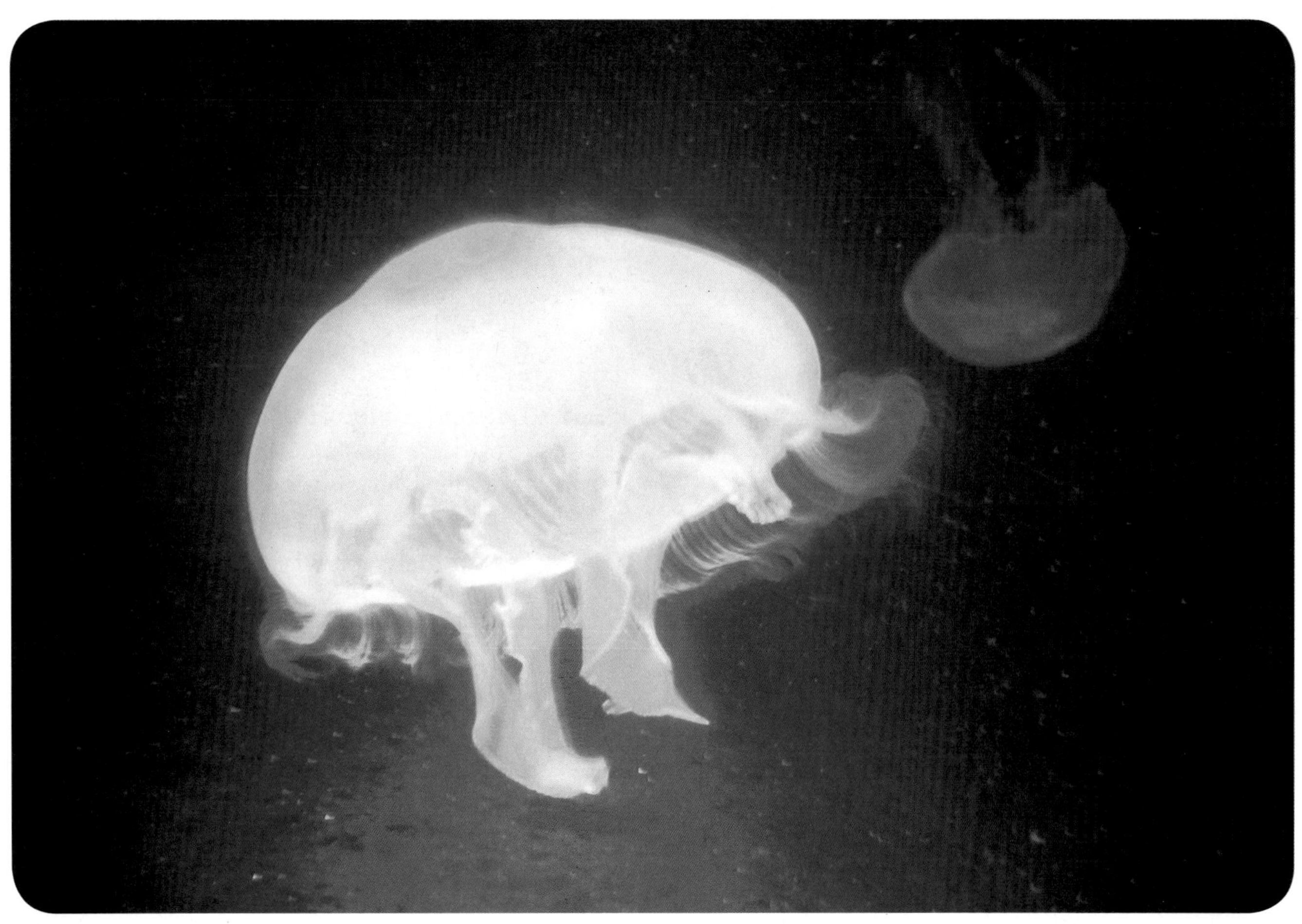

Figure 13.4 Jellyfish. *Photo courtesy of Seann Dwyer.*

war, have long tentacles that inflict painful stings. Some shells and coral can inject venom or inflict sharp cuts. Reactions to these contacts can range from a mild stinging sensation to shock, nausea, and respiratory difficulty. If the reaction is severe, seek medical attention immediately.

There are two main steps in first aid for jellyfish and Portuguese man-of-war stings (Markenson et al. 2010): inactivating the venom and relieving the pain. First, rinse the affected area with vinegar (or a baking soda slurry) to remove any remaining stingers. Second, immerse or shower the affected area in hot water (as hot as tolerable) as soon as possible and for as long as the pain persists. Do not rub the skin or apply a pressure bandage. Encourage the injured person to stay out of the water until the pain subsides. Contact EMS if the victim does not know what stung him or her, if the sting is on the face or neck, or if the victim displays any allergic reaction or difficulty in breathing.

On surf beaches, predatory fish such as sharks, barracuda, and bluefish are threats, and you must be on the lookout for them. Shark attacks are exceedingly rare, and the bites of bluefish or barracuda are usually minor. Most shark attacks occur near shore, most often between the first sandbar and the shore, but sometimes they occur between sandbars where sharks may be trapped at low tide or near steep drop-offs. See the box on this page for more information.

As a lifeguard, you have the responsibility to alert patrons to the presence of all dangerous marine life. Learn about the types in your area so you know the proper precautions.

Rivers and streams

In rivers and streams, as in the ocean, currents can be particularly dangerous because they change so frequently. As currents shift, unsuspecting swimmers can be caught in a current and carried

Avoiding Shark Attacks

Here is some advice you can give patrons to reduce the chances of a shark attack:

- Always swim in a group. A shark is less likely to attack a group of people than an individual.
- Do not swim too far from shore because it isolates you and reduces the ability to rescue you quickly.
- Avoid swimming in darkness or at dawn or dusk, when light is limited and sharks have a competitive advantage.
- Do not enter the water if you are bleeding from an open wound or menstruating—sharks have an extraordinary sense of smell.
- Avoid wearing shiny jewelry, which resembles the sheen of light on fish scales.
- Avoid water with known effluents or sewage.
- Avoid waters being used for commercial or sport fishing, especially if there are signs of baitfish or feeding activity that attract sharks. Diving seabirds are a good indication of such activity.
- Use extra caution when water is murky.
- Avoid brightly colored clothing—sharks see contrast particularly well.
- Refrain from excessive splashing.
- Exercise caution when occupying the area between sandbars or near steep drop-offs—these are favorite hangouts for sharks.
- Do not enter the water if a shark is known to be present, and evacuate the water if a shark is seen.
- Do not provoke sharks.

By permission from Florida Museum of Natural History n.d.

away from shore. Watch for changes in the currents and be prepared to act.

Current strength is very deceptive. If you are caught in a river current, do not try to swim directly against it—you will only tire yourself out. Swim diagonally across the current until you escape its strength (**figure 13.5**).

Never run and plunge into moving water. As in oceans, the current may carry debris, which in addition to being potentially hazardous may change the bottom contour. Such changes make running dives very dangerous.

Lakes, ponds, and quarries

Although the water in lakes and quarries (open, excavated holes created to mine rock) is not as active as in oceans and rivers, the bottom contour may

Figure 13.5 Swim diagonally across the current to escape its strength.

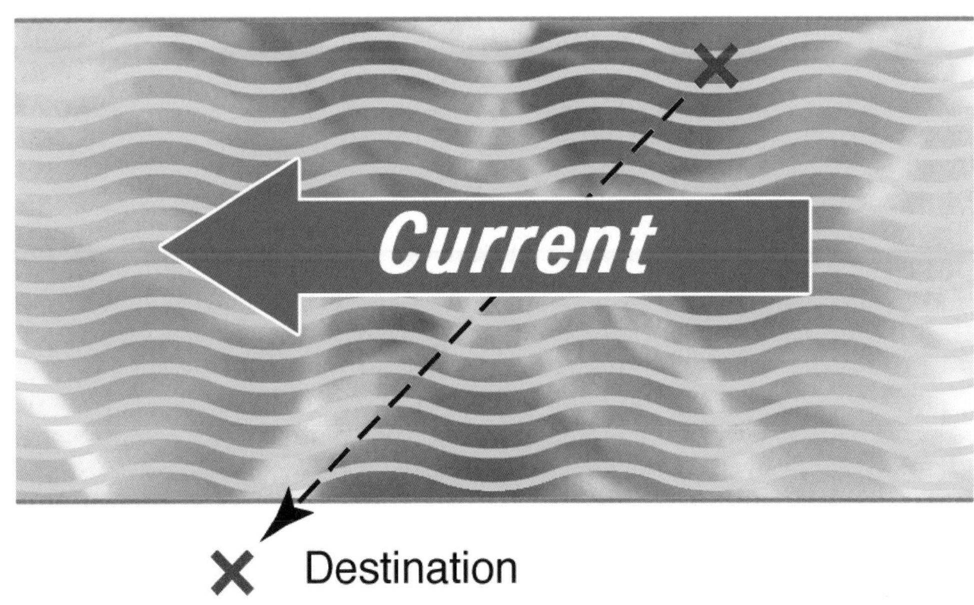

Warm Water Amoeba Hazard

An amoeba called ***Naegleria fowleri***, common in warm freshwater throughout the south, causes a few deaths each year.

Naegleria enters the body through the nose and travels to the brain, where it causes an infection and swelling called ***amoebic encephalitis***. It is nearly always fatal, though it can be treated with antibiotics if caught quickly enough. Symptoms appear—headache, fever, nausea, and vomiting, followed by lethargy, stiff neck, and confusion—usually 1 to 14 days after infection. Death usually occurs 3 to 10 days after symptoms occur.

Naegleria lives in the top few inches of muddy sediment of any body of freshwater and thrives when the water temperature reaches 80°F or above. It can be present at lower temperatures. Warmer water temperatures in lakes that have warmed up over the summer would logically indicate that this amoeba may be a hazard at more northern lakes in the coming years. Flowing rivers tend to be cooler than shallow lakes or ponds and may not harbor as many of the amoebae, though scientists are not certain. Health officials say that the amoeba does not occur in well-maintained swimming pools, but the key phrase is "well-maintained."

Stirring up the sediment suspends the amoeba in the water, so it can reach the nasal passages. Scientists do not know how many of the amoebae need to be in the water to present a danger. Though most of the people who have died have been fairly young, doctors are not certain if age is a factor or if younger people tend to be more active swimmers and do things to stir up the water, making them more susceptible.

For more information about ***Naegleria fowleri*** and other recreational water illnesses (RWIs), visit the CDC website at www.cdc.gov/ncidod/dpd/parasites /naegleria/default.htm. Also see the appendix on RWIs.

still change and present hazards. Wind and wave action can carry submerged debris close to shore and deposit it on the bottom. Artificial lakes or reservoirs may have submerged tree stumps or logs close to shore. Large rocks or boulders may also be under the water in lakes and especially in quarries.

In quarries, boulders, rock slabs, ledges, and even mechanical equipment left behind by former mining operations may create hazards for swimmers. These additional hazards make it important to prohibit diving in quarries. In freshwater such as lakes, ponds, or quarries, underwater weeds and other plant life pose potential danger. The plants themselves are not dangerous, but they catch swimmers by surprise. A swimmer who panics at contact with weeds could become entangled as a result of frantic and erratic attempts to escape. The panic, not the entanglement, is the real danger.

If you encounter weeds yourself, remain calm and use slow, subtle shaking movements to escape the entanglement. If you must rescue someone who has become entangled, your first task will be to calm the victim and get him or her to stop thrashing about. Give the victim your rescue tube or buoy to provide flotation; it will provide some security and give you a chance to untangle the victim's feet. When swimming out of an area of underwater weeds, modify your crawl or breaststroke by kicking minimally to avoid entanglement.

Docks at lakes and ponds present another danger: risk of spinal injury from diving. Prohibit diving from a dock into water less than 9 feet deep. Signs that say "Danger! Shallow Water—No Diving" should be located on dock areas where water is less than 9 feet deep.

The excitement of outdoor swimming areas brings with it certain hazards, some obvious and others more subtle. One key to your effectiveness as an open-water lifeguard is how well you know your environment and how carefully you play attention to its changing conditions. You may have to re-educate yourself about certain assumptions or instincts—swimming against a current, what is dangerous and not dangerous.

Review

Review Topics

Lifeguarding outdoors has unique challenges related to the forces of nature. This chapter gave you tools for keeping swimmers safe from adverse weather, wildlife, and other natural hazards. Here are some key points to remember from this chapter:

1) Sources for news and information about weather conditions
2) Dangerous weather conditions and related safety procedures
3) Dangers of fair weather and related safety procedures
4) Dangers of sun exposure and how to protect yourself
5) Importance of water temperature and clarity
6) Particular hazards of ocean, rivers, and lakes and how to manage them
7) How to recognize, avoid, and escape currents, especially rip currents

Review Questions

1. Name three sources of weather information mentioned in this chapter.
2. Fair weather is not often considered a hazard, but what safety issues does it present?
3. Why is it important to monitor water temperature and clarity?
4. Name five ocean hazards and why they can be dangerous to swimmers.
5. What are the common causes of spinal injury on beaches?
6. Describe a rip current, listing the seven characteristics from the text.
7. Describe how you would coach someone to escape a river current.
8. What is the procedure for treating a jellyfish sting?

OFF THE STAND

CHAPTER 14

Understanding Pool Maintenance

As a lifeguard, your most important job is to monitor the pool area to help prevent accidents and to respond appropriately if an incident does occur. However, you may also be asked to help with some pool and facility operations when not guarding a pool. This chapter provides an introduction to pool maintenance that will help you keep the pool and the pool area clean and safe. You can learn more about pool maintenance by taking the YMCA POOL (Pool Operator on Location) course.

In this chapter, you will learn the following:

- Safety inspections
- Chemical safety and other precautions
- Water testing and correcting pool chemistry
- Fecal contamination risks and procedures
- Common water problems

CHAPTER 14

Safety Inspections and Maintenance

Aquatic facilities require routine inspections for potential hazards. Your facility will have policies for completing and recording inspections. As a lifeguard, you may be assigned some inspection responsibilities when you are not on the guard. Safety inspections are governed by regulations and are an important part of risk management and maintenance planning. Most inspections cover not only the pool or waterfront but also structures on the facility grounds. Be sure you are aware of the procedures to be followed and that you fill out any necessary inspection forms. As a general guideline, inspections include checking the following:

- Deck
    - Deck chairs or furniture
    - Lifeguard chairs
    - Entry and exit areas
    - Surfaces that may become slippery
- Pool equipment and features
    - Pool bottom
    - Filtration system
    - Drain areas
    - Ladders
    - Lifelines and lane lines
    - Diving areas, including boards and stands

- Starting blocks
- Slides
- Play elements
- Signage
- Water
  - Clarity
  - Chemical readings
  - Temperature
- Equipment
  - Radio or phone system for ordinary communications
  - Emergency communication system
  - First-aid and emergency equipment
- General environment
  - Air temperature
  - Entry and exit areas
  - Water fountains
  - Lights
  - Shower and locker room areas

Record and report the results of your inspection to facility management. Problems noted in any of the above areas require maintenance to fix the condition and to protect patron safety as well as to guard against legal action in the event of any related injury. In any situation when you are aware of a hazard that requires maintenance attention, keep patrons away from that area until the hazard is removed or fixed.

Among the regulations governing safety inspections and maintenance that you are required to be aware of is the federal Virginia Graeme Baker (VGB) Act, which took effect in 2008. Named for a 7-year-old girl who was trapped by a hot-tub drain and drowned, the VGB Act requires specific types of drain covers and maintenance standards for all public and private pools and spas. While management is responsible for installation and maintenance of all material regulated by VGB standards, as a lifeguard, expect to be held responsible for inspecting drains, inlet covers, and other hardware before your shift and for immediately reporting any concerns to management. While on duty, keep children from exploring grates and other hardware and monitor water clarity to ensure all areas of your zone are visible at all times.

In addition to regular inspections, daily maintenance is also key to a clean and safe aquatic facility. Testing pool water; sweeping walkways and locker room floors; emptying trash cans; and disinfecting floors, benches, toilet seats, and fixtures are all important to the cleanliness and healthfulness of your facility.

Chemical Safety

Because you may be asked to assist in handling pool chemicals, be aware of the potential dangers involved with these materials. Federal right-to-know legislation requires employers to inform and train staff who may be exposed to chemicals (or leaks or spills) about chemical handling and personal protection. An important part of this requirement is that employers provide material safety data sheets (MSDS) for each chemical in use. MSDS provide information on the properties of a chemical, necessary safety precautions and safe-handling instructions, and potential health effects and emergency procedures. By Occupational Safety and Health Administration (OSHA) standards, employers are required to provide this information and training to employees before requiring employees to work with harmful chemicals.

Another safety requirement of employers is labeling all hazardous materials with the appropriate names

First Aid for Chemical Accidents

In the event of a chemical accident, **call EMS immediately**. To flush eyes, whenever possible use an eyewash unit (pictured).

Chlorine gas

In case of inhalation of chlorine gas, remove the victim from the area and keep him or her warm and quiet. Place the victim on his or her back with the head elevated. If the victim is breathing, administer oxygen. If the victim is not breathing, begin rescue breathing or CPR immediately, supplementing it with oxygen.

Liquid chlorine

In the case of skin contact with liquid chlorine, flush the skin with cold water. If the chemical splashes on clothing, remove and wash the skin with cold water. If the victim has swallowed liquid chlorine, have someone call the poison control center in your area after calling EMS. If liquid chlorine gets in the eyes, flush them with cold water for 15 to 30 minutes. A hospital visit is recommended whenever liquid chlorine makes contact with a person's eyes.

Hydantoin bromine

If liquid hydantoin bromine gets in the eyes, flush them with cold water for 15 to 30 minutes. If clothing is splashed with the chemical, remove the clothing and wash the skin with cold water. For contact with skin, flush with cold water. If the victim has inhaled fumes from a dry chemical fire, give oxygen. If the victim has swallowed the chemical, have someone call the poison control center in your area after calling EMS.

Dry chlorine compounds

In case of skin contact with dry chlorine compounds such as calcium or lithium hypochlorite and chlorinated cyanurates or sodium bisulfate, flush the skin with cold water. In case of contact with eyes, flush them with cold water for 15 to 30 minutes. For contact with clothing, remove the clothing and flush the skin with cold water. If the victim has inhaled fumes from a chemical fire, give oxygen. If the chlorine compound was swallowed, have someone call the poison control center in your area after calling EMS.

Muriatic acid (hydrochloric acid)

In case of contact with skin or eyes, flush with cold water for 15 to 30 minutes. If clothing is splashed, remove the clothing and flush the skin with cold water for 15 to 30 minutes.

Soda ash or diatomaceous earth

In case of skin contact, flush the skin with cold water. If in the eyes, flush them with cold water for 15 to 30 minutes. If the victim inhaled large amounts of the substance, have someone call EMS.

Test kit reagent

If the reagent comes in contact with the skin, flush it with cold water. In case of contact with eyes, flush them with cold water for 15 to 30 minutes. For contact with clothing, remove the clothing and flush the skin with cold water. If the chemical was swallowed, have someone call the poison control center in your area after calling EMS.

and warnings. It is critical that hazardous materials signs be posted on the doors of filter rooms and chemical storage rooms. (See chapter 6 for an example of a hazardous materials sign.)

Before you move or use a chemical, consult the safety signs and the MSDS to ensure that you know how to safely handle that substance. If you have questions or are unsure, contact your pool operator or management before you attempt to assist in chemical operations.

When asked to work with pool chemicals, follow the guidelines on the MSDS and use these general safety precautions:

- Never smoke near chemicals.
- Wear a dust mask or breathing apparatus, rubber gloves, a wide-brimmed hat, a rubber apron, and rubber boots when handling chemicals.
- Avoid inhaling the fumes or dust of any chemical.
- Avoid spilling chemicals on your clothes or body.
- Avoid mixing chemicals together.
- Always add acid to water—never add water to acid—when diluting.
- Dissolve powders or crystals in warm water before adding them to the pool.
- Add to the pool when the pool is not in use.
- Divide the total amount required of a chemical into three equal parts. Add one-third of the chemical every 3 to 4 hours.
- Use chemical feed pumps and control the amount of the chemical that is released.
- Avoid adding chemicals to vacuum filter tanks, skimmers, or gutters.

Be sure that you understand and practice your facility's plans for chemical emergencies. In the event of a chemical accident, contact EMS, fire department, or hazardous materials team immediately. For additional help, contact the Chemical Transportation Emergency Center (CHEMTREC) at 800-424-9300. These professionals can provide advanced care for the victim. While awaiting help, you can provide some emergency first aid. See the sidebar First Aid for Chemical Accidents for steps you can take in the event of a chemical accident.

Check that the phone number of the poison control center in your area is posted by phones in the aquatic area. Call the center and EMS whenever chemicals have been inhaled, absorbed, or swallowed.

Other Safety Concerns

Because of the presence of water in pool environments, things you might take for granted as being safe require additional attention and care in aquatics. Electrical devices, surfaces that may become slippery, and effective signage all require your monitoring to help ensure a safe environment for patrons.

Pools pose the potential for electrical shock because electrical outlets and fixtures in aquatic facilities may come in contact with water. The National Electrical Code has established stringent requirements for the location of electrical fixtures in pool areas. Outlets are typically required to have covers and ground-fault circuit interrupters. Your facility is required to meet these safety requirements, but it is also critical to exercise caution and common sense in preventing electrical accidents. Refrain from using any electronic devices, such as music players or portable electric fans, near the water's edge. Be careful not to stand in water while plugging a device into an electrical outlet. Do not use extension cords in the pool area.

In and around pools and other water recreation attractions, surfaces may become slippery. Be sure to follow your facility's procedures for regularly checking and cleaning surfaces that have the potential to become a hazard should patrons slip and fall.

Another aspect of facility safety that you can assist management to monitor and maintain is proper signage. It is important that patrons can easily see and understand the rules and warnings for the safe use of a facility. You can help protect patron safety by checking that signs are visible, not worn or otherwise hard to read, and that they are up-to-date and accurately reflect the facility's equipment and precautions. Notify management of any problems with signage and follow your responsibilities as a lifeguard to communicate and enforce rules.

Figure 14.1 Example of a filtration system.

Cleaning the Pool

Each aquatic facility has its own systems and procedures for cleaning and maintaining the pool environment. Filtration systems and vacuums can remove foreign particles and debris and help keep the water clear, which is important to visibility and also makes the pool more attractive for patrons.

Filtration systems

In general, the filtration system in a pool (**figure 14.1**) is designed to continuously recirculate the water, keeping it clean, safe, and enjoyable for all swimmers. If the filtration system is working properly, all the water in the pool will pass through the filter every 6 to 8 hours.

The system serves a number of important functions:

- Removes hair, lint, leaves, and other items
- Filters out any impurities that are dissolved in the water
- Adds fresh water to replace water lost through leakage, splashing, evaporation, cleaning, and skimming

A filtration system has a catcher that removes foreign matter from the water. This protects the pumping unit. If debris flows through the system, it causes unnecessary wear and reduces the pump's effectiveness.

Pool vacuums

While filters remove the fine dirt that is suspended in the water, some matter settles to the pool bottom. Removing this residue takes some of the strain off the filters and improves the clarity of the water, which is important to scanning, and makes the pool more attractive.

The extra dirt can be removed by a pool vacuum. There are various models of vacuums available, and your management will train you in the proper operation of the one used at your facility. In smaller pools, vacuuming can be done from the deck using a long pole with a vacuum head attached; the operator moves the vacuum head along the bottom of the pool. In larger pools, automatic vacuums may be used to move across the pool bottom.

Regardless of the type of vacuum used, the best time to vacuum is in the morning when no one is in the pool. Sediment tends to settle overnight and is most effectively cleaned before the pool is opened.

Testing Pool Water

Maintaining safe, clean water for swimming requires the use of chemicals to kill bacteria and to keep the proper pH balance. The correct balance of pool chemistry helps reduce the risk of communicable diseases, damage to the filtration system, and growth of algae, and it helps to keep patrons comfortable in the water. Pool chemistry is monitored by testing the water. For proper testing, aquatic facilities require a commercial-grade testing kit (**figure 14.2**) that measures disinfectant levels, pH, alkalinity, and calcium hardness (dissolved minerals). It is also important to test the water for the amount of total dissolved solids (TDS)—the sweat, lotions, hair spray, disinfectants, minerals, and other solids that would be left if all of the pool water evaporated.

Figure 14.2 Example of a commercial-grade testing kit.

Monitoring pH

The water's pH is the most commonly known measure of pool water chemistry, and it can affect swimmers' comfort as well as the life span of equipment. All substances have a pH factor, which is measured on a 0.0 to 14.0 scale. Those substances with a pH between 0.0 and 6.9 are considered acidic; those with a pH between 7.1 and 14.0 are considered basic. Water that is acidic causes swimmers' eyes to burn and is corrosive to pool equipment. When water is basic, it can cause scale formation on surfaces in the pool, make chlorine less effective as a disinfectant, and make water cloudy. This is why an appropriate balance of the water's pH level is important. The recommended pH for pool water is within the range of 7.2 to 7.5.

The pH level is also affected by anything that goes into the pool, such as anything that may be on swimmers' bodies or other chemicals. This is why it is recommended that facilities test the pH of pool water every two hours. Your facility's procedures will tell you how often to test the water while the pool is in use. More frequent testing may be necessary depending on the number of swimmers, the temperature, and other factors. If you are responsible for adding chemicals to maintain the proper balance, you will need additional training (such as that provided by the YMCA Pool Operator on Location course). At the very least, you require

> **Remember**
>
> While on duty, a lifeguard's job is to be vigilant and guard the pool. Do not test water while on duty. Instead, an off-duty lifeguard or aquatic staff member should complete the water tests.

knowledge of the kind and quantity of chemicals to add to maintain the balance of the pool and how and when to administer the chemicals safely. As with all pool chemicals, add them to the pool only when no one is in the pool and wait the appropriate amount of time (at least 15 minutes) before allowing people to reenter pool water.

Lowering pH

If the water becomes too basic, that is, the pH level is too high, your facility will use chemicals to lower the pH level. The most common chemicals used to lower pH are acid or carbon dioxide. Follow the safety protocols established by your facility if asked to administer these chemicals. Be especially aware of high pH levels if your pool uses liquid chlorine (sodium hypochlorite) as a disinfectant because it has a very high pH and will raise the pH level of the pool's water.

Raising pH

Similarly, if pool water becomes too acidic, that is, if the pH level is too low, your facility will use chemicals to raise the pH level. The substances used to raise pH are soda ash (sodium carbonate) or caustic soda (sodium hydroxite). Follow your facility's procedures for the safe administration of these chemicals if you are asked to handle them. Be especially alert to low pH levels if your pool uses gas chlorine as a disinfectant because it lowers pH in pool water.

Water balance

Controlling the water's pH is one part of maintaining balanced pool chemistry. Other characteristics of water that affect people's comfort and safety as well as the efficiency and maintenance of pool equipment include total alkalinity, calcium hardness, and total dissolved solids (TDS). The Langelier Saturation Index measures each of these qualities and is a tool that aquatic facilities use to monitor and maintain the proper balance of water chemistry.

Langelier Saturation Index

The Langelier Saturation Index (LSI) uses five variables to calculate water balance: pH, temperature, calcium hardness, alkalinity, and total dissolved solids. Computing the LSI once a week helps ensure proper water balance at a specific pool temperature. This index is important because unbalanced water can affect both patron comfort and the life of the pool itself and the pool's operating system. For additional information about the LSI, consult the *YMCA Pool Operations Manual* (3rd edition).

Pool volume calculation

Chemical testing of pool water usually requires you to know the volume of water in the pool, sometimes known as *facility capacity*. A variety of formulas exist for calculating pool volume based on the type of pool. Once you know the capacity, you can then determine the quantity of chemicals needed following the manufacturer's instructions for proper chemical application.

In general, you can determine the volume of a rectangular pool by using the following formula:

$$\text{Volume in gallons} = (\text{length} \times \text{width} \times \text{average depth}) \times 7.5$$

Where 7.5 is the number of gallons in a cubic foot of water, and the average depth is calculated by adding the depth of the shallow and deep ends and then dividing that number by 2.

Disinfecting Pool Water

Chlorine is the most common chemical used as a water disinfectant. It acts quickly and remains in the water for continuous disinfection. Although chlorine can be corrosive and poisonous, it does not pose any great difficulty in distribution or handling when safe-handling procedures are followed.

A common method of chlorination is using hypochlorites in liquid, granular, or powder form. Hypochlorites are compounds that can produce HOCl, a disinfecting compound. Such substances are applied by a chemical feeder that must operate constantly to maintain a steady amount of free chlorine residual in the water.

Water must be tested for the residual, or free available, chlorine. Residual chlorine is the amount of chlorine in pool water that is available to clean the water by chemically bonding with contaminants. YMCA of the USA recommends that chlorine levels be between 2 to 3 ppm (parts per million) for water temperatures 86°F or lower and 3 to 5 ppm for water that is warmer. The acceptable level of chlorine residual varies among states, so check with your health department to learn the local standards.

To check the level of chlorine residual, you can use the colorimeter test. This involves mixing a sample of pool water with the test solution in a test tube. The solution changes color immediately, indicating the amount of chlorine residual present. By comparing the color to a fixed scale, you can determine the amount of chlorine residual in a few seconds.

An FAS-DPD test kit is best for determining both free and combined chlorine levels. The test is complete when the red color in the sample tube turns crystal clear. There are also electronic testing devices available. Your management team will determine the best testing tools for your facility.

Fecal Contamination of Pool Water

Fecal matter in the water is a very serious incident that requires immediate action. Feces can cause recreational water illness (RWI) and can transmit many different bacteria, viruses, and parasites, including blood-borne pathogens.

Preventing fecal contamination

You can reduce the occurrence of fecal accidents in several ways. One action you can take is to encourage parents to take their children to the restroom during scheduled breaks, when the lifeguards can test water quality. To prevent transmission of germs and to encourage people to use the restrooms, help management monitor and make sure that the facilities are clean, restrooms have toilet paper, and there is ample soap for hand washing.

Management may find it helpful to post signs with the following guidelines. You can use the signs to help inform and remind patrons of these safety measures:

- Infants and preschoolers must wear plastic covers with tight elastic legs.
- Do not enter the water if you have diarrhea.
- Wash your child thoroughly, especially the bottom, with soap and water before entering the pool.
- Do not swallow the pool water.
- Change diapers in the restroom and not at poolside.
- Take your child to the restroom often.
- Wash your hands with soap and water after using the restroom or changing diapers.

Encourage swimmers to shower with soap and water before entering the pool. This could reduce the risk of pool contamination by removing invisible fecal matter from their bodies. A quick rinsing of cold water over a swimsuit will not do much good. It is helpful if hot water is available in swimmers' shower facilities.

Other precautions against fecal contamination include maintaining chemical feed equipment and pool chemicals at optimal levels within state and local government regulations. Management can prevent facilities from running out of chlorine through regular monitoring and system checks. When monitoring chlorine levels, check the water in the pool itself, rather than using samples taken from the filter room. Remember that poor pH control can compromise chlorine's effectiveness as a disinfectant.

If your facility operates a wading pool and its filtration system is connected with other pools, this increases the chance that fecal contamination can be dispersed from the wading pool to the other pools. Your facility might consider keeping diapered children in pools with closed filtration systems.

Cleanup procedures

Upon finding any amount of fecal matter in the pool, notify your aquatic director or pool manager immediately so he or she can activate your facility's cleanup policy. YMCA of the USA recommends the following cleanup procedures for different kinds of fecal contamination (following CDC requirements, which can be found at www.cdc.gov/healthywater/swimming/):

- **Solid feces, high chlorine level:** If the feces are solid and the free chlorine level is 2.0 ppm or higher, clear the pool, remove the fecal matter, and confirm that the free chlorine level in three different locations is 2.0 ppm or higher. Take samples from shallow, transitional, and deep water, and not from water in front of inlets. Close the pool for 30 minutes.
- **Solid feces, low chlorine level:** If the feces are solid and the free chlorine level is below 2.0 ppm, follow the same steps as in the previous example. However, in this case, after closing the pool, treat the water until the free chlorine residual is 2.0 ppm in three different locations. Do not reopen the pool until 30 minutes after the free chlorine residual has reached 2.0 ppm.
- **Diarrhea/cryptosporidium contamination:** If the feces are liquid and include particulates, or if the person who had the fecal accident has had diarrhea in the last two weeks, or if your health department has identified your pool as the source of cryptosporidium, a parasite that causes diarrhea, use the more extensive procedures on the CDC's Healthy Swimming website (www.cdc.gov/healthywater/swimming/).

For more information on the prevention and control of fecal contamination in swimming pools, see the appendix.

Common Water Problems

Water problems begin when the water is not tested systematically and adjusted to maintain proper disinfectant levels. When the water chemistry becomes unbalanced, the following problems may result:

- Low levels of disinfectant
- Algal growth
- Turbidity, or cloudiness

Low levels of disinfectant

Safe swimming requires your facility to maintain an appropriate level of disinfectant in the water. The amount of free chlorine residual or other disinfecting chemical in the water may decline for a number of reasons:

- Increased bather load
- Use of old chemical disinfectant
- Slow circulation at the end of the filter cycle
- Increased sunlight and air temperature
- Wave and water action from pool activities

Algal growth and control

Algae are slimy green or brown plant organisms that grow in pools that are not maintained well. Because wind and rain can introduce algae to water, growth of algae is more of a problem in outdoor than in indoor pools. If conditions are right, algae can multiply enough within 24 to 48 hours to create visible growth on the pool walls and make the water appear green or brown.

Warm water encourages the growth of algae and bacteria. Controlling algae has been a perplexing problem for outdoor pool operators. The best method to control algae is to prevent it from growing in the first place. Once algae begin their growth cycle, the chief method for control is super chlorinating the water or applying an algaecide. For safety reasons, this procedure is to be done when the pool is not in use and involves raising the chlorine residual to 3.0 to 5.0 ppm.

Although algae themselves are not life threatening, they require immediate elimination to avoid odors, slippery surfaces, decreased visibility, and a stale taste to the water. Good pool maintenance, proper chlorine levels, and meticulous attention to filtration and vacuuming will reduce the likelihood of developing algal problems.

Turbidity

Turbidity, or cloudy water, may mean that impurities are present in the water. If you cannot see the drain cover at the bottom of the pool, the pool should not be open. Close the pool until the problem is corrected. The problem may be caused

Table 14.1 YMCA Pool and Spa Maintenance Guidelines

	Pools	Spas
1. Residual free chlorine	2.0–3.0 ppm	3.0–5.0 ppm
2. Weekly chlorine shock to	5.0 ppm	10.0 ppm
3. pH	7.2–7.5	7.5–7.8
4. Saturation Index	0 – +.1	0 – +.1
5. Total dissolved solids	< 1,500 ppm	< 1,500 ppm
Total alkalinity	100–120 ppm	100–200ppm
Calcium hardness	200–400 ppm	100–150 ppm
6. Temperature	80–84°F	85–102°F
7. Humidity (indoor)	50%–60%	50%–60%
8. Clarity	Drain cover slots clearly visible from pool deck	Drain cover slots clearly visible from pool deck
9. Biological values	Bacteria, virus, and parasite free	Bacteria, virus, and parasite free
10. Chlorine and pH testing	Every 2–3 hours	Hourly

by water contamination, a malfunctioning filter, or unbalanced water chemistry. The best solution is to prevent turbidity in the first place. If it does occur, check to see that you have maintained the pool according to the recommended water chemistry values. The following guidelines can help you prevent and overcome cloudy water:

- Maintain appropriate water chemistry levels (see the section on testing pool water in this chapter).
- Maintain the appropriate water level.
- Follow cleaning procedures for filters on a systematic schedule.
- Keep pool entrances and deck areas clean.

Spas

Hot tubs and whirlpools, which are popular at many aquatic facilities, pose some hazards—electrocution, drowning, and the transmission of disease are the most common. A few rules and some common sense will help make spas safe for patrons to enjoy. Review the rules discussed in chapter 2 for some suggestions to make the spa at your facility hazard free.

The health-related problems associated with spas can be reduced if management does the following:

- Maintains the spa water at a temperature between 98°F and 102°F
- Keeps the water chemistry balanced
- Tests for the presence of bacteria and treats the water as necessary

In this section, you have learned about how to maintain proper chemical balance of pool water. You can use **table 14.1** as a reference when you have to work on maintaining the recreational water in your facility. This table provides maintenance guidelines, or acceptable conditions, for both pools and spas.

For more on pool operations, see the *YMCA Pool Operations Manual* (3rd edition) and consider taking the YMCA of the USA course, Pool Operator on Location (POOL). For more on pool management, see the *YMCA Aquatic Management* manual. Both books are available from the Program Store, 800-747-0089 or www.ymcaprogramstore.com.

Review

Review Topics

Part of your duties as a lifeguard may include helping to keep the pool water safe and comfortable for swimmers. From this chapter, you learned about pool chemistry and inspection, signage, and how to fix common water problems. Here are some key points to remember from this chapter:

1) Areas to check in a safety inspection
2) Information on pool chemicals, how to handle them, and procedures for an accident
3) How to clean a nonslip surface
4) How to clean up solid and liquid fecal matter in pool water
5) Tips for reducing fecal contamination of pool water
6) Recommended signs and sign formats for certain areas
7) Purpose of a filtration system
8) How the different kinds of filtration systems work
9) Methods for cleaning the bottom of the pool
10) How to disinfect pool water
11) What pH means, why it is important, and how to test it

Review Questions

1. What does MSDS stand for? What kind of information does it contain?
2. List eight general safety precautions for working with chemicals.
3. What steps should you take if someone gets test-kit reagent in his or her eyes?
4. What does a filtration system do?
5. Why is water testing an important part of pool maintenance?
6. Why is residual chlorine important, and how can you test for it?
7. Why is acid-base balance important in pool chemistry? How do you test pH, and what is the ideal pH range for pool water?
8. How do you handle a solid fecal incident when the residual chlorine is less than 2.0 ppm? When there is a diarrheal incident?
9. Why is it important to vacuum the pool bottom?

CHAPTER 15

Pursuing Your Job and Your Future

The Y works every day to nurture everyone's potential and to make sure everyone has the opportunity to learn, grow, and thrive. As a YMCA-certified lifeguard, that includes you. When you become a lifeguard through the Y, you have the opportunity to become part of something larger and to give back to your community. As a lifeguard, you can help people stay safe and have fun while developing the skills and relationships they need to be healthy, confident, and connected to others.

In this chapter, you will learn the following:

- Getting and keeping a job
- YMCA Leadership Competencies and additional training opportunities
- Opportunities for continued personal growth

15
CHAPTER

Getting a Job

At the Y, we recognize that everyone has personal strengths. We support and help people develop through encouragement—including our own staff—and we are always there rooting for their success. For many people, lifeguarding is their first job. If that is true for you, we want you to know that the Y is a great place for you to start. The YMCA Lifeguard course is designed to help you develop not only your skills and knowledge but also your confidence, your health, and your ability to help make the world a better—and safer—place. Because we recognize that not everyone who becomes a lifeguard is experienced with getting and keeping a job, this chapter includes some basic information to support new lifeguards in finding opportunities to use their skills and be of service. If you are experienced with the work world, you may want to go directly to the subsequent sections on additional aquatic training opportunities later in this chapter.

Preparing a resume

The first step in getting a job is to prepare your resume, which is a brief history of your background. This information tells prospective employers what kind of experience you have and forms the basis for their decisions on whom to interview and what questions to ask.

Your resume gives a prospective employer a first impression about you, so be careful in your presentation. In general, a resume

- is neat;
- is as complete as possible;
- uses correct grammar, spelling, and punctuation;
- provides your name and address prominently;
- organizes information into clear categories; and
- is as short as possible (two pages maximum).

Include the following information in your resume:

- Name, address, phone number, and e-mail address
- Statement that you meet the age requirement for becoming a lifeguard
- Educational background, including dates of attendance
- Awards and honors you have earned
- Current certifications and their expiration dates
- Job-related experience, including employers' names, dates of employment, and positions or roles (listed with the most recent job first)
- Volunteer experience including the organization's name, dates of service, roles, and age group you worked with
- Statement that references are available upon request

The people you select as your references are very important. First, think about the people you know who could tell a prospective employer about your reliability, your character, and your ability to perform the tasks the position would require. Teachers, mentors, previous employers, and religious leaders are commonly listed as references (do not use family members or your peers).

Before you list people as references on your resume, as a courtesy, ask if they are willing to serve as references for you. Doing so gives you the opportunity to reconnect with them and possibly get their advice on getting a job or conducting an interview. Find out how and when they prefer to be contacted. Tell them about the job you are applying for so they can focus their comments on what is most relevant to the job and the employer. Most people want time to think about what they would say about you to a prospective employer.

When listing your references, include their names, addresses, telephone numbers, and how they know you. You want to make it easy for employers to reach people who will tell them about your abilities. Listing how the reference knows you helps tell what kind of information the reference can supply. A neighbor will provide different information from a previous employer.

Searching for jobs

Once your resume is ready, you can begin looking for job opportunities. Think about where you want to work, and then contact your local Y. You can also contact park districts, county recreation departments, or other aquatic facilities to see if they have openings. Seek out current lifeguards or aquatic supervisors to let them know you are interested in working at their facilities. Ask friends who have connections with aquatic facilities if they know of any positions. If you are looking for a summer job, start your search in early spring. Summer jobs go quickly, and facilities will want to train you before the season gets busy.

Be sure to check online and newspaper ads for job listings but go further with your search. You can find job opportunities in places such as community bulletin boards and the public library and through school counselors, public or private employment agencies, and personnel offices at large companies.

Applying for a job

The first time you apply for a job, you will be nervous. Do not worry—it is normal to feel nervous and it shows that you care. What is important is that you leave a positive first impression, and by showing that you have prepared and care about the job, you can do just that.

Figure 15.1 Filling out a job application online.
Photo courtesy of Kate Smiley.

Job applications can be completed online (**figure 15.1**) or in person. If you apply in person, be sure to dress neatly and appropriately for your visit to a prospective employer and be polite and friendly. The person who hands you the application is rarely the person who will interview you; however, demonstrate your values and treat everyone with the same respect. After all, this person may tell the person who does the hiring that you were friendly, confident, and polite.

Although job application forms differ from employer to employer, most include the same types of information. Bring your resume with you. You will find it helpful in completing the form, and it gives a professional impression if you include it. Some employers may even accept your resume rather than having you complete the application.

When you complete an application form, keep the following guidelines in mind:

- Fill in all blanks to the best of your ability.
- If a question does not apply to you, mark it NA (not applicable). Avoid leaving questions blank.
- Be honest; present yourself as you are.
- Double-check your spelling and verify that the contact information you provide is correct, especially your phone number and e-mail address.
- Feel free to ask questions if you do not understand something. If you fill out an application by hand, write neatly so the employer can read your application easily.

Figure 15.2 Practice interview.

Preparing for an interview

When a prospective employer contacts you for an interview, your best chance for success is to be well prepared. Consider the interview an opportunity to learn more about the position and the employer as well as to present yourself and your abilities.

Before any interview, take these steps:

- Learn all you can about the employer and the type of facility.
- Think about the qualities you have that will make you a good employee for that specific employer and facility.
- Prepare a list of questions you would like to ask about your responsibilities and the procedures at the facility. You want to work at a facility that will support you, train you, and help you succeed at your job. Find out about the training the employer provides and the quality and safety standards in place.
- Select a neat and appropriate outfit to wear to your interview. Represent yourself in the best light and make sure your clothing is modest and not too casual. Be aware of any slogans on your clothes that could give the wrong impression about you, your values, or your maturity and professionalism.

Another way to prepare is to practice answering interview questions. Ask a parent or an adult friend to play the role of the interviewer and conduct a practice interview (**figure 15.2**). Here are some typical interview questions:

- What led you to apply for this job?
- What do you think you can add to our organization?
- What would you consider your greatest strength?

- What do you consider are some of your weaknesses?
- What have you learned from your previous work experiences? How have you handled specific situations similar to the ones you will face on the job? (Be prepared with specific examples.)
- Tell me why I should hire you instead of all the other applicants.

Interviewing

The most important thing to remember going into an interview is to present yourself in a favorable light. This includes phone interviews, which employers may use to select whom to interview in person. Treat a phone interview with as much seriousness and preparation as an in-person interview. Be sure you are in a quiet place where you will not be distracted or interrupted. When you interview in person, arrive early—it tells the prospective employer that you are punctual. Dress neatly and do not chew gum. Turn off your cell phone before going into the interview.

When the interviewer comes to get you, stand up and greet him or her with a firm handshake. Establish eye contact and smile. It is amazing how confident those actions can make you feel. They also present the image of a confident candidate. Try to maintain eye contact throughout the interview. Be aware of nervous behavior that might distract the interviewer and affect the impression you give (such as biting your fingernails, tapping your fingers or feet, or scratching your head).

Listen carefully to the interviewer's complete question—try not to interrupt. Then think before you speak. Answer the question clearly and directly. Be aware of any nervous tendency toward rambling or repeating yourself. When your opportunity to ask questions arises, be sure your questions show you are interested in the job, have researched the organization, and are interested in progressing with the organization. As you leave, thank the interviewer for contacting you. Indicate that you are interested in the position (if you are) and you hope to be considered. Then simply shake the interviewer's hand, thank him or her, and leave in a polite manner. When you get home, handwrite a note thanking the interviewer for the opportunity to interview.

You may not get the first job you apply for, but each attempt can be a great learning experience. Your interviewing skills will improve and eventually you will get your first job. Congratulate yourself—you are on your way. Getting a job is a great start, and keeping it is the next step. Be a good employee—keep trying to learn as much as you can about your position and about the facility.

Keeping a Job

Jobs held early in your career are important learning opportunities. You learn work habits and responsibility. You learn about yourself and the world. How you challenge yourself and demonstrate the values of caring, honesty, respect, and responsibility are important in your job. Here are some ways you can show these values:

- Report to work on time.
- Provide constant and dedicated attention to your duties.
- Attend staff meetings and in-service training when scheduled and actively participate.
- Plan for recertification in CPR/AED, first aid, and oxygen administration, and lifeguarding to maintain your certification as a lifeguard.
- Stay in good physical condition.
- Minimize the number of times you need a substitute for your duty shift.
- Be friendly and courteous to patrons.
- Get along with other staff and show that you are a team player.
- Exhibit a positive attitude.

Professional Development and Training

YMCA of the USA's Training and Leadership Development is one of the most extensive professional development and education programs in the nonprofit sector. In fact, for

Figure 15.3 YMCA Leadership Competency Model.

three years in a row *The Princeton Review* cited YMCA of the USA's leadership development program as a major factor in including the Y among the 112 best employers for recent college graduates.

At the Y, helping kids, families, and communities learn, grow, and thrive requires strong, cause-driven leadership. Whether it is leading a swim class, keeping people safe, participating in in-service training, or providing superior member service, lifeguards and all other YMCA staff are expected to exhibit strong leadership skills every day. To support the work of its leaders, the Y uses a Leadership Competency Model (**figure 15.3**, previous page) that promotes lifelong development among 18 leadership competencies or characteristics. These 18 leadership competencies have been identified through extensive research and define the knowledge, skills, and behaviors required for success in the Y.

Training Opportunities

Remember that your certification as a lifeguard depends on keeping your CPR and first-aid certifications current. More important, your moral and legal duties call for you to have adequate first-aid, CPR Pro/AED, and oxygen-administration training. In addition to these training requirements, you have further opportunities to pursue additional and advanced training in aquatics.

Maintaining your CPR Pro/AED, first-aid, and oxygen-administration certifications

YMCA Lifeguard certification remains valid only if you maintain current certification in CPR Pro/AED, first aid, and oxygen administration issued by one of the following national organizations:

- American Heart Association
- American Red Cross
- American Safety and Health Institute
- National Safety Council

Note: YMCA of the USA recognizes only the first year of a CPR Pro/AED certification. See www.ymcaexchange.org for detailed information on CPR Pro/AED, first aid, and oxygen administration certification.

In-service training at your facility is also a valuable tool in your ongoing training and development. Each time you review a procedure or learn a new technique, you become more valuable as a professional lifeguard and more capable of taking on additional responsibility.

Successful lifeguards regularly practice their skills in prevention and recognition (especially scanning), emergency action plans, rescue, CPR and resuscitation, backboarding, and emergency care. Practice on your own and participate in the in-service trainings held at your facility. Such training may include the following:

- Review of CPR/AED, first-aid, and oxygen administration skills (**figure 15.4**)
- Conditioning workouts
- Suggestions for providing service to patrons
- Practice of emergency procedures
- Discussion of lifeguarding scenarios
- Practice of evacuation procedures (in case of fire, chemical spills, power outages, inclement weather, medical emergencies, missing persons, etc.)
- Backboarding skills

Your facility manager will document your participation in any in-service training, and it is a good practice to keep a record for yourself.

Keep in mind, too, that if you enjoy aquatics or just working with people, you can have a lifetime career at the Y. The Y is the nation's leading nonprofit committed to strengthening communities through youth development, healthy living, and social responsibility. YMCAs across the country offer full-time job opportunities in many different aspects of swimming, sports, and play, and other areas of healthy living and social responsibility. If you care about others and want to make a difference in their lives, join us at the Y.

Additional YMCA aquatic safety training and programs

YMCA of the USA also offers a variety of aquatic safety trainings and programs that you might find valuable, including the following:

- YMCA Lifeguard Instructor
- YMCA Lifeguard Trainer
- YMCA Aquatic Safety Assistant course (YASA)

- YMCA Junior Guard and Aquatic Leadership program
- Aquatic Personal Safety course
- Aquatic Safety course
- YMCA Splash

YMCA Lifeguard Instructor

Certification as a YMCA Lifeguard instructor allows you to train future lifeguards. YMCA Lifeguard instructors can train and issue certifications in the following courses: YMCA Lifeguard, CPR Pro/ AED, First Aid, and Oxygen Administration. A currently certified YMCA Lifeguard trainer must conduct the YMCA Lifeguard Instructor certification course.

YMCA Lifeguard Trainer

Obtaining certification as a YMCA Lifeguard trainer allows you to train YMCA Lifeguard instructors. YMCA Lifeguard trainers can train and issue certification in the following courses: YMCA Lifeguard, YMCA Lifeguard Instructor, CPR Pro/AED, First Aid, and Oxygen Administration. The YMCA Lifeguard Trainer certification course must be conducted by a currently certified YMCA Lifeguard faculty.

YMCA Aquatic Safety Assistant course

The YMCA Aquatic Safety Assistant course (YASA) provides the knowledge and skills necessary to recognize and prevent aquatic risks and to assist a lifeguard in an emergency. The YASA certification does not train an individual to become a lifeguard, swim instructor, water exercise instructor, or other aquatic professional; rather, YASA

Figure 15.4 Practicing emergency procedures.

A

B

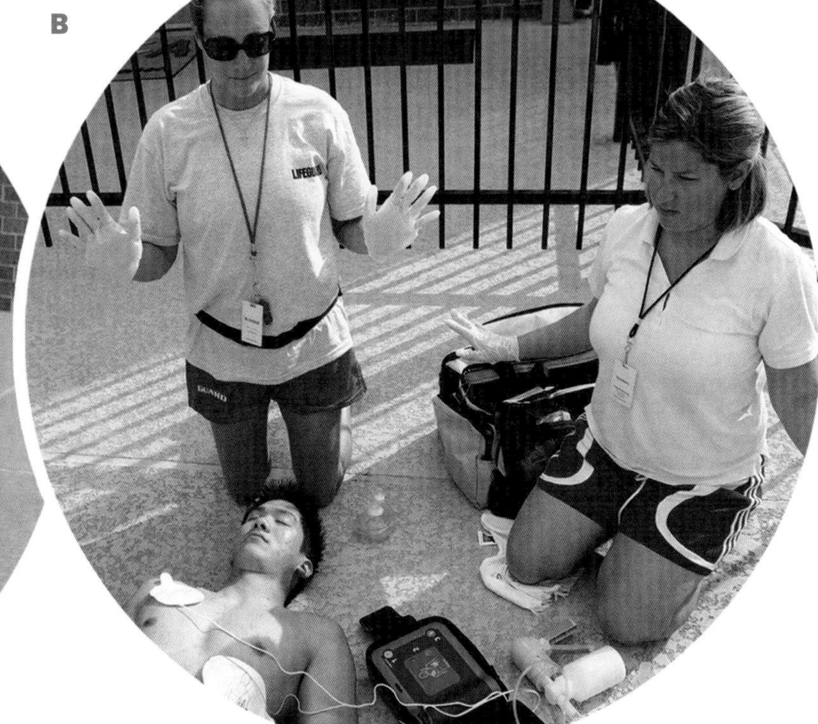

certification trains a person only for assisting a lifeguard during an emergency.

YMCA Junior Guard and Aquatic Leadership program

This course trains people who are too young to become certified lifeguards in the various aspects of aquatic leadership and safety. Each participant is given a practical evaluation and receives a recognition award for successfully completing the evaluation. The course modules cover the following topics:

- Leadership
- The Y's cause
- Diversity
- Job training
- CPR Pro/AED, first aid, and oxygen administration
- Facility maintenance
- Healthy lifestyles
- Rescue skills
- Swimming skills
- Character development
- Aquatic safety
- Community service

Once participants have become certified, they may become involved in a number of program activities, including the following:

- Lifeguard in-service (as an assistant)
- Aquatic course teaching (as an assistant)
- YMCA Splash (as an assistant)
- Competitions
- Mentoring programs (either being mentored or mentoring younger children)

Aquatic Personal Safety course

This course trains participants in personal safety and survival skills in and around aquatic environments. Participants receive a certificate from the local YMCA upon successful completion or participation in the course. Consult your local YMCA or call YMCA of the USA at 800-872-9622 for course prerequisites and certification requirements.

Aquatic Safety course

This introduction to water safety requires no swimming ability or previous training. It is designed to meet the basic water safety needs of individuals who participate in activities in aquatic environments ranging from corporate fitness programs to home pools.

YMCA Splash

YMCA Splash is an introduction and orientation to swimming and water safety skills. It is primarily for grade-school children and families, but it can be modified for use with older children and adults. Typically, YMCA Splash is a 5-day program held at a pool or in a classroom, but a 1-day specialty course is also available. An optional parents' presentation can be used with the 5-day program to instruct parents on the topics covered in the classes. Each participant who completes the course is given a certificate of participation.

Further YMCA aquatic training opportunities

YMCA of the USA offers a variety of aquatic leadership and management courses that you might find valuable. For example, certification courses are available for the following positions:

- YMCA Swim Lessons instructor to teach parent/child, preschool, youth, and adult classes
- Water exercise instructor
- YMCA/Arthritis Foundation Aquatic Program instructor
- Pool Operator on Location (YMCA POOL)
- YMCA aquatic manager (YAM)
- Competitive swim coach
- Competitive swim official

Continued Personal Growth

In addition to professional development and job-related skill building, your personal development is important to your living a healthy and meaningful life. At the Y, we seek to help everyone learn, grow, and thrive. "Thriving" is a term used to describe a way that experts are studying and supporting healthy personal development. Thriving focuses on how you are doing at any given point in time and on the path you are taking into the future—perhaps a summer lifeguarding job that may be the start to a career in recreation, the medical field, or community service such as working for the Y. The skills you have learned in this YMCA Lifeguard course will help you in many aspects of your life.

As you consider your lifeguarding job—which is perhaps your first job—and your future, give some thought to what your spark is. A spark is something that gives your life meaning and purpose. It is an interest, a passion, or a gift. Ask yourself: What are your passions? What are your capabilities and contributions to the world? What do you bring to the world that is good, beautiful, and useful? Sparks are the hidden flames in kids and adults that excite them and tap into their true passions. Sparks come from within. They motivate and inspire. They are authentic passions, talents, assets, skills, and dreams.

Purpose and passion are the hallmarks of a life that matters, a life worth living. They are the source of joy and happiness.

Research conducted by Search Institute, in Minneapolis, with thousands of teenagers and parents shows that young people who identify their sparks and get support in developing them

- have higher grades in school;
- are more socially competent;
- are more likely to be physically healthy;
- are more likely to volunteer to help other people;
- are more likely to be good stewards of the earth and its resources; and
- are more likely to have a sense of purpose.

As you start on your first lifeguarding job, remember the spark that led you to want to become a lifeguard and do the work necessary to become one. Seek out ways to fan that spark and keep your fire burning, whether through additional training, more challenging jobs, or pursuing a career path that will allow you to expand upon what you have learned in this course.

As a YMCA-certified lifeguard, you have the opportunity to make a difference in people's lives. At the Y, we are here to support you as you grow and develop, nurture your skills and potential, and give back to your community.

Congratulations and good luck!

Review

Review Topics

Your experience as a lifeguard will teach you valuable on-the-job skills and will give you opportunities to grow as a person. This chapter covered getting and keeping a job, training, personal growth, and leadership development. Here are some key points to remember from this chapter:

1) How to prepare a resume
2) Tips for searching and applying for a job, including completing an application form
3) How to prepare for an interview
4) Pointers for keeping a job
5) The re-certification, training, and development opportunities available through YMCA of the USA
6) How lifeguarding can help you in other areas of life

Review Questions

1. A friend is preparing a resume, and you are helping her. What are some tips you can give her? What should she include on the resume?
2. What are some important things to keep in mind regarding using references?
3. Before going in for an interview, what are some steps you can take to prepare?
4. You are coaching a friend who is practicing his interviewing skills. What are some pointers you give him?
5. What are some of YMCA of the USA's programs that might be beneficial to a lifeguard?
6. How might lifeguarding work benefit you in other areas of life?

APPENDIX A

Child Abuse Prevention

The Y is committed to helping people of all ages learn, grow, and thrive. This means providing a healthy and safe environment for children and youth, one that protects young people from abuse and mistreatment. Because of our concern for the welfare of children, the Y has developed guidelines and training to aid in the detection and prevention of child abuse.

Each YMCA provides local training, policies, and guidelines to its staff and volunteers for preventing, recognizing, documenting, and reporting suspicions or cases of abuse. In addition, Ys screen staff members and volunteers and conduct background checks upon hiring.

As a lifeguard, you will have direct contact with people of all ages, including children, youth, and vulnerable adults. This means you will have important responsibilities not only for preventing abuse but also for preventing the potential for abuse or the appearance of it and also for identifying potential cases of abuse happening outside the Y.

Below is a list of what you can expect to receive from your employer as a lifeguard, followed by sample elements of a code of conduct required of a professional lifeguard. Also included is a list of possible indicators of abuse, which will help you be more effective in your work, and a list of resources and further information to help you in this area.

Expectations of a professional lifeguard

As a YMCA lifeguard, you may be expected to know or do the following:

- Understand that abuse occurs and that abusers may be of any age, background, ability, race, religion, income, etc.
- Pledge to do everything in your power to prevent abuse
- Know who your Y's point person is for abuse prevention
- Read and sign a code of conduct and policies and understand the repercussions of not following it
- Be trained in prevention within 30 days of your start date and every year thereafter
- Recognize potential for abuse, including characteristics and behavior patterns of victims and abusers (see below)
- Be aware of the signs of abuse
- Be aware of the responsibilities and requirements for reporting suspicions of abuse, including laws, standards, and organizational policies
- Be trained in what to do if a person discloses abuse to you or in your presence
- Cooperate fully and in good faith with any investigation

Sample code of conduct

1. At no time during a Y program may a staff person be alone with a single child where he or she cannot be observed by others. Staff members should space position themselves in such a way that other staff can see them.
2. A child may not be left unsupervised.
3. Staff shall not abuse or mistreat children in any way, including
   a. physical abuse—striking, spanking, shaking, slapping;
   b. verbal abuse—humiliating, degrading, threatening;
   c. sexual abuse—touching or speaking inappropriately or showing children inappropriate materials;

d. mental abuse—shaming, withholding kindness, being cruel, belittling; and

e. neglect—withholding food, water, or basic care.

4. No type of child abuse will be tolerated. Any abuse by an employee will result in disciplinary action, up to and including termination of employment.
5. Staff members may not transport children in their own vehicles.
6. Profanity, inappropriate jokes, displays of intimate affection, sharing intimate details of one's personal life, and any kind of harassment in the presence of children, parents, volunteers, or other staff is prohibited.
7. Outside of the Y, staff members may not be alone with children whom they meet in Y programs. This includes babysitting, sleepovers, driving or riding in cars, and inviting children to their homes.
8. Staff members may not single out children for favored attention and may not give gifts to youth or their parents.
9. Program rules and boundaries must be followed, including appropriate touch guidelines. Children may be informed, in an age-appropriate manner, of their right to set their own "touching" limits for personal safety.
10. Children may not be disciplined by use of physical punishment or by failing to provide the necessities of care.
11. Staff members may not date program participants who are under the age of 18.
12. Under no circumstances should staff members release children to anyone other than the authorized parent, guardian, or other adult authorized by the parent or guardian (authorization on file with the Y).
13. Staff members are to make sure the rest room is not occupied by suspicious or unknown individuals before allowing children to use the facilities. Staff members will stand in the doorway of the rest room while children are using the rest room. This policy allows privacy for the children and protection for the staff members (i.e., not being alone with a child). If staff members are assisting younger children, doors to the facility must remain open. No child, regardless of age, should be allowed to enter a bathroom alone on a field trip or at other off-site locations. Always send children in threes (known as the rule of three) and, whenever possible, with staff.

Recognizing child abuse and neglect: Signs and symptoms

The first step in helping abused or neglected children is learning to recognize the signs of child abuse and neglect. The presence of a single sign does not prove child abuse is occurring in a family, but a closer look at the situation may be warranted when these signs appear repeatedly or in combination. The following information, including the signs of abuse, is adapted from the Child Welfare Information Gateway, www.childwelfare.gov/pubs/factsheets/signs.cfm.

If you do suspect a child is being harmed, reporting your suspicions may protect the child and get help for the family. Any concerned person can report suspicions of child abuse and neglect. Some people (typically certain types of professionals) are required by law to make a report of child maltreatment under specific circumstances—these are called mandatory reporters. For more information, see the Child Welfare Information Gateway publication, Mandatory Reporters of Child Abuse and Neglect: www.childwelfare.gov/systemwide /laws_policies/statutes/manda.cfm.

For more information about where and how to file a report, contact your local child protective services agency or police department. An additional resource for information and referral is the Childhelp National Child Abuse Hotline (800-4-A-CHILD).

Recognizing child abuse

The following signs may signal the presence of child abuse or neglect.

The child:

- Shows sudden changes in behavior or school performance
- Has not received help for physical or medical problems brought to the parents' attention

- Has learning problems (or difficulty concentrating) that cannot be attributed to specific physical or psychological causes
- Is always watchful, as though preparing for something bad to happen
- Lacks adult supervision
- Is overly compliant, passive, or withdrawn
- Arrives early, stays late, and does not want to go home

The parent:

- Shows little concern for the child
- Denies the existence of—or blames the child for—the child's problems in school or at home
- Asks teachers or other caregivers to use harsh physical discipline if the child misbehaves
- Sees the child as entirely bad, worthless, or burdensome
- Demands a level of physical or academic performance the child cannot achieve
- Looks primarily to the child for care, attention, and satisfaction of emotional needs

The parent and child:

- Rarely touch or look at each other
- Consider their relationship entirely negative
- State that they do not like each other

Types of abuse

The following are some signs often associated with particular types of child abuse and neglect: physical abuse, neglect, sexual abuse, and emotional abuse. It is important to note, however, that these types of abuse are more typically found in combination than alone. A physically abused child, for example, is often emotionally abused as well, and a sexually abused child also may be neglected.

Signs of physical abuse

Consider the possibility of physical abuse when the child:

- Has unexplained burns, bites, bruises, broken bones, or black eyes
- Has fading bruises or other marks noticeable after an absence from school
- Seems frightened of the parents and protests or cries when it is time to go home
- Shrinks at the approach of adults
- Reports injury by a parent or another adult caregiver

Consider the possibility of physical abuse when the parent or other adult caregiver:

- Offers conflicting, unconvincing, or no explanation for the child's injury
- Describes the child as "evil," or in some other very negative way
- Uses harsh physical discipline with the child
- Has a history of abuse as a child

Signs of neglect

Consider the possibility of neglect when the child:

- Is frequently absent from school
- Begs or steals food or money
- Lacks needed medical or dental care, immunizations, or glasses
- Is consistently dirty and has severe body odor
- Lacks sufficient clothing for the weather
- Abuses alcohol or other drugs
- States that there is no one at home to provide care

Consider the possibility of neglect when the parent or other adult caregiver:

- Appears to be indifferent to the child
- Seems apathetic or depressed
- Behaves irrationally or in a bizarre manner
- Is abusing alcohol or other drugs

Signs of sexual abuse

Consider the possibility of sexual abuse when the child:

- Has difficulty walking or sitting
- Suddenly refuses to change for gym or to participate in physical activities
- Reports nightmares or bedwetting
- Experiences a sudden change in appetite
- Demonstrates bizarre, sophisticated, or unusual sexual knowledge or behavior
- Becomes pregnant or contracts a venereal disease, particularly if under age 14
- Runs away
- Reports sexual abuse by a parent or another adult caregiver

Consider the possibility of sexual abuse when the parent or other adult caregiver is unduly protective of the child or severely limits the child's contact with other children, especially of the opposite sex

- Is secretive and isolated
- Is jealous or controlling with family members

Signs of emotional maltreatment

Consider the possibility of emotional maltreatment when the child:

- Shows extremes in behavior, such as overly compliant or demanding behavior, extreme passivity, or aggression
- Is either inappropriately adult (parenting other children, for example) or inappropriately infantile (frequently rocking or head-banging, for example)
- Is delayed in physical or emotional development
- Has attempted suicide
- Reports a lack of attachment to the parent

Consider the possibility of emotional maltreatment when the parent or other adult caregiver:

- Constantly blames, belittles, or berates the child
- Is unconcerned about the child and refuses to consider offers of help for the child's problems
- Overtly rejects the child

Resources on the Child Welfare Information Gateway website

- Child Abuse and Neglect
  www.childwelfare.gov/can/index.cfm
- Defining Child Abuse and Neglect
  www.childwelfare.gov/can/defining/
- Preventing Child Abuse and Neglect
  www.childwelfare.gov/preventing/
- Reporting Child Abuse and Neglect
  www.childwelfare.gov/responding/reporting.cfm

Source: Child Welfare Information Gateway, www.childwelfare.gov/pubs/factsheets/signs.cfm. This factsheet was adapted, with permission, from Recognizing Child Abuse: What Parents Should Know. Prevent Child Abuse America. © 2003. This material may be freely reproduced and distributed; however, when doing so, please credit Child Welfare Information Gateway. Available online at www.childwelfare.gov/pubs/factsheets/signs.cfm.

APPENDIX B

Recreational Water Illnesses, Including Fecal Contamination

The best defense against an outbreak of intestinal disease in a pool, or recreational water illnesses (RWIs), is to establish a series of preventive measures. The following procedures for prevention of fecal contamination are recommended for all YMCA aquatic facilities. YMCAs should also refer to local bathing codes if additional procedures are required.

The following recommendations for dealing with fecal incidents in pools are adapted from the Centers for Disease Control publication *Healthy Swimming: Fecal Incident Response Recommendations for Pool Staff* (2010).

What are recreational water illnesses (RWIs)?

RWIs are spread by swallowing, breathing, or having contact with contaminated water from swimming pools, spas, lakes, rivers, or oceans. Recreational water illnesses can cause a wide variety of symptoms, including gastrointestinal, skin, ear, respiratory, eye, neurologic, and wound infections. The most commonly reported RWI is diarrhea. Diarrheal illnesses can be caused by germs, or disease-causing agents. Germs include viruses, protozoa, bacteria, and parasites. Common germs include *Cryptosporidium* (or crypto), *Giardia*, *E. coli* O157:H7, *Shigella*, and norovirus.

CT inactivation time

Table 1 shows the inactivation time for these common germs in chlorinated water. Inactivation time is the time that a disease-causing agent can remain in the water and still be able to infect a person.

Table 1: Germ Inactivation Time for Chlorinated Water*

Germ	Time
E. coli 0157:H7 bacterium	Less than 1 minute
Hepatitis A virus	About 16 minutes
Giardia parasite	About 45 minutes
Crypto protozoa	About 15,300 minutes or 10.6 days

* Assume water with 1 part per million (ppm) or 1 mg/L free chlorine at pH 7.5 or less and a temperature of 77°F (25°C) or higher.

The **CT inactivation value** is the concentration (C) of free chlorine in parts per million (ppm) or milligrams per liter (mg/L), multiplied by time (T) in minutes at a specific pH and temperature. The formula is

$$\text{CT inactivation value} = \text{C} \times \text{T}$$

The CT inactivation value for *Giardia* is 45, and the CT inactivation value for crypto is 15,300 (assuming a pH of 7.5 or less and a temperature of 77°F [25°C] or higher). If you choose to use a different free chlorine concentration or inactivation time, you must ensure that the CT inactivation values remain the same.

For example, to determine the length of time needed to disinfect a pool after a diarrheal incident at 15 ppm, use the following formula:

$$C \times T = 15{,}300$$

Insert the value for concentration (C):

$$15 \times T = 15{,}300$$

Solve for time (T):

$$T = 15{,}300 \div 15 \text{ ppm}$$

$$= 1020 \text{ minutes} = 17 \text{ hours}$$

It would take 17 hours to inactivate crypto at 15 ppm.

Should all fecal incidents be treated the same?

No, all fecal incidents should not be treated the same. A diarrheal fecal incident is a higher-risk event than a formed-stool incident. With most diarrheal illnesses, the number of germs found in each bowel movement decreases as the diarrhea stops and the person's bowel movements return to normal. Therefore, a formed stool is probably less of a risk than a diarrheal incident that you may not see.

A formed stool may contain no germs, a few, or many, which can cause illness. You won't know. The germs that may be present are less likely to be released into the pool because they are mostly contained within the stool. However, formed stool also protects germs inside from being exposed to the chlorine in the pool, so prompt removal is necessary.

Should you treat a formed fecal incident as if it contains crypto?

No, a formed fecal incident should not be treated as if it contains crypto. In 1999, pool staff volunteers from across the country collected almost 300 samples from fecal incidents that occurred at water parks and pools. CDC then tested these samples for crypto and *Giardia*. None of the sampled feces tested positive for crypto, but *Giardia* was found in 4.4% of the samples collected (CDC 2001). These results suggest that *formed* fecal incidents pose only a very small crypto threat but should be treated as a risk for spreading other germs (such as *Giardia*). Remember a diarrheal fecal incident is considered to be a higher-risk event than a formed-stool fecal incident.

CDC strategies for dealing with visible fecal contamination

When dealing with a visible incident of fecal contamination, any type of bacteria, virus, or parasite might be in the water.

Formed-stool fecal incidents

Formed stools can act as a container for germs. If the fecal matter is solid, removing the feces from the pool without breaking it apart will limit the degree of pool contamination.

1. Close the pool to swimmers. If you have multiple pools that use the same filtration system, all pools will have to be closed. Do not allow anyone to enter the pool(s) until the disinfection process is completed.
2. Remove as much of the fecal material as possible, using a net or bucket, and dispose of the material in a sanitary manner. ***Vacuuming stool from the pool is not recommended.*** Clean and disinfect the item used to remove the fecal material. For example, after cleaning the net or bucket, leave it immersed in the pool during disinfection.
3. If the free chlorine level is less than 2 ppm, raise the free chlorine to 2 ppm and ensure that the pH is 7.5 or less. Also make sure that the water is at a temperature of 77°F (25°C) or higher. This chlorine concentration was selected to keep the pool closure time to approximately 30 minutes. Other concentrations or closure times can be used as long as the contact time (CT) inactivation value is achieved.
4. Maintain free chlorine concentration at 2 ppm and a pH of 7.5 or less for at least 25 minutes before reopening the pool. State or local regulators may require higher free chlorine levels in the presence of chlorine stabilizers[1], which are known to slow disinfection. Ensure that the filtration system is operating while the pool reaches and maintains the proper free chlorine concentration during the disinfection process.

---

[1] Chlorine stabilizers include compounds such as cyanuric acid, dichlor, and trichlor.

Diarrheal fecal incidents

Those who swim when ill with diarrhea place other swimmers at significant risk for getting sick. Diarrheal incidents are much more likely to contain germs than formed stool. Therefore, it is important that all pool managers stress to patrons that swimming when ill with diarrhea is an unhealthy swimming behavior.

1. Close the pool to swimmers. If you have multiple pools that use the same filtration system, all pools will have to be closed. Do not allow anyone to enter the pool(s) until the disinfection process is completed.
2. Remove as much of the fecal material as possible (for example, using a net or bucket) and dispose of it in a sanitary manner. ***Vacuuming stool from the pool is not recommended.*** Clean and disinfect the item used to remove the fecal material. For example, after cleaning the net or bucket, leave it immersed in the pool during disinfection.
3. If necessary, consult an aquatics professional before attempting the hyperchlorination of any pool to determine the feasibility, the most optimal and practical methods, and needed safety considerations.
4. Raise the free chlorine concentration to 20 ppm,[2,3] and maintain a pH of 7.5 or less and a temperature of 77°F (25°C) or higher. **The free chlorine and pH should remain at these levels for at least 12.75 hours to achieve the CT inactivation value of 15,300 (Shields et al. 2009).** Crypto CT inactivation values are based on killing 99.9% of crypto. This level of crypto inactivation cannot be reached in the presence of 50 ppm chlorine stabilizer, even after 24 hours at 40 ppm free chlorine, pH 6.5, and a temperature of free chlorine levels at 77°F (25°C) (Shields et al. 2008). Extrapolation of these data suggest it would take approximately 30 hours to kill 99.9% of crypto in the presence of 50 ppm or less cyanuric acid, 40 ppm free chlorine, pH 6.5, and a temperature of 77°F (25°C) or higher.
5. Confirm that the filtration system is operating while the water reaches and is maintained at the proper chlorine level for disinfection.
6. Backwash the filter after reaching the CT inactivation value. Be sure the effluent is discharged directly to waste and in accordance with state or local regulations. Do not return the backwash through the filter. Where appropriate, replace the filter media.
7. Allow swimmers back into the water only after the required CT inactivation value has been achieved and the free chlorine and pH levels have been returned to the normal operating range allowed by the state or local regulatory authority.

[2] Many conventional test kits cannot measure free chlorine levels this high. Use chlorine test strips that can measure free chlorine in a range that includes 20–40 ppm (such as those used in the food industry) or make dilutions with chlorine-free water when using a standard DPD test kit.

[3] If pool operators want to use a different free chlorine concentration or inactivation time, they need to ensure that CT inactivation values always remain the same (see Tables 2 and 3).

Fecal incident log

For both formed and diarrheal fecal incidents, establish a fecal incident log. Document each fecal incident by recording date and time of the event, whether it involved formed stool or diarrhea, and the free chlorine and pH levels at the time or observation of the event. Before reopening the pool, record the free chlorine and pH levels, the procedures followed in response to the fecal incident (including the process used to increase chlorine levels if necessary), and the contact time.

Pool disinfection time

How long does it take to disinfect the pool after a fecal incident? This depends on what type of fecal incident has occurred and at which free chlorine levels you choose to disinfect the pool. If the fecal incident is formed stool, follow Table 2, which displays the specific time and free chlorine levels needed to inactivate *Giardia*. If the fecal incident is diarrhea, follow Figure 2, which displays the specific time and free chlorine levels needed to inactivate crypto.

Table 2: *Giardia* Inactivation Time for a Formed-Stool Fecal Incident

Free Chlorine Level (ppm)	Disinfection Time*
1.0	45 minutes
2.0	25 minutes
3.0	19 minutes

* These closure times are based on 99.9% inactivation of *Giardia* cysts by chlorine at pH 7.5 or less and a temperature of 77°F (25°C) or higher. The closure times were derived from the U.S. Environmental Protection Agency (EPA) Disinfection Profiling and Benchmarking Guidance Manual. These closure times do not take into account "dead spots" and other areas of poor pool water mixing.

Table 3: Crypto Inactivation Time for a Diarrheal Fecal Incident

Free Chlorine Level (ppm)	Disinfection Time*
10	1,530 minutes (25.5 hours)
20	765 minutes (12.75 hours)
40	383 minutes (6.5 hours)

* At pH 7.5 or less and a temperature of 77°F (25°C) or higher.

For YMCAs

It is important that YMCA pool operators seek recommendations and procedural guidelines from state or local health department regarding fecal contamination incidents. Additionally, it is recommended that YMCAs review the procedures with their medical advisory committee.

- Be sure your staff is trained and certified in the YMCA POOL (Pool Operator on Location) course.
- Maintain all components of the circulation, filtration, and disinfection systems in good working condition.
- Use some form of chlorine as a disinfectant (e.g., Cl_2 gas, sodium hypochlorite, calcium hypochlorite).
- Maintain an effective chlorine residual: pool, 2.0 ppm; whirlpool/spa, 3.0–5.0 ppm; wading pool, 2.0–3.0 ppm. Keep the pH between 7.2 and 7.5.
- Use a chemical feeder to dispense chlorine into the pool 24 hours a day. Never batch or hand feed chlorine.
- Operate the pool, whirlpool, and wading pool circulation system 24 hours a day.
- Test, adjust, and record chlorine and pH levels every 2 hours for swimming and wading pools and once an hour for whirlpools.
- Calculate a Langelier Saturation Index once a week and adjust the balance to 0.
- Drain and scrub the walls and pool bottom once a year. If the pool cannot be drained because of a high water table, then dilute the old water from the pool by draining one third of the pool water and refilling. Repeat this procedure six times to achieve the best result.
- Avoid the use of stabilized chlorine if possible.
- Establish and enforce personal hygiene rules for the pool and whirlpool:
  1. Swimmers are required to take a warm soap-and-water shower before using the pool or whirlpool.

2. After swimmers use the whirlpool and before they enter the swimming pool, swimmers are required to take a warm soap-and-water shower.
3. Infants, preschool children, and adults who may experience incontinence must use some form of diaper that keeps fecal material inside the diaper.

- Provide diaper-changing stations in both the men's and women's dressing rooms for parents or caregivers with infant responsibilities.
- Install "child acceptable" toilet facilities and strongly recommend to parents and caregivers that they encourage their toddler or preschooler to use them before bringing the child into the pool for instruction and recreational swimming.
- Add a rule to facility behavioral signs requesting that anyone currently experiencing diarrhea not use the pool, wading pool, or spa.
- Be sure that spray pools for toddlers and preschoolers do not have any standing water or untreated recirculating water.
- Educate patrons on prevention of disease transmission and water safety. The Center for Disease Control National Center for Infectious Diseases recommends the following tips (2000):
  1. Do not enter the water if you have diarrhea. (People can spread germs in the pool without having an "accident.")
  2. Do not swallow the pool water. (Remember: It's everybody's bath water, and chlorine doesn't kill all germs.)
  3. Do wash your hands and bottom thoroughly with soap and water after using the bathroom, including changing diapers. (Germs on hands end up everywhere, including in the water.)
  4. Do notify the lifeguard if you see fecal matter in the pool or if you see behaviors, such as changing a diaper at poolside, that may spread disease.
  5. If you are a parent or caregiver:
     - Do take your child on bathroom breaks often.
     - Do change diapers in a bathroom, not at poolside. (Germs can contaminate surfaces and objects around the pool and spread disease.)
     - Do wash your hands thoroughly with soap and water after changing diapers, and make sure that your child's hands are washed.
     - Do wash your child thoroughly (especially his or her bottom) with soap and water before swimming.
     - Do not count solely on swim diapers or pants to stop accidents from leaking into the pool. (These products are not leak proof.)
     - If you have questions about the diseases or think you have a parasitic infection, consult a health care provider.

Works cited

Centers for Disease Control and Prevention. 2010. Healthy Swimming: Fecal Incident Response Recommendations for Pool Staff. www.cdc.gov/healthywater/pdf/swimming/pools/fecal-incident-response-recommendations.pdf.

———. 2001. Prevalence of Parasites in Fecal Material from Chlorinated Swimming Pools—United States, 1999. *Morbidity and Mortality Weekly Report (MMWR)* 50(20):410–2. www.cdc.gov/mmwr/preview/mmwrhtml/mm5020a4.htm.

Shields, J. M., M. J. Arrowood, V. R. Hill, M. J. Beach. 2009. The effect of cyanuric acid on the chlorine inactivation of Cryptosporidium parvum. *J Water Health* 7(1):109–14. Quoted in Centers for Disease Control and Prevention 2010.

Shields, J. M., V. R. Hill, M. J. Arrowood, M. J. Beach. 2008. Inactivation of Cryptosporidium parvum under chlorinated recreational water conditions. *J Water Health* 6(3):513–20. Quoted in Centers for Disease Control and Prevention 2010.

APPENDIX C

Risk Management Involving Starting Blocks or Platforms, Water Depth, Deep Diving Starts, and Supervision

Research has proven that it is dangerous to dive in water less than 5 feet deep. Key factors in preventing diving injuries are correct use of starting blocks and platforms, proper diving instruction, observation of water depth, appropriate use of deep dives, and swimmer/diver supervision.

Starting blocks or platforms

Follow these guidelines when using starting blocks or platforms:

- Place starting blocks or platforms at the deep end of the swimming pool only. They are never to be placed in the shallow end or in water less than 5 feet deep.
- When not in use, remove starting blocks or platforms from the pool area. Cap them off to avoid any unintended use, or regulate their use by signage.
- Regularly inspect starting blocks or platforms for stability, surface characteristics (traction), and signs of wear.
- Starting blocks or platforms are considered competitive swimming equipment ONLY and are to be used with proper supervision and safety instruction. They are not to be used as recreational devices or toys.
- Starting blocks and platforms should have safety warnings posted regarding their use.

Diving instruction and water depth

In order to minimize the risk of injury, conduct diving instruction from the deck in no less than 9 feet of water[1] and from a 1-meter board in no less than 11 feet 6 inches of water.

Long, shallow dives should be taught in no less than 9 feet of water. Once participants are proficient in such dives, warn them that they are allowed to perform these dives only in water at least 5 feet deep and when participating in a competitive swimming or lifeguard training program. Standing front dives should be performed in no less than 9 feet of water.

Deep diving starts

Deep diving starts are sometimes referred to as scoop starts, pike starts, spoon starts, hole-in-the-water starts, and no-resistance starts. This type of start causes a swimmer to enter the water at a steeper angle than the traditional long shallow water dive or flat start.

Deep dives are being used more frequently by competitive swimmers. It should be noted that they are of questionable value and present a potentially dangerous dive unless the water is greater than 5 feet deep.

The water, unfortunately, may be deep enough in one pool, but not in another. This presents a problem for swimmers and coaches in determining when deep dives can be safely used. During the excitement of a swimming meet, the swimmer or coach may use the deep dive in a shallow pool and cause or suffer injury.

Supervision

Coaches and instructors should supervise the use of starting blocks or platforms. These devices are to be used only by trained swimmers under supervision in the deep end and in water at least 5 feet deep. Starting blocks and platforms should be removed or capped off to prevent use in all other situations, or their use should be regulated by posted rules.

---

[1]Height and weight of the participant and the design of the pool bottom are factors to be considered in determining the safety of the diving area.

Coaches and instructors will use proper sequential training techniques and enforce safe starting skills. Swimmers will be instructed not to abort a poor start during its execution. Somersaulting, tucking, or jerking to one side may increase the risk of hitting the pool bottom.

Lifeguards, instructors, and aquatic personnel control shallow-water areas and starting blocks. Lifeguards will be alert and will strictly enforce all rules.

APPENDIX D

Quick Reference for First Aid

Chapter 9 of *On the Guard* presents some of the conditions and accidents in an aquatic setting that may require first aid. The table below summarizes the symptoms and responses for these common occurrences for ease of reference. See chapter 9 for more information.

Table 9.3 First Aid Quick Reference

Condition	Symptoms	First aid	Necessary to call EMS?
Asthma	Constant coughing, worsening at night and early morning Anxiety Sudden onset of wheezing Chest tightness and pounding heart Shortness of breath Extreme difficulty breathing Bluish color to lips and face Sweating Altered mental status	Position person for ease of breathing Help person take prescribed medication Alert EMS if no improvement within 15 to 20 minutes Reassure and calm the person	Sometimes

Table 9.3 First Aid Quick Reference (continued)

Condition	Symptoms	First aid	Necessary to call EMS?
Allergy (anaphylactic shock)	Itchy raised lumps or hives on face and chest Nausea Abdominal pain or cramping Swelling of the lips, eyelids, face Extreme difficulty in breathing Wheezing may be heard Blueness of the skin, lips, and nail beds Complete airway obstruction	Assist victim in finding comfortable position to breathe Loosen any tight clothing Calm, comfort, and reassure the person Assist victim in using prescribed epinephrine auto-injector; administer it yourself if victim is unable	Yes
Diabetes (very low or very high blood sugar)	Altered mental status Pale, cool, and sweaty skin Fainting Unconsciousness A strong fruity breath Drowsiness or difficulty waking up	Provide any substance containing sugar (e.g., fruit juice, candy) If the victim has oral glucose gel, give that instead Do not provide anything with artificial sweetener Calm, comfort, and reassure the person NOTE: Insulin is not considered an emergency medication. *Do not* administer insulin to a person with diabetes in an emergency setting.	Yes, if no improvement within 15 minutes

Table 9.3 First Aid Quick Reference (continued)

Condition	Symptoms	First aid	Necessary to call EMS?
Dental injury	Dislocated or broken tooth Lips or gums bleeding	Evaluate for additional injuries, noting dizziness, head trauma, or neck soreness Handle knocked-out tooth by chewing surface only Keep tooth moist; have the person spit into a cup and place tooth in saliva (if that is not possible, place tooth in milk, mild contact lens solution, or sports drink; avoid using water) *Do not* scrub tooth or remove attached tissue; let tooth dry; or wrap in tissue, cloth, or gauze	Send to dentist immediately (within 30 minutes—the faster you act, the better the chance of saving the tooth)
Seizure	Rigid muscles Jerky, convulsive movements Loss of consciousness Loss of bowel and bladder control Apnea (not breathing for a period)	Provide privacy Provide safe environment Lay victim down; protect and support head Loosen restrictive clothing Put nothing in mouth Move away from pool side Monitor until EMS arrives	Yes
Heart attack	Chest pains Squeezing sensation in the chest Shortness of breath Weakness Profuse sweating Pale, sweaty skin Nausea and vomiting	Keep person calm Make comfortable Help person take any heart medication Monitor condition Be ready for CPR, use an AED, and/or administer O2 if necessary	Yes

Table 9.3 First Aid Quick Reference (continued)

Condition	Symptoms	First aid	Necessary to call EMS?
Heat cramps	Cramps in calves, arms, abdominal muscles, and back Sweaty skin Increased heart rate Exhaustion Dizziness	Get person out of the heat Give water Apply moist towels Do not massage Gently stretch cramping muscles	Only in severe cases
Heat exhaustion	Heavy sweating Thirst Pale, cool skin Headache Nausea and vomiting Weakness and dizziness Feeling faint or collapsing	Move person out of the heat Give water or a sports drink if conscious Lay or sit victim down Loosen restrictive clothing Cool body with moist, cold towels or a cool shower Use fan to lower temperature Apply cold compresses to neck, groin, and armpits	Yes Warning: If left unattended, can escalate to heatstroke
Heatstroke	Symptoms of heat exhaustion* plus the following: Altered mental status (confusion, hallucination, bizarre behavior) Heavy sweating may be present, especially when exertion is the cause Skin will become red, very warm (even hot), and completely dry Seizure Unconsciousness	Establish airway, breathing, and circulation Begin cooling immediately (pour or spray water on victim, fan, place ice packs on groin and armpits, cover body with wet sheet) Place victim on side in recovery position to protect airway Provide continuous cooling until EMS arrives Do not give anything by mouth if vomiting or unconscious	Yes, immediately

* Per Markenson 2010.

Table 9.3 First Aid Quick Reference (continued)

Condition	Symptoms	First aid	Necessary to call EMS?
Hypothermia	Shivering Pale, cold skin Clumsiness or lack of coordination Slurred speech or mumbling Stumbling Confusion or unclear thinking Poor decision making (for example, trying to remove warm, dry clothing) Progressive lack of consciousness Cardiac arrest may occur	Move to warmer place Remove wet clothing Dry victim Cover with something dry; cover head and neck to retain body heat Provide warmth unless cold water drowning Give warm liquids (nonalcoholic, noncaffeinated) If cold water drowning, begin CPR and do not rewarm	Yes
Neck and back injuries	Sitting, standing, or walking patron complains of neck or back pain	Stabilize head and neck by placing your hands on each side of the victim's head near or over the ears Tell victim not to move, Ask: Are you OK? What happened? Do you feel pain anywhere? Can you move your fingers? Can you move your toes? Do you have any pain in your neck? Have second lifeguard palpate back of neck to see if pain is present	Yes, especially if there is a history of activity that may have resulted in spinal trauma

Table 9.3 First Aid Quick Reference (continued)

Condition	Symptoms	First aid	Necessary to call EMS?
Severe bleeding—external	Bleeding from open wound	Apply direct pressure Cover wound with bandage Treat for shock: Keep airway open and monitor breathing Control bleeding Maintain normal body temperature Have victim lie flat If available, give emergency O2	Yes, if extensive
Severe bleeding—internal	Bleeding from mouth, rectum, or vagina or blood in urine Visible bruises or cuts Rapid pulse Sweaty, cool skin Dilated pupils Nausea, vomiting Pain or tenderness, abdominal rigidity, or bruising Chest bruising or rib fractures	Call EMS Treat for shock Monitor pulse and breathing Prepare for vomiting	Yes

GLOSSARY

A

abrasion – a scrape wound. An abrasion affects only the surface of the skin.

acid-base balance – in pool chemistry, a pH between 7.2 and 7.4. This pH level is comfortable for swimmers and maximizes chlorine use.

acidosis – a condition where the blood is overly acidic. Acidosis is caused by too much carbon dioxide in the blood, a condition that is called *hypercapnia*. See also *hypercapnia*.

acquired immunodeficiency syndrome (AIDS) – a life-threatening condition in which the immune system is damaged, leaving the body susceptible to infections. AIDS is the final stages of infection caused by the human immunodeficiency virus (HIV). See also *human immunodeficiency virus*.

ADA – See *Americans with Disabilities Act*.

AED – See *automated external defibrillator*.

after-drop syndrome – in a victim of hypothermia, a condition caused by cold blood flowing back to the vital organs from the extremities after he or she is warmed. After-drop syndrome can be minimized by keeping the victim still, and it requires medical attention.

AGE – See *arterial gas embolism*.

AIDS – See *acquired immunodeficiency syndrome*.

alkalinity – the measure of water's ability to reduce the effect of acids. Alkalinity produces a pH higher than 7.0. Water with high alkalinity may be cloudy and leave scale on pool plumbing.

alveolus (pl. **alveoli**) – an air sac in the lungs. The membrane of the alveolus allows for the transfer of oxygen to and carbon dioxide from the blood.

Americans with Disabilities Act (ADA) – a law that protects people with disabilities by requiring them to have equal opportunities to access and use all public facilities. The ADA also requires that aquatic professionals and first responders treat people with disabilities the same as those without disabilities.

anaphylactic shock – a deadly, severe allergic reaction that includes breathing problems, hives, and a drop in blood pressure. Anaphylactic shock requires immediate medical attention.

apnea – the temporary absence of breathing; breath-holding. Apnea occurs during the initial stage of drowning. Apnea may also be experienced by a person who suffers a grand mal epileptic seizure. See also *initial apnea* and *terminal apnea*.

arterial gas embolism (AGE) – a medical emergency that occurs when gas bubbles enter the arteries. If these bubbles reach vital organs such as the heart and brain, they can cause unconsciousness and death. AGE happens when a scuba diver surfaces while holding his or her breath.

aspiration pneumonia – a condition caused by breathing water or other fluid into the lungs. During the second stage of drowning, the victim may suffer from aspiration pneumonia.

automated external defibrillator (AED) – a device used to analyze the heart rhythm and help restore a normal heartbeat. When the normal electrical impulses that cause the heart to beat become irregular, the heart muscle fibrillates, or quivers. An AED can deliver an electrical current to the heart to help it beat with a normal rhythm again.

avulsion – the tearing away of tissues or a body part by an accident or a surgery. Avulsions may be caused by explosives or machinery. The avulsed body part should be retrieved and taken with the patient to a medical facility.

B

backrush – the return flow of water from waves that have rolled ashore. Contrary to popular belief, backrush does not pull objects out to sea. Its strength, which depends on the slope of the beach, lessens at around three feet of depth.

bag-valve mask (BVM) – a hand-held rescue breathing device used in first aid to help someone breathe properly. A BVM consists of a self-inflating bag, a valve, and a mask. When used alone, a BVM provides 21 percent oxygen; when attached to an oxygen source, it can supply 90 to 100 percent oxygen.

biological death – the stage that follows clinical death that represents the start of irreversible brain damage. Biological death occurs during the fourth stage of drowning.

blood-borne pathogen – a disease-causing agent found in human body fluids. Three of the most serious blood-borne pathogens are the hepatitis B virus (HBV), the hepatitis C virus (HCV), and the human immunodeficiency virus (HIV), all of which can be life threatening.

breach of duty – the failure to exercise that care which a reasonable and prudent professional would exercise under similar circumstances. A lifeguard who breaches his or her duty could be held responsible in a lawsuit.

breakpoint – the area of the pool where the shallow end meets the deep end. The breakpoint is usually marked by lifelines.

buddy system – a safety check system that involves pairing every swimmer to a buddy of similar ability. When using the buddy system, swimmers pair up when they hear a predetermined signal so that staff members can account for all swimmers.

buoyancy – the tendency to float or sink; the upward force exerted by a fluid on an object submerged in it. Buoyancy can be positive (floating), negative (sinking), or neutral (hovering between floating and sinking).

BVM – See *bag-valve mask.*

C

calcium hardness test – a type of water quality test. Calcium hardness refers to water with excess minerals in it, or hard water. An appropriate level of calcium hardness for pools is 200–400 ppm.

cardiac arrest – See *sudden cardiac arrest.*

cardiopulmonary resuscitation (CPR) – a series of steps, administered by a certified individual, that can help a person start breathing again after cardiac arrest. The CPR procedure includes clearing the airways, administering rescue breathing, and massaging the heart by pushing downward on the chest.

carotid pulse – the beating of the heart felt in the carotid artery in the neck. The carotid artery is located between the front of the neck and the windpipe. The carotid pulse can be used to assess circulation.

clinical death – the point at which both breathing and pulse have stopped (referred to as respiratory and cardiac arrest). Clinical death lasts approximately four minutes before the onset of biological death.

colorimeter – a common test for residual chlorine. The colorimeter requires a test solution, a sample, and a test tube. To determine how much residual chlorine is present, the sample is mixed with the test solution in the test tube. Then the resulting color is compared to a fixed scale.

contour depth line – a line marked on a wall or fence near a pool that provides a profile of the pool's depth. The contour line allows patrons to see how deep the water is in relation to their height. Also known as a *contour line.*

contracture – a condition that causes the muscle fibers to shorten and cease functioning. Contracture occurs when the oxygen level in the muscle drops, causing the accumulation of lactic acid. Contracture causes considerable pain and is one of the triggers of a cramp.

coping – the material that encases the wall of the pool shell. Depth markers can be inserted on the pool's coping.

Cryptosporidium – a microscopic parasite that causes a diarrheal disease. Cryptosporidium may be present in liquid feces in the pool, so use an extensive cleanup procedure. Also known as *crypto.*

CT value – the concentration (C) of free chlorine in parts per million (ppm) or in milligrams per liter (mg/L), multiplied by time (T) in minutes at a specific pH and temperature. The formula is CT inactivation value = C × T.

current – a flow of water in a body of water. Ocean currents can be strong after set waves. See also *flash rip current*, *parallel current*, *rip current*, and *river current*.

D

damages – the monetary compensation awarded to or on behalf of a person who has been injured by the action of another. Damages may be awarded based on breach of duty.

DAN – See *Divers Alert Network.*

DCS – See *decompression sickness.*

deck-level pool – a swimming pool in which the level of the water in the pool comes to the level of the walking surface that surrounds the pool. In some rescue scenarios, a second rescuer may sit on the edge of a deck-level pool.

decompression sickness (DCS) – a condition caused by the formation of gas bubbles in the blood or tissues during or following ascent from an open-water scuba dive that was too long and too deep. Decompression sickness requires treatment in a recompression chamber.

defibrillation – the process of passing an electrical current through the heart to temporarily stop the natural electrical impulses that cause it to beat. Defibrillation allows the heart to restore its normal rhythm. See also *automated external defibrillator.*

diatomaceous earth – a material used in some filtration systems. Diatomaceous earth is made up of fossilized marine plant life, or diatoms.

distressed swimmer – a person who is struggling to stay on the surface of the water. Lifeguards should learn to recognize the signs of a distressed swimmer.

Divers Alert Network (DAN) – a not-for-profit scuba organization that provides a hotline to assist in diving emergencies. DAN's hotline (919-684-9111) is available at all times and may be called collect from anywhere in the world. Call DAN only after calling EMS.

drowning – the breathing difficulties caused by submersion in a liquid, especially water. There are four stages to drowning.

duty – a legal obligation to act. A lifeguard's duty is to act in an emergency.

dyspnea – difficulty breathing. Dyspnea occurs when the glottis partially relaxes.

E

ear squeeze – a pain in the ears when submerged in water due to a difference in pressure between the outer and middle ears. Ear squeeze may affect a lifeguard's ability to carry out his or her duties.

electrolyte – any of various atoms or molecules that have an electrical charge, like sodium or chloride. Electrolytes help control the water that flows in and out of a cell. Hyperthermia causes loss of electrolytes.

emergency medical services (EMS) – the organizations, resources, and medical professionals in a community who help people who suddenly become sick or injured. EMS groups include ambulance services and rescue squads.

EMS – See *emergency medical services.*

entire-area coverage – a type of lifeguard supervision system where a single lifeguard supervises an entire swimming area. The entire-area coverage system requires backup staff to maintain vigilance and respond to an emergency. Also known as *total coverage.*

epiglottis – the piece of flexible cartilage that covers the glottis. The epiglottis prevents food stuff, fluids, or other foreign material from entering the trachea.

esophagus – the passageway that carries food and liquids from the throat to the stomach. Water normally passes through the open glottis into the esophagus.

eustachian tube – the passage that connects the throat and middle ear. The Valsalva maneuver can open a blocked eustachian tube.

F

fixed-flow regulator – a device that releases a continuous stream of gas from a cylinder of compressed oxygen. A fixed-flow regulator will not fully inflate a bag-valve mask because it only provides 6 to 12 liters per minute. Also known as a *constant-flow regulator.*

flash rip current – a temporary, short-term rip current that is related to heavy surf. A flash rip generally results from unusual wind or water conditions changing quickly, such as those seen in a hurricane.

G

glottis – the area at the top of the trachea that connects to the lower part of the throat. The epiglottis closes the glottis to prevent food and liquids from entering the airway during the swallowing process.

Good Samaritan law – a regulation that provides legal protection from liability to a trained person, acting in good faith while off duty, who provides emergency medical assistance at the scene of an accident or emergency. Good Samaritan laws differ from state to state.

H

head-immobilizer pad – a pillow or wedge that supports a victim's head and neck while he or she is on a backboard. Head-immobilizer pads are used if a lifeguard thinks the victim has a spinal injury.

head-splint technique – a rescue method designed to keep the head and neck still by pulling the arms above the head, with the palms together. By squeezing the arms together, you immobilize the head by trapping it between them. The head-splint technique is used if a lifeguard thinks a victim in deep water has a spinal injury.

Health Insurance Portability and Accountability Act (HIPAA) – a law passed in 1996 that protects the privacy of individually identifiable health information. HIPAA prevents lifeguards from sharing medical information about a victim with non-medical personnel.

heart attack – the death of or damage to heart muscle due to a blockage in the coronary arteries. A heart attack can cause sudden cardiac arrest, which is when the heart stops beating. See also *sudden cardiac arrest.*

heat cramp – a painful muscle contraction caused by loss of electrolytes and salt due to sweating. Heat cramps are a mild form of hyperthermia. See also *hyperthermia.*

heat escape lessening position (HELP) – a survival position for cold water that protects the areas of the body critical to maintaining core temperature: head and front of the neck, armpits, chest, and groin. The HELP position is most easily assumed if you are wearing a PFD.

heat exhaustion – the nausea, weakness, and dizziness caused by the loss of electrolytes and water through excessive sweating. Heat exhaustion is a serious form of hyperthermia. Because it can lead to heatstroke, heat exhaustion requires medical attention. See also *hyperthermia.*

heatstroke – a potentially life-threatening form of hyperthermia that results from the body's temperature-regulation system shutting down. The body's heat is recycled internally, causing systems to malfunction. Heatstroke is the most serious form of hyperthermia and requires emergency medical attention. See also *hyperthermia.*

HELP – See *heat escape lessening posture.*

HIPAA – See *Health Insurance Portability and Accountability Act.*

HIV – See *human immunodeficiency virus.*

hopper-bottom pool – a pool whose sides angle down toward the deepest point, a small area possibly as small as 2 feet by 2 feet. Hopper-bottom pools present risks for diving.

human immunodeficiency virus (HIV) – a pathogen that damages the immune system and makes the body vulnerable to infections and cancers. HIV is spread through contact with blood and body fluids. HIV leads to AIDS, but it is possible for a person to be HIV positive and not have the symptoms of AIDS. See also *acquired immunodeficiency syndrome.*

hypercapnia – an excess of carbon dioxide in the blood. Hypercapnia makes the blood more acidic and causes acidosis. See also *acidosis.*

hyperthermia – a condition that occurs when prolonged exposure to heat causes the body's core temperature to rise. A person with severe hyperthermia (heat exhaustion or heatstroke) requires emergency medical attention. Also known as *overheating.* See also *heat cramps*, *heat exhaustion*, and *heatstroke.*

hyperventilation – excessively deep, rapid breathing. Hyperventilation can cause a person to pass out before the body feels that it needs to breathe.

hypochlorite – a substance that can be used to chlorinate water and disinfect surfaces. Examples include sodium hypochlorite, lithium hypochlorite, and calcium hypochlorite. Hypochlorites come in liquid, granular, or powder form. When used to chlorinate a pool, they are applied by a chemical feeder that operates constantly to maintain a steady amount of free residual chlorine in the water.

hypothermia – a condition that occurs when prolonged exposure to cold causes a person's core temperature to drop below 95°F. Someone with hypothermia requires emergency medical attention. See also *immersion hypothermia*.

hypoxia – a lack of oxygen in the body's cells. Hypoxia causes a victim to become irrational due to lack of oxygen to the brain.

I

immersion hypothermia – the cooling of the body's core temperature caused by suspension in cold water. Immersion hypothermia can occur even in warm weather because water cools the body more quickly than air. See also *hypothermia*.

incision – a cut. The edges of an incision are smooth, and there may be severe bleeding. Incisions can be caused by sharp objects in the pool.

initial apnea – the first stage of the drowning process. During initial apnea, the victim is unable to inhale air and expel carbon dioxide, and he or she starts to panic. See also *apnea* and *terminal apnea*.

in-line stabilization – the process of using external means to limit the movements of the head and neck to prevent further injury. In-line stabilization is used when a victim has or may have spinal injury. The head-splint technique is a manual method of in-line stabilization.

in-service training – ongoing training during the course of employment. In-service training gives professional lifeguards a chance to regularly practice skills, test their knowledge, and enact rescue scenarios to ensure peak performance in the event of an emergency.

J

jaw-thrust technique, modified – a procedure for positioning a victim for rescue breathing if the victim may have a spinal injury. The modified jaw-thrust technique involves moving the victim's jaw forward without tilting the head back.

L

laceration – an injury that tears the skin. A laceration can be caused by a blunt object and may affect veins or arteries, causing severe bleeding.

Langelier Saturation Index (LSI) – a formula that determines if pool water is chemically balanced. The LSI protects patrons' comfort and the life of the pool. The LSI uses five variables to calculate water balance: pH, temperature, calcium hardness, alkalinity, and total dissolved solids.

liability – legal responsibility. *Liability* is a synonym for *duty*, *responsibility*, or *obligation*. Even if patrons have signed a waiver of liability, a lifeguard is still responsible to protect them.

lifeline – a rope strung across a pool or beach to separate different areas. A lifeline can separate shallow water from deep water, lap-swimming areas from open-swimming areas, and so forth. Lifelines are also intended to provide support to panicky swimmers who get into water that is too deep.

LSI – See *Langelier Saturation Index*.

M

manual suction device – a simple, nonelectrical device used to help remove foreign material from a person's airway. The manual suction device creates a vacuum that withdraws debris. Manual suction devices are used with victims suffering from or at risk of an airway obstruction (e.g., victims who have vomited, been underwater, or inhaled fluid or debris, or who are bleeding from the nose or mouth). Also called a *manual hand-held suction device.*

material safety data sheet (MSDS) – a paper that lists information about handling chemicals that are in an area where people work. Material safety data sheets are required by OSHA standards, and aquatic facilities must have them on hand.

medical alert tag – a piece of jewelry worn around the wrist, ankle, or neck that provides medical information about a person. For example, a medical alert tag will state if the person has epilepsy, diabetes, or certain allergies, or if he or she needs regular medications. Some medical alert tags include a phone number to call for current medical information about the person.

metered-dose inhaler – a portable dosing apparatus that releases asthma medication directly into the lungs. Metered-dose inhalers deliver a specific amount of medication when you push the pressurized canister into the *l*-shaped mouthpiece.

modified jaw-thrust technique, modified – See *jaw-thrust technique, modified.*

MSDS – See *material safety data sheet.*

muriatic acid – a pool chemical used to correct a positive LSI reading. Muriatic acid is a form of hydrochloric acid and can be harmful if it comes into contact with the skin or eyes.

N

Naegleria fowleri – a freshwater amoeba that causes amoebic encephalitis, or infection and swelling of the brain. *Naegleria fowleri* lives in the top inches of mud in very warm water, such as lakes, and it may also live in soil.

nebulizer – a device that converts liquid medication to a fine mist, which can be inhaled. Nebulizers allow a person to directly treat the lungs with asthma medication.

negligence – actions that fall below the standards established by law for protection of others against unreasonable risks. Negligence occurs when a lifeguard does not perform his or her duty according to accepted standards.

P

PACA – See *problem, alternatives, consequences, and action.*

parallel current – a flow of water that follows the shoreline and is usually caused by waves that break on the shore at an angle. Parallel currents can sweep a swimmer down the length of the shore. Also known as *longshore current*, *lateral current*, or *littoral current.*

pathogen – disease-causing agent. Pathogens include bacteria, viruses, and parasites.

personal flotation device (PFD) – a device that can be worn, such as a life jacket or vest, and that provides buoyancy. A PFD may or may not be inflatable. The U.S. Coast Guard approves PFDs that proven and tested buoyancy.

personal protective equipment (PPE) – the supplies that OSHA requires employers to provide to lifeguards who might be exposed to blood or other infectious materials during first aid, CPR, and rescue breathing. Personal protective equipment includes breathing barriers, resuscitation masks, disposable gloves, gowns, masks, shields, and protective eye wear.

PFD – See *personal flotation device.*

pH – a measure of the alkalinity and acidity of a substance. A pH test is used to monitor pool water. The recommended pH range for pool water is 7.2 to 7.4.

pool volume – the amount of water that a pool holds. Pool volume is an important factor in testing and balancing pool chemistry. Pool volume is calculated using different formulas, depending upon the type of pool. Also known as *facility capacity.*

PPE – See *personal protective equipment.*

problem, alternatives, consequences, and action (PACA) – the four steps in the YMCA decision-making process. The steps of PACA help you consider the consequences of the available alternatives.

proximate cause – an occurrence that leads to an injury. Proximate cause is one of the four elements required to prove a legal claim of negligence. If the proximate cause of an injury or loss was the lifeguard's negligence, or failure to perform his or her duty, the lifeguard may be held legally responsible in a lawsuit.

puncture – a stab wound. A puncture is caused by a sharp, pointed object, which the lifeguard should not remove from the wound.

Q

quaternary ammonium disinfectant – a cleaning and deodorizing compound that lacks color and smell. Quaternary ammonium disinfectants are used to kill bacteria and may kill fungi and viruses.

R

reflex closure of the glottis – the involuntary, or automatic, process of swallowing. The reflex closure of the glottis is disrupted during the drowning process. Also known as the *swallow reflex.*

rescue breathing – a procedure that involves forcing air into the mouth and lungs of a person who is not inhaling and exhaling. Rescue breathing provides enough oxygen to temporarily support life. Also known as *artificial respiration.*

rescue flotation device (RFD) – a piece of equipment that can be secured to the body with a strap and that serves as a flotation aid to assist the lifeguard in performing a rescue. Rescue flotation devices include rescue tubes or buoys.

residual bromine – the amount of bromine in pool water that is available to clean the water by chemically bonding with contaminants. Residual bromine is similar to residual chlorine. Also known as *free available bromine.*

residual bromine test – a water quality test that measures the amount of bromine that is available to chemically bond with contaminants, disinfecting the water. YMCA of the USA considers the appropriate level of residual bromine to be 2.0 ppm.

residual chlorine – the amount of chlorine in pool water that is available to clean the water by chemically bonding with contaminants. Maintaining a proper level of residual chlorine can prevent lifeguard lung. Also known as *free available chlorine.*

residual chlorine test – a water quality test that measures the amount of chlorine that is available to chemically bond with contaminants, disinfecting the water. YMCA of the USA considers the appropriate level of residual chlorine to be 2.0–3.0 ppm.

respiratory arrest – See *terminal apnea.*

resuscitation mask – a device designed to allow mouth-to-mask rescue breathing while protecting a rescuer from disease transmission. A resuscitation mask provides enough oxygen to the victim to keep him or her alive.

RFD – See *rescue flotation device.*

rip current – a channel of water flowing away from and perpendicular to the shore. Rip currents are hazardous for all swimmers. A swimmer can escape a rip current by swimming in a direction parallel to the shore. See also *current.*

river current – a seaward flow of water in a river that may vary in strength and location. A river current may carry debris. A swimmer can escape a river current by swimming diagonally across the current. See also *current.*

roll call system – a safety check system used to monitor patrons that involves a lifeguard taking attendance before and after a swimming session. The roll call system does not provide a way to check on swimmers in the water.

rotation system – a procedure designed to help lifeguards stay vigilant by providing a change of position. YMCA of the USA recommends that lifeguards rotate every 20 to 30 minutes. The rotation system defines timing, direction, order, and location of the positions through which lifeguards cycle.

roving lifeguard – a lifeguard who walks around a pool deck or waterfront area and who is closer to patrons. A roving lifeguard is often used in crowded facilities and shallow-water areas and serves as a communication link between lifeguard towers.

S

safety check system – a procedure used by lifeguards to be aware of the number and location of swimmers in an aquatic area. Safety check systems include safety swim testing and banding, the buddy system, and the tag board system.

saturation index – See *Langelier Saturation Index*.

scanning – a system of visual observation in which a lifeguard performs systematic visual sweeps of the facility, patrons, and activity. Scanning is the cornerstone of accident prevention in the YMCA lifeguarding program.

shallow water – a measurement of water depth, based on a swimmer's height. For swimmers, the surface of shallow water is below the individual's armpits; for divers, shallow water is less than 5 feet deep.

sinus squeeze – a sharp pain in the cavities in the front of the face that happens when a person with nasal congestion submerges in water. Sinus squeeze can cause damage to sinus membranes.

soda ash – sodium carbonate. Soda ash is a chemical used to raise the pH of pool water to make it more alkaline (or less acidic).

spa – a facility that may include a hot tub or whirlpool. Spas present several hazards, including electrocution, drowning, and transmission of disease.

Special Marine Warning – an alert issued by the National Weather Service when a waterspout is spotted, whatever its strength. A Special Marine Warning means all patrons need to get to safety.

spoon-shaped pool – a pool with contoured sides that gives a false sense of depth in the deep section of the pool, which presents risks for diving. The distance between the diving board and the upslope in a spoon-shaped pool is greatly reduced.

standard of care – the care that a "reasonable and prudent" professional would use in the same or similar situation. Standard of care is, by law, the level of ordinary care, practice, and conduct within the profession.

starting block – a raised surface from which swimmers enter the water. Starting blocks are used for competitive swimming competitions. Also called *starting platform*.

starting platform – See *starting block*.

stream current – See *river current*.

sudden cardiac arrest (SCA) – the abrupt stopping of the pumping action of the heart. Sudden cardiac arrest happens during the fourth stage of drowning. Also known as *cardiac arrest*.

surf – (*n*) breaking waves; (*v*) to move forward in the water on a wave. The amount of surf on a beach determines what kind of rescue techniques a lifeguard uses.

surf zone – the shallow area where waves break. The surf zone is not a good place to use a paddleboard because it may be crowded.

surfactant – a substance that acts on the surface of something; in this case, a substance in the fluid covering the surface of the air sacs in the lungs that makes it easier for the air sacs to exchange oxygen and carbon dioxide. The surfactant is washed away when a person is drowning, which makes exchange of gases more difficult.

T

tag board system – a safety check system that uses tags on a pegboard to monitor swimmers as they enter and exit the water. The tag board system requires that swimmers be responsible for their own tags.

terminal apnea – respiratory arrest; the cessation of breathing. Terminal apnea is the fourth and final stage of the drowning process. See also *apnea* and *initial apnea*.

total dissolved solids – the sweat, body lotion, hair spray, disinfectant, and other solids that would be left if the water in a pool evaporated. The amount of total dissolved solids in the pool should be less than 1,500 ppm.

trachea – the passageway that carries air from the throat to the lungs. The trachea is protected by the epiglottis, which keeps foreign materials from entering. Also known as the *windpipe*.

turbidity – cloudiness. Turbidity is a common water quality problem in pools and may indicate that impurities have not been filtered out.

U

upslope – the angled section of the pool bottom that marks transition between the deep and shallow ends. Many diving accidents happen when the diver misjudges the depth and distance to the upslope of the pool bottom.

V

Valsalva maneuver – a method used to open the eustachian tubes by blocking the nostrils, closing the mouth, and gently trying to exhale. The Valsalva maneuver is used to equalize pressure while skin diving.

variable-flow regulator – a device used with a tank of compressed oxygen to control the flow of gas from the tank. A variable-flow regulator can provide up to 15 liters of oxygen per minute and can be used with a bag-valve mask. Also known as an *adjustable-flow regulator*.

ventricular fibrillation – an uncoordinated beating of the heart. Ventricular fibrillation can be stopped with a shock from an automated external defibrillator, which may reset the heart.

vital capacity – the maximum amount of air that can be pushed out of the lungs after a maximum inhalation. Vital capacity affects a body's ability to float.

W

waterfront – a place where water meets land. Because the waterfront conditions are different from pool conditions, waterfront lifeguards need to know additional procedures.

waterspout – a tornado that occurs over water. Waterspouts can be weak or strong, but either type is dangerous enough to warrant action. The National Weather Service issues a Special Marine Warning whenever a waterspout is spotted, whatever its strength.

Z

zone – a defined swimming area for which a lifeguard is responsible while on duty. Zones help lifeguards identify behavior that is appropriate in a particular area.

zone coverage – a system of dividing a swimming area into smaller units, called zones. The zone coverage system assigns one lifeguard to each zone.

REFERENCES

American Academy of Dermatology (AAD). 2010. Sunscreen safety and effectiveness. www.aad.org/stories-and-news/news-releases/sunscreen-safety-and-effectiveness.

American Cancer Society (ACS). 2010. How do I protect myself from UV rays? www.cancer.org/Cancer/CancerCauses/SunandUVExposure/SkinCancerPreventionandEarlyDetection/skin-cancer-prevention-and-early-detection-u-v-protection.

American Red Cross (ARC). 2007. *Lifeguarding*, 3rd ed. Yardley, PA: StayWell.

American Safety & Health Institute (ASHI). 2008. *Basic first aid for the community and workplace: Student handbook.* Eugene, OR: ASHI.

Anderson, C., and J. Horne. 2006. A high sugar content, low caffeine drink does not alleviate sleepiness but may worsen it. *Human Psychopharmacology* 21(5):299–303.

Ballard, J. C. 1996. Computerized assessment of sustained attention: A review of factors affecting vigilance performance. *Journal of Clinical and Experimental Neuropsychology* 18(6):843–63.

van Beeck E. F., C. M. Branche, D. Szpilman, J. H. Modell, and J. J. Bierens. 2005. A new definition of drowning: Towards documentation and prevention of a global public health problem. *Bulletin of the World Health Organization* 83(11):853–6. www.scielosp.org/scielo.php?pid=S0042-96862005001100015&script=sci_arttext.

Centers for Disease Control and Prevention (CDC). 1987 (updated 1996). Universal precautions for prevention of transmission of HIV and other bloodborne infections. www.cdc.gov/ncidod/dhqp/bp_universal_precautions.html.

———. 2009a. Hepatitis B FAQs for health professionals. www.cdc.gov/hepatitis/HBV/HBVfaq.htm.

———. 2009b. Basic information about HIV and AIDS. www.cdc.gov/hiv/topics/basic/index.htm.

———. 2010a. Unintentional drowning: Fact sheet. www.cdc.gov/HomeandRecreationalSafety/Water-Safety/waterinjuries-factsheet.html.

———. 2010b. Vomit and blood contamination of pool water. www.cdc.gov/healthywater/swimming/pools/vomit-blood-contamination.html

De Lisle Dear, G., and N. W. Pollock, eds. 2009. *DAN Dive and Travel Medical Guide*, 5th ed. Durham, NC: Divers Alert Network (DAN).

DeMers, G. 1983. Head splint method of rescue for aquatic related neck injuries. *Journal of Physical Education, Recreation, and Dance* 9:66–67.

Fenner, P., S. Leahy, A. Buhk, and P. Dawes. 1999. Prevention of drowning: Visual scanning and attention span in lifeguards. *Journal of Occupational Health and Safety—Australia and New Zealand* 15(1):61–66.

Field, J. M., M. F. Hazinski, M. R. Sayre, L. Chameides, S. M. Schexnayder, et al. Part 1: Executive summary: 2010 American Heart Association guidelines for cardiopulmonary resuscitation and emergency cardiovascular care. *Circulation* 2010;122(suppl 3):S640–S656.

Florida Museum of Natural History. n.d. Reducing the risk of a shark encounter: Advice to aquatic recreationists. International Shark Attack File, Univ. of Florida. www.flmnh.ufl.edu/fish/sharks/Attacks/relariskreduce.htm.

Graver, D. 2003. *Scuba Diving*, 3rd ed. Champaign, IL: Human Kinetics.

Hancock, P. A. 1984. Effect of environmental temperature on display monitoring performance: An overview with practical implications. *American Industrial Hygiene Association Journal* 45(2):122–126.

Idris, A. H., R. Berg, J. Bierens, L. Bossaert, C. Branche, A. Gabrielli, S. A. Graves, et al. 2003. Recommended guidelines for uniform reporting of data from drowning: The "Utstein style." *Circulation* 108:2565–74.

Institute of Sport and Recreation Management (ISRM). 2009. The use of play equipment and water features in swimming pools: A recommended code of practice. Loughborough, England, UK: ISRM.

International Critical Incident Stress Foundation Inc. (ICISF). 2001. Critical incident stress information sheets. www.icisf.us/images/pdfs/rar/Critical%20Incident%20Stress%20Information%20Sheet.pdf.

International Life Saving Federation (ILS). 2003a. ILS policy statement no. 9: Positioning a patient on a sloping beach. www.ilsf.org/sites/ilsf.org/files/filefield/medicalpolicy09.pdf

———. 2003b. ILS policy statement no. 8: Statements on the use of oxygen by lifesavers. www.ilsf.org/sites/ilsf.org/files/filefield/medicalpolicy08.pdf.

Irwin, R., J. Drayer, C. Irwin, T. Ryan, and R. Southall. 2010. Constraints impacting minority swimming participation: Phase II. Department of Health and Sport Sciences. Univ. of Memphis. www.usaswimming.org/_Rainbow/Documents/121d4497-c4be-44a6-8b28-12bf64f36036/2010%20Swim%20Report-USA%20Swimming-5-26-10.pdf.

Lavine, R. W., J. L. Sibert, M. Gokturk, and B. Dickens. 2002. Eye-tracking measures and human performance in a vigilance task. *Aviation, Space, and Environmental Medicine* 73:367–72.

Leclerc, T. 1997. A comparison of American Red Cross and YMCA preferred approach methods used to rescue near-drowning victims. MA thesis, Alabama A&M Univ.

Lepore, M., G. W. Gayle, and S. F. Stevens. 2007. *Adapted Aquatics Programming: A Professional Guide*, 2nd ed. Champaign, IL: Human Kinetics.

Lifesaving Society. 2007. *Alert: Lifeguarding in action.* North York, Ontario, Canada: Royal Life Saving Society Canada.

Mackworth, N. 1957. Some factors affecting vigilance. *The Advance of Science.* Quoted in Wickens, C. and J. Hollands, *Engineering Psychology and Human Performance* (New York: Harper Collins, 1992), 7–8.

Markel Insurance Company. 2007. Better practices. Presentation at American Camp Association National Conference, February 14, in Austin, TX.

Markenson, D., J. D. Ferguson, L. Chameides, P. Cassan, K.-L. Chung, et al. Part 17: First aid: 2010 American Heart Association and American Red Cross guidelines for first aid. *Circulation* 2010;122(suppl 3):S934–S946. http://circ.ahajournals.org/cgi/content/full/122/18_suppl_3/S934.

Mayo Clinic. 2009. Heart attack symptoms: Know what signals a medical emergency. www.mayoclinic.com/health/heart-attack-symptoms/HB00054.

Modell, J. 1997. The drowning process and lifeguard intervention, ed. B. C. Brewster. Paper presented at the International Medical-Rescue Conference. San Diego: International Life Saving Federation Americas Region.

National Institutes of Health (NIH). 2009. What I need to know about hepatitis C. National Institute of Diabetes and Digestive and Kidney Diseases (NDDIC). http://digestive.niddk.nih.gov/ddiseases/pubs/hepc_ez/.

National Oceanic and Atmospheric Administration (NOAA). 2009. A severe weather primer: Questions and answers about lightning. National Severe Storms Laboratory. www.nssl.noaa.gov/primer/lightning/ltg_faq.shtml.

———. 2005. Rip current safety. National Weather Service. www.ripcurrents.noaa.gov/overview.shtml.

National Transportation Safety Board (NTSB). 1998. Safety study: Personal watercraft safety. www.ntsb.gov/publictn/1998/SS9801.pdf.

Occupational Safety and Health Administration (OSHA). 1992. Occupational safety and health standards: Toxic and hazardous substances. Bloodborne pathogens. Personal protective equipment. Standard 29 CFR. 1910.1030(d)(3). www.osha.gov/pls/oshaweb/owadisp.show_document?p_table=STANDARDS&p_id=10051.

———. 1993 (updated 2007). Coverage of lifeguards under 29 CFR 1910.1030. Standard interpretation: Clark, R. L., memorandum to L. R. Anku. www.osha.gov/pls/oshaweb/owadisp.show_document?p_table=INTERPRETATIONS&p_id=21197.

Personal Watercraft Industry Association (PWIA). n.d. Riding rules for personal watercraft. www.pwia.org/pdf/RidingRulesBro.pdf.

Porter, R. R. 1997. Comparison of the American Red Cross and Young Men's Christian Association rescue procedures for a passive near-drowning victim. MA thesis: Indiana Univ. of Pennsylvania.

Quan, L., and P. Cummings. 2003. Characteristics of drowning by different age groups. *Injury Prevention* 9:163–8.

Richardson, W. J. 1997. Recognition and observation of potential rescue victims in an open water environment, ed. B. C. Brewster. Paper presented at the International medical-rescue conference, San Diego: International Life Saving Federation Americas Region.

Search Institute. 2010. What kids need: Sparks. www.search-institute.org/what-kids-need-sparks.

———. 2010. What kids need: Thriving. www.search-institute.org/thriving.

Smith, T. 2006. Seeing is believing: A technique called Vigilance Voice can help your lifeguards identify problems at your pool. *Parks & Recreation* Nov.

United States Coast Guard (USCG). 2008. PFD selection, use, wear, and care: Cold water survival. www.uscg.mil/hq/cg5/cg5214/pfdselection.asp.

———. 2009. Recreational boating statistics 2008. U.S. Department of Homeland Security; U.S. Coast Guard; and the Office of Auxiliary and Boating Safety. www.uscgboating.org/assets/1/Publications/Boating_Statistics_2008.pdf.

———. n.d. How to choose the right life jacket: A handy guide from your United States Coast Guard. www.uscgboating.org/assets/1/Publications/howtochoosetherightlifejacket_brochure.pdf.

United States Department of Commerce. 1999. December 16 Letter to Cleveland County YMCA. National Weather Service Forecast Office.

United States Department of Labor. 1995 (updated 2002). Communicating with and about people with disabilities. Office of Disability Employment Policy; the Media Project, Research and Training Center on Independent Living, Univ. of Kansas, Lawrence, KS; and the National Center for Access Unlimited, Chicago. www.dol.gov/odep/pubs/fact/comucate.htm.

United States Lifesaving Association (USLA). 2003. *Open water lifesaving—The United States Lifesaving Association manual*, 2nd ed., ed. B. C. Brewster. Boston: Pearson Custom Publishing.

———. n.d. Training guide for USLA safety tips. www.usla.org/PublicInfo /safety_guide.asp#1.

Williamson, A. M., and A.-M. Feyer. 2000. Moderate sleep deprivation produces impairments in cognitive and motor performance equivalent to legally prescribed levels of alcohol intoxication. *Occupational Environmental Medicine* 57(10):649–55.

Xu, J. Q., K. D. Kochanek, S. L. Murphy, and B. Tejada-Vera. 2010. Deaths: Final data for 2007. National vital statistics reports; vol 58 no 19. Hyattsville, MD: National Center for Health Statistics. www.cdc.gov/ nchs/data/nvsr/nvsr58/nvsr58_19.pdf

YMCA of the USA (Y-USA). 2006. *YMCA Pool Operations Manual*, 3rd ed. Chicago: Y-USA.

INDEX

Page references followed by f or t refer to figures or tables, respectively.

A

F

G

H

I

M

N

O

P

S

Y

Z

Notes